CU00692873

# THE
# LIVERPOOL
# DOCK
# ENGINEERS

# THE
# LIVERPOOL
# DOCK
# ENGINEERS

## ADRIAN JARVIS

ALAN SUTTON PUBLISHING LIMITED

First published in the United Kingdom in 1996
Alan Sutton Publishing Limited
Phoenix Mill · Far Thrupp · Stroud · Gloucestershire
in association with the Trustees of the National Museums & Galleries on
Merseyside

Copyright © the Trustees of the National Museums & Galleries on
Merseyside, 1996

All rights reserved. No part of this publication may be reproduced, stored in
a retrieval system, or transmitted, in any form or by any means, electronic,
mechanical, photocopying, recording or otherwise, without the prior
permission of the publishers and copyright holders.

British Library Cataloguing in Publication Data

A catalogue record for this book is available from the British Library.

ISBN 0-7509-1093-3

Typeset in 10/12 Bembo.
Typesetting and origination by
Alan Sutton Publishing Limited.
Printed in Great Britain by
Hartnolls, Bodmin, Cornwall.

# Contents

# List of Illustrations

Abbreviations for credits:

NMGM. The Trustees of the National Museums & Galleries on Merseyside.

CP. Colin Pitcher, ABIPP.

CP/ICE. Photograph by Colin Pitcher, original by courtesy of the Institution of Civil Engineers.

CP/MAL. Photograph by Colin Pitcher from an original in the Maritime Archives & Library, Merseyside Maritime Museum.

CP/LRO. Photograph by Colin Pitcher, original by courtesy of Liverpool City Record Office.

# Acknowledgements

This book has been some four years in the writing, during which time I have created problems for many people: without the generous responses of friends, colleagues and a number of librarians and archivists it would have taken far longer.

But I must begin with the fundamentals. I am in the happy and unusual position of being employed primarily as a research historian, which is, as a university friend acidly remarked, a bit like being a university lecturer but without the students. That this should be so is the result of a policy decision of the Trustees of National Museums & Galleries on Merseyside soon after they were established, that research and scholarship were to be key activities. That was, and remains, a far-sighted and courageous decision at a time when many museums are eating their intellectual seed-corn.

Next, I must mention the role of Merseyside Development Corporation. They did not contribute directly to this publication as they have to some previous ones, but it is no exaggeration to state that much of the momentum which has been built up in the study of the history of the Port of Liverpool results from their long-term support of historical research within their 'designated area'. A number of the works most frequently cited in this book resulted directly from projects wholly or partly funded by MDC. In particular, Tony Potter, formerly Chief Engineer and later Director of Development, has been a source of constant help and encouragement.

The vast majority of the primary materials used comes from the enormous MD&HB archive, which is, at least in engineering matters, the biggest most and complete for any port in the country. The easiest thing to do with obsolete paperwork nowadays is to bin it, and the public-spirited attitude of the Mersey Docks and Harbour Company, successors to MD&HB, in ensuring that their obsolete paperwork ended up in a public repository will continue to benefit scholarship far into the future. It is probably invidious to mention individuals in such a large organization, but perhaps I may be excused for mentioning the two with whom I have mainly dealt, namely

Albert Nute (formerly Assistant Secretary) and Peter Lucas (Chief Engineer). The latter gentleman also saved me a huge amount of time by providing me with a run of *Minutes of the Proceedings of the Institution of Civil Engineers* from 1858 to 1935, which now lives in my office.

Among my colleagues at Merseyside Maritime Museum, my greatest debt is to Gordon Read, Curator of Archives, and his assistant Dawn Littler. They have patiently allowed me to rootle through their stacks and through recently acquired material before it was listed, a privilege which must be worth literally months of work. I have also presumed on the patience of the rest of the staff of the Maritime Archives and Library on many occasions and thank them for their consistent helpfulness.

Helping researchers is all in the day's work for archivists and librarians, but I cannot omit mention of the staff at the Institution of Civil Engineers, especially Mary Murphy and Carol Arrowsmith, who have been helpful far beyond the call of duty.

A debt which is impossible to quantify, but none the less important for that, is owed to everyone who discusses port history with me at conferences and seminars in Britain and overseas. It was, for example, a chance remark about Buenos Aires made by Mike Stammers, Keeper of Merseyside Maritime Museum, which first made me realize the closeness of the engineering connections between Liverpool and some of the other great ports of the world. How can I acknowledge debts like that to dozens of fellow-historians (and some engineers)? I can only hope that they know who they are, and that they have paid the modest cost of this book to learn of my gratitude now.

Having been rather a sickly child with a large Meccano set, I have a reasonable intuitive grasp of mechanisms and structures, but I have no engineering training. Ken Smith (Lecturer in Civil Engineering, University of Liverpool) has spent a great deal of time scribbling rude comments on various draft sections and has also helped me to a better understanding of the way engineers think. Any solecisms which remain must be in bits I dared not show him.

This is the conventional point at which to claim that my greatest debt is to my wife. I cannot tell a lie: it is not, for she, poor lost soul, thinks dock engineering is boring. My greatest debt is to Gordon Jackson (University of Strathclyde). At one level it is the debt I share with everyone who writes about port history, for his work virtually defines the subject. At another, it was when discussing his comments on the draft text of my *Liverpool Central Docks* that he suggested the need for this book, though he cannot be held responsible for the form it eventually took. Finally, he agreed, despite his formidable workload, to read this draft as well and made many astute and helpful comments.

I have probably left people out, for which I can only apologize. I close with my thanks to the staff at Alan Sutton Publishing. The relationship between author and publisher inevitably produces minor differences of opinion, but their belief in a rather esoteric subject has never faltered and their constant amiability has made them a real pleasure to work with.

# Costs and Measurements

Everything described in this book was measured according to the Imperial System and paid for in pre-decimal money. In the interests of easier reading, conversions into metric, SI and decimal currency have not been interpolated in the text. For those unfamiliar with the old systems, the following conversion factors are offered.

*1. Money*

The old system divided the pound into 20 shillings (s) and the shilling into 12 pence (d). In some cases, such as rates of wages, it was conventional *not* to reduce shillings to pounds, so that a well-paid craftsman might be described as receiving 55*s* – i.e. £2.75 – per week.

1 shilling = 5 new pence.
1 old penny = 0.42 new pence.

*2. Distance*
1 mile = 1,760 yards = 1,609 metres.
1 yard = 3 feet = 0.914 metres.
1 nautical mile = 6,080 feet = 1,855 metres.

*3. Heights and Depths*
Are normally measured in feet and inches above or below the level of the sill of Liverpool's first dock, normally known as Old Dock Sill, occasionally Old Dock datum.
1 foot = 12 inches = 0.305 metres.
1 inch = 25.4 mm.

*4. Area*
1 acre = 4,840 square yards = 0.405 hectares.

1 square yard = 9 square feet = 0.836 square metres.
1 square foot = 0.304 square metres.

## 5. *Volume*

Solids, such as spoil or masonry, are measured in cubes of linear measurements, while liquids (and quasi-liquids like bulk grain) are measured in bushels, gallons etc.

1 cubic yard = 27 cubic feet = 0.764 cubic metres.
1 bushel = 8 gallons = 36.4 litres.
1 gallon = 8 pints.

## 6. *Weight*

1 ton = 20 hundredweight (cwt) = 1.016 tonnes.
1 cwt = 112 pounds (lbs) = 50.8 kilograms.

## 7. *Pressure*

1 pound per square in (lb/in$^2$) = 6.895 kilopascals = 0.0703 kg/cm$^2$.

## 8. *Power*

1 horsepower = 33,000 ft/lb per minute = 0.746 kilowatts.

# Introduction

# The Boundaries of Engineering History

The history of engineering is still affected to a surprising degree by a single publication, namely Samuel Smiles' *Lives of the Engineers*. This began life in 1857 as a *Life of George Stephenson* and grew a volume at a time until it reached five volumes in what was effectively the last edition (though much reprinted) in 1874.[1] It is an extraordinary fact that, although there had been a number of engineering biographies before then, notably Rickman's *Life of Thomas Telford*,[2] Smiles' work provided the first lengthy treatment of most of his subjects and was certainly the first engineering biography to sell in large quantities and to general readers.

Anybody who has read Smiles' other famous work, *Self-Help*, can immediately recognize a hidden agenda in *Lives of the Engineers*: it is to provide a series of exemplars of the benefits, both material and spiritual, of the practice of self-help. George Stephenson is the best example of all: born into a poor working-class family and starting work as a pit boy at the age of thirteen, he overcame endless difficulties, financial, technical and social, to become possibly the most famous and distinguished engineer in all history. It was Smiles who made him so.

There is, however, another hidden agenda in *Lives of the Engineers*, and it is a less wholesome one. There had been severe doubts about the ethics and finances of railway companies since the early 1840s, when what we like to call the Railway Mania got going. This manifested itself in a number of ways, but there were three which caused particular disquiet. Railway companies were buying up canals in order to suppress competition. They had completely discarded the legal fictions of public benefit which were incorporated in their enabling Acts and some were making dividends as absurdly large as those which had earlier brought the canal industry into disrepute. Above all, lines were being built and bought and sold which bore little or no connection with actual use, but were merely financial speculations. In the worst cases, the use of capital to pay inflated dividends to raise share prices became routine.The exposure, in 1848, of the machinations of George Hudson 'The Railway King'[3] (a man to whom present-day white-collar criminals could teach nothing) brought into the open the ethical problems within what was already among the largest industries in the country.

Such revelations could not fail to produce results unhealthy for the industry as a whole. As early as 1844, the Regulation of Railways Act included powers to nationalize railways, and railway companies became the targets for what McKendrick has termed 'Literary Luddites'. As Dentith has shown, the crooked speculator became a stock villain in novels.[4] The editorial policies of some newspapers, notably *The Times*, consistently suggested that the railway industry was the home of financial malpractice.

This was extremely bad news for the engineering profession: the railway industry was by a long way its biggest source of business. When Smiles, with his benign view of self-help[5] came seeking information from Robert Stephenson, a past president of both the engineering institutions, to write a biography of his father, George, a golden opportunity offered itself. Here, in Robert's hand, was the means to undo the harm done by Spencer, Dickens, Carlyle[6] and the like and show the engineering profession in what he considered its true light. Smiles was introduced to many of the most distinguished engineers of the older generation and to the already considerable accumulations of information in the libraries of the Institutions. There is little doubt that some of the people involved, Robert Stephenson included, deliberately misled Smiles.[7]

By the late 1850s, there were many aspects of engineering which were highly distasteful to a lot of those middle-class people who did not make their living from it. Most of the extractive industries and all of what existed of the chemical industry did horrible damage to the landscape, to the atmosphere and to watercourses. Some industries, particularly shipbuilding and boilermaking, produced gross noise pollution. Occupational diseases and the consequences of urban overcrowding were the cause of considerable doubt and worry. Contrary to what we might at first expect, there was strong and widespread objection to these and other problems, reflected not only in books and articles in periodicals, but also in major enquiries such as that of the Royal Commission which investigated the pollution of rivers in 1870. The engineering profession was in danger of being perceived as the designer of more effective abrasives for grinding the noses of the poor.

The Charter of the Institution of Civil Engineers refers to 'harnessing the great sources of power in Nature to the use and service of man'. Certain works of engineering convey very obvious benefits to the population at large. Bridges have quite strong emotional (and superstitious) connotations: they save people and livestock from being drowned when trying to use fords in time of flood and they save lengthy detours. Several medieval bridges are attributed to saints, though only St Benezet was canonized specifically for bridgebuilding. Nevertheless, bridges clearly went beyond the beneficial into the positively virtuous. In most cases they also looked prettier than the average alkali works. Quite as virtuous was the building of lighthouses, which saved countless sailors' lives, and the image of the honest hardworking sailor, always ready to volunteer for the navy to defend his island home in time of war still exercised a hold on the dewier-eyed portions of the reading classes. The reclamation of fens was virtuous too: if the mere fact of making previously useless land available for growing food seemed insufficiently virtuous, it was possible to resort, as Smiles did, to legends of demons in the fens and the victory won over them by the holy reclamation engineer, St Guthlac, thus making an explicit connection between civil engineering and saintliness.[8]

The end result of such influences is that much of Smiles' writing, and most of the really popular and influential part of it, is concerned with civil engineering at the expense of other kinds and within the field of civil engineering, works which involved land reclamation, travel and transport predominate. Smiles was a powerful story-teller, and he attracted a stream of imitators which has still not quite dried up. His work effectively defined the boundaries of the history of engineering at the time, and the lines he drew have not yet been fully erased. The shelves of any general library will reveal great footages of history of Smiles' favourite subjects – railways, canals, roads, bridges and even (to a much lesser degree) lighthouses. If we seek biographies of engineers, we find that Smiles' major subjects – the Stephensons, Telford, Watt, Rennie, Brindley, for example – have several each, published over a long period of time. Other men, like William Jessop, who were quite as important, have just one recent biography. Others just as prominent, like James Walker, have no biography at all.[9]

Many areas of engineering have continued to be short-changed by historians in this way. The impression is conveyed that all the truly great engineers were dead by 1860,[10] with the predictable result that the pioneers of electrical engineering are poorly covered. The Smilesian undertone that engineers achieved success through a combination of inborn genius, perseverance and sheer hard work has led to a relative dearth of books on theoretical engineers. Despite the work on thermodynamics by such as Cardwell, even Rankine, one of the nineteenth century's great theoreticians and engineering teachers, has yet to become the subject of a full-length work.

Dock engineering has been almost as badly served, perhaps in part because some of the most spectacular works were post-1860. Smiles did include some accounts of dock works, notably in his life of Rennie, but he barely mentioned others like Jessop who were significant dock builders. In other cases, he wrote lives of men who, like Telford, or indeed Robert Stephenson, built at least some docks, without laying much emphasis on that aspect of their work. Here as elsewhere, we find that the choices Smiles made have remained with us: of the engineers whose work features in this book, only Rennie received the Smiles treatment. As is well known, if an engineer did not appear in Smiles, he almost certainly did not appear in *Dictionary of National Biography*, and it seems that dock engineers are likely still to be thinly represented in the *New DNB* now in preparation. Finally, we must recognize that not one of Smiles' famous engineers was a salaried employee: all were consultants. This was probably for reasons of variety of interest to the general reader: the life of the chief engineer of a railway company was pretty unvaried compared with that of a consultant.

## The Role of Liverpool

Although there have been books on the history of ports which included elements of dock engineering and there have been biographies of engineers who did at least some work on docks, this is the first book to be written specifically on dock engineers and their work. It is based almost entirely on the men who engineered the docks of Liverpool and Birkenhead, an apparently foolhardy narrowing of the subject area which is in need of some explanation, even after taking into account the fact that the archives of the Mersey Docks & Harbour Board are, in engineering matters, the best and most complete in the country.

The Port of Liverpool was effectively brought into being by a royal charter of 1207 as the answer to specific political and military problems faced by King John. His actions did not depend on any rational commercial decision, or even consideration, so it need not come as too great a surprise to us that Liverpool's location was far from ideal for a commercial port. The Mersey estuary has little shelter from the prevailing wind, especially on the Liverpool side, and it has a large tidal range of over 10 metres at equinoctial spring tides. The large capacity of the broad part of the river couples with that tidal range to produce a rip through the narrows by Liverpool which can reach seven knots. It was, in short, a difficult and even dangerous place for loading or discharging goods or passengers, for anchoring or for winter laying-up. That is why, in 1715, Liverpool opened the first commercial wet dock in the country, and why it continued to build new docks at an ever-increasing rate. During the period of its most rapid growth, say about 1780–1850, Liverpool was probably more dependent on the skills of dock engineers than any other major port in Britain except Bristol, which was built in an equally stupid place, on a narrow, winding river with a tidal range even bigger than Liverpool's. In ports like London, vessels could anchor and load and discharge by lighter. Without Jessop's 'Floating Harbour' Bristol would have declined sooner and faster than it did, and without its docks it is doubtful whether Liverpool could have risen to prominence at all.

Needing the services of dock engineers was one thing, paying for them another. Liverpool was fortunate in two principal respects. The first was that the Corporation Estate was of enormous value compared with most others, so that the Dock Trustees, who were the Common Council under a different name, were able to borrow large sums of money on bond, the revenues of the Estate underwriting the loans. Crucially, those revenues included the right to levy town dues on goods crossing the foreshore, which yielded a significant income. The second was that a string of happy circumstances led to the potential for a dramatic and continuing growth in the trade of Liverpool. Although the rate of growth began to slacken after about 1850, the tonnage

*Just as unlikely a place as Liverpool. . .*
*the approach to Bristol Docks (with their*
*entrance just visible top left) at low tide.*

and value through the port remained vastly in excess of every other British port except London, and continued to rise each year until after the First World War. As late as 1930 Liverpool still surpassed the total tonnage of the next six largest ports put together. The financing of the port had gained, perhaps even earned, a very high reputation for probity and security, so that while debt charges were sometimes unduly high in relation to dues income, raising money was not generally a problem before 1900. The result was that while the port had its financial ups and downs, it was generally better placed for almost constant investment, and thus the employment of engineers, than were most other ports.[11]

From the beginnings in 1709, when the first Liverpool Dock Act was passed, to 1824 the Liverpool docks were engineered in much the same way as others, namely by the employment of an engineer on what was effectively a part-time basis. When there was too much work for him, when a second opinion was required or when it was felt that part or all of the work was beyond his capabilities, consultants were hired in. In 1824, the Dock Trustees appointed Jesse Hartley as Dock Surveyor: he became the first full-time salaried dock engineer to be responsible for every aspect of the engineering of the Dock Estate. As such, he became the first civilian specialist dock engineer in the country. He was a man who liked to control as much as he could, so he gradually built up an integrated system which anticipated the great railway works: his 'Dock Yard', as he called his main depot, contained the men, machinery and skills for every aspect of the design and execution of dock construction and maintenance.

This was an entirely different way of undertaking dock construction, and, as we shall see, it led to highly talented and ambitious young men making their way to Liverpool: if you wanted to learn dock engineering the Liverpool Dock Yard was the place where the action was. A colleague of the author once passed through Buenos Aires docks and remarked that some of the retaining walls looked surprisingly like the work of Jesse Hartley, but they were built in the late 1880s, nearly 30 years after Hartley's death. The connection was that the Principal of the firm of consulting engineers responsible for the design was Sir John Hawkshaw, who had, over 40 years earlier, worked under Jesse Hartley.[11] Until the establishment of the Port of London Authority in 1908, what we think of as the Port of London was in fact a rather chaotic assemblage of small-to-medium sized private dock companies engaged in fairly futile competition with each other. Liverpool was by a huge margin the largest and most important port under the management of a single authority and its revenues were correspondingly large. As the technical difficulties of dealing with the escalating demands of shipowners increased, so did the size and expenditure of the Engineer's Department, so that we find Liverpool-trained dock engineers turning up with greater frequency in the pages of the *Minutes of the Proceedings of the Institution of Civil Engineers* and in employment at docks around the world.

It seems more or less *de rigueur* in any book on a subject connected with the processes of industrial growth to claim that the particular industry, product, service or activity under consideration was the one truly indispensable ingredient in the industrialization of the world. Such arguments are almost invariably over-simplifications and may even arise from motives less worthy than local pride or a desire to 'puff' the book. The argument that life as we know it today would be impossible without the nineteenth century dock engineers is perhaps a little tenuous, but worth a passing mention. The processes of the industrial revolution resulted in ever-increasing demands for the raw materials of manufactured goods and an ever-increasing supply of the goods themselves. Britain was ill-adapted to producing some of the raw materials – silk, cotton or sulphur, for example – and was simply not big enough to consume all the goods it could produce. The Lancashire cotton or Cheshire silk industries could only expand within limits imposed by the ability to carry their raw materials and their products across oceans. Further, the process of urbanization encouraged by those and other industries resulted in and to an extent depended upon Britain becoming a net importer of foodstuffs. Although it has been fairly generally agreed that Britain was in relative economic decline from at least 1870 onwards,[12] that relative decline arose more from growth in other countries than from a decrease in British output, so the amounts of goods needing moving about continued to grow rapidly. It is significant that major exceptions to the relative decline occur in shipbuilding and operation – and in dock construction.

The continuing success of the shipping industries was largely rooted in significant technical improvements in shipbuilding and marine engineering in the 1860s and '70s which slashed the duration of longer voyages and produced considerable cost reductions. They posed, as we shall see, problems of great cost and technical difficulty for dock engineers, but without their being overcome, there would have been much greater obstacles to industrial expansion in Britain than there were. The dock engineers may not quite deserve the rousing cheers accorded to some of Samuel Smiles' heroes, but a polite ripple of applause might be in order.

# 1
# Dock Engineers:
# the Professional Origins

## Stage 1: Thomas Steers and the Beginning of Dock Engineering in Liverpool

The argument in favour of the importance of the Liverpool Dock Yard as a 'centre of excellence' for the training of dock engineers assumes that there were skilled professionals there to do the training. What, then, was the situation when Thomas Steers came to begin work on Liverpool's first dock? What were the necessary skills, and where did he acquire them?

The two main problems in constructing even the most rudimentary dock are the retaining walls and the gates. Other problems may arise later, but the basics, of preventing the sides of the hole falling in the water and of maintaining the level of the water while still permitting vessels to come and go must be solved before the engineer starts to worry about accessories like cranes, bridges or sheds. It was in any case far from uncommon, as happened to Steers, for all the estimated cost to have been spent before even the rudiments were completed, so that the embellishments had to wait until there was some revenue coming in.[1]

The job of the retaining wall is to maintain a nice tidy vertical or near-vertical edge to the dock for ships to tie up to in order to do their business. The ships themselves can impose loads on the walls, for example by crashing into them or by using the mooring bollards to come to a halt. Normally the main load, however, is that imposed in preventing the ground behind the wall from doing what it otherwise would, namely slipping gracefully into the dock until it reaches its natural angle of repose, which is usually something of the order of 45°.[2] The weight of any goods stacked on the quayside ('surcharge') increases the forces acting on the wall. The need for retaining walls was not, however, peculiar to docks, and the technology was a very old one which could, by the end of the seventeenth century be 'borrowed' from a variety of sources. As early as the first century BC, Vitruvius was able to describe what were clearly retaining walls for both military and harbour purposes.[3] How successful or otherwise they were need not concern us here, for we can observe large and eminently durable retaining walls on the mounds and/or moats of almost any castle in Britain.

Those of us who were weaned on Smiles and his historical followers tend to associate the beginnings of canal building with James Brindley. Britain was in fact rather a late-comer in the canal-building business, as Smiles himself acknowledges in later editions of *Lives of the Engineers* by including a short account of Pierre-Paul Riquet, who completed the great *Canal du Midi* in 1688. Canals may not have needed retaining walls of the scale of those of a castle, or of a dock, but they needed large quantities of them, they needed to be waterproof and, in the locks, they needed to be several feet high. The employment of pound locks (i.e. those with gates at both ends) certainly dates back into the fourteenth century, and the Stecknitz Canal of 1391 had a summit level requiring the use of two locks.[4] By the time that Steers was learning about engineering at the end of the seventeenth century, the *Canal du Midi* was complete. It involved some massive masonrywork, including a dam no less than 105 ft high to retain the water for supplying the summit level.

The second strand, the construction of gates, has a similarly long pedigree. The gates of the Stecknitz Canal's locks were probably vertical 'guillotine' type, though pivoted gates had been in use to control flood protection works in Holland considerably earlier. The critical invention was the mitre gate, employed by Leonardo da Vinci on the *Naviglio Interno* at the very end of the fifteenth century. (Though some have it that, while Leonardo undoubtedly used it, the idea belonged to Philippe Visconti, some fifty years earlier.) It is surprising that the use of the mitre gate spread only comparatively slowly, for it is one of the world's great inventions. It is to a degree both self-aligning and self-sealing, allowing it to be made with a hemispherical bottom 'hinge' and just a comparatively light iron strap to retain it at the top. Because it is able to 'float' in its mountings, it does not need to be made to such a high standard as guillotine or flap gates, and because it closes only half the width of the lock or entrance passage, wider passages are proportionately much less of a problem in construction, maintenance and operation. Finally, because most of the forces imposed on the gate by the head of water it controls are resolved along the line of the gate into the walls of the lock, it spreads its load more evenly over more of the masonry. The design of large mitre gates eventually became quite a precise science, to which Liverpool engineers made significant contributions.[5]

Engineers have always needed other skills than building walls or gates. In particular they have needed the ability to persuade other people to provide them with lots of money for the execution of their proposals. Riquet's idea of building a canal large enough to carry a small ship right across France from the Atlantic to the Mediterranean could very easily have appeared an absolutely lunatic venture. His ability to convince Louis XIV and (which was more difficult) Colbert of its feasibility was the essential preliminary: before the first sod could be raised a great many *livres* had to be.

Large works of civil engineering have never been cheap and they have until recently inevitably involved large amounts of manual labour. The engineer needed, therefore, to be able to estimate costs, purchase and control materials, hire labour and schedule its output. We know, of course, that the problems of discharging all these functions have often defeated the engineers: the outrage expressed in the popular press at the overspending and delay on the Channel Tunnel arose from a failure to recognize that engineering was ever thus. Nevertheless, Vauban, Louis XIV's celebrated siege engineer and fortress-builder commanded huge resources (including 21,000 labourers at the siege of Mons in 1691) and was in the habit of producing detailed plans, specifications and estimates before work began. It was just that engineers often got it wrong, not that they did not try. Vauban was also among the moving forces for systematizing French engineering, civil as well as military, and it is probably no coincidence that a French edition of Vitruvius appeared in 1674. Presumably as a result of the 'Auld Alliance', the University of Glasgow has a number of French engineering texts from this early period.

What manner of man, then, was Thomas Steers, to have learned such skills? The first remarkable thing about him is that that he does not have proven contact with any of the thirteen engineers listed by Swann as undertaking dock or harbour works at an earlier date. Specifically, there seems to have been no technology transfer from the comparatively sophisticated works undertaken in the Royal Dockyards to his works for merchant shipping, which were comparatively few and humble.[6] The second is how little work has been done on him, for he is the *fons et origo* of dock engineering in Liverpool. After Steers, the basics of civilian dock engineering in England were tolerably well established, and we have no need to wonder where his successor learned his skills, for his successor was Henry Berry, Steers' clerk. A paper published in 1930 by Henry Peet remained the only original work for half a century, though it has been cited by almost every following author.[7] More recently, Clarke has gone back to the source material and brought forward some new information.[8]

The rudiments of Steers' career may be summarized fairly simply. The date of his birth is open to some doubt, but is thought by Clarke to be 1672. Little is known of his early life, but he was commissioned in the 4th Regiment of Foot, and served as Quartermaster in campaigns against the French in Flanders in the mid-1690s. As Quartermaster, he would inevitably have some knowledge of and interest in technical matters, and because much of the Flanders campaigning involved protracted sieges, it is not stretching speculation very far to assume that he would occasionally have time on his hands. We know from Malet that the Duke of Bridgewater acquired a fair amount of engineering knowledge by 'technological tourism'[9] and there seems no reason to differ from Clarke's contention that Steers did likewise in a region which boasted some excellent water engineering, perhaps the best in Europe. His normal duties would involve him in survey work and probably excavations as well. Above all, the role of Quartermaster required then, as it does today, a shrewd business head to acquire supplies at a reasonable price and an equally shrewd understanding of book-keeping and human nature to ensure that they were not 'liberated' by the men.

Steers, then, returned from Flanders around 1697, already equipped with some useful technical knowledge and managerial skills. Clarke suggests that he may have made some influential contacts as well, making out a case for the possible exertion of influence on his behalf by Lord Derby. He next appears getting married, in his native county of Kent, and settling down to live in Rotherhithe. Now the reason Liverpool historians have always been careful to describe Liverpool's original dock as the first commercial, as distinct from merely civilian, wet dock is that John Wells designed a small wet dock at Rotherhithe, known as The Howland Great Dock and completed in 1699. Steers could not fail to become aware of its construction (which had already begun when he arrived in the area) and he certainly drew up a survey of the site. There is no indication that he had any direct involvement in either design or construction of the dock, but if the 'technological tourism' suggestion is valid, here was some more of it. He leased some land from Elizabeth Howland, and his occupation is given in the agreement as 'house carpenter'. If correct, this adds a valuable and relevant manual skill to his CV, for dock construction has always required large amounts of heavy carpentry for temporary and protective works.[10]

There were a number of men in Britain at the time capable of undertaking harbour and water control works, and two of them, Henry Huss and George Sorocold of Derby, came to Liverpool in 1708 and 1709 respectively to survey and design a dock. In the event, their scheme was used only as the basis of the parliamentary bill, and the following year Steers began work to a plan of his own.

The situation in which Steers found himself in Liverpool was a rather odd one. It has become customary to refer to him as Liverpool's first dock engineer, and to imagine him in a line of succession which leads directly to Peter Lucas, the present Chief Engineer of the Mersey Docks & Harbour Company. In a sense that is entirely legitimate, for it does not appear that any of the engineering work of the Dock Estate between Steers' appointment in 1710 and his death in 1750 was undertaken outside his control. But there were two fundamental differences.

The first, and very obvious one, is the small scale of the works involved. Liverpool's first dock may have been a pioneering venture, but at 3.5 acres it was not very big. The reasons it took so long to build were that the technology was a bit experimental and (as always) the money ran out before it was complete, enforcing something of an hiatus. These reasons were, of course, linked. Ritchie-Noakes, following Bird, refers to Steers' plan of building within the Pool rather than excavating *de novo* from dry land as George Sorocold had suggested as being 'bolder'.[11] In fact, as Jackson has pointed out, a number of early dock builders fell for the idea that squaring off the sides of an existing tidal inlet was the cheap, easy way to build a dock, and they were wrong. The saving in spoil lifting was normally wiped out by the difficulty of finding a sound foundation for the retaining walls.[12] But even allowing for the unforeseen problems and the additions made after

5

the nominal completion, there was never going to be enough high-grade engineering work to keep a highly-paid man like Steers gainfully occupied.

'The past is a foreign country: they do things differently there' is a remark which has been so much quoted as almost to conceal the very important truth in it. If we imagine Thomas Steers as being employed in a similar manner to, say, G.F. Lyster, his successor in the late nineteenth century, we delude outselves very seriously. In addition to being employed by the Council in its *alter ego* as Dock Trustees, he was also, from 1713, a freeman, a councillor from 1717 and mayor in 1739. The linkage in the other direction was just as odd by modern standards, since he was also the contractor for the construction of the dock. It must be emphasized that there was nothing necessarily corrupt or unethical about such an arrangement in which as a councillor he voted to employ himself as engineer and then as engineer decided to employ himself as contractor. The question of conflict of interest was not addressed by the Dock Trustees until 1824, when the excesses of John Foster (Dock Surveyor 1799–1824) forced them to.[13] Even that was quite a 'forward-looking' move, for the bye-laws of the Institution of Civil Engineers did not specifically proscribe conflict of interest until 1910. Steers was as much a politician as a local government officer, but we must remember the requirement for fund-raising skills in engineers, and recognize that he had found an effective way, perhaps at the time the most effective way, of securing adequate funding for his projects.

The flexibility of Steers' arrangements with the Council extended much further. We need not be surprised that he was allowed to take on outside work – that was a practice which continued until 1840 – though we might be a little surprised that he spent many months in Ireland working on the Newry Canal (completed in 1741) for which he was paid the large sum of £1,651, corresponding to about £100 per month. He worked on a number of other canal projects, in at least one of which he was both engineer and contractor. Furthermore, he was involved in a number of other projects in Liverpool which were nothing to do with the docks, including St George's Church and the Old Ropery Theatre. Even these activities nowhere near exhaust the interests, or indeed the sources of income, of this many-faceted man: he was at one time employed as Dockmaster and later as Water Bailiff as well, he owned an anchor-smithy, and was part-owner of a ship and of a salt-works in Ireland. Several of Samuel Smiles' heroes worked themselves to an early grave, but Steers was made of sterner stuff than that and despite his prodigious activity, was about 80, and still working, when he died.

The construction of the Old Dock is still a matter of some obscurity. During the widening and re-alignment of the Dock Road in 1980, part of the wall of the Old Dock was uncovered, and recorded by the Field Archaeology Department of what was then Merseyside County Museums (now National Museums & Galleries on Merseyside). Severe time constraints prevented major excavation, but a yellow sandstone coping was uncovered, standing on top of a sturdy brick wall.[14] The word 'sturdy' appears substantiated not merely by the archaeologists' description of what they saw, but by Ian Weir's calculations. From the best data he was able to find, it seems that Steers' walls were actually slightly more strongly built than would be required by the formula propounded by Bernard Forest de Belidor, one of the pioneers of retaining wall theory, in 1729.[15] The bricks were made on site: suitable clay for brickmaking underlies much of the old foreshore of Liverpool and continued to be used well into the days of G.F. Lyster.

Sandstones are a notoriously difficult material on which to get geologists to make any very firm suggestions as to exact origin. The stone used was apparently of a very distinct yellow colouring, and we know that it was not until John Foster was Dock Surveyor that stone supplies from the Corporation quarries at Brownlow Hill and St James' Mount became insufficient and needed to be supplemented with 'imports' from Runcorn.[16] Near the West Front of Liverpool Cathedral, there is still visible a small outcrop of sandstone so yellow that it looks almost artificial, and a similar stone was observed when a drainage trench was cut through the wall of the former Chester Basin in 1990. It therefore seems reasonable to suppose that the stone came from the Corporation quarries. It may not, however, have come direct, since both Sorocold and Steers had remarked on the possibility of re-using stone from the nearby ruins of Liverpool Castle as a way of reducing costs.

Without wishing in any way to detract from Steers' achievement, one must remember that some of the difficulties he faced were not as great as local historians have sometimes suggested. It is well known that Portland Cement was not invented until 1824, and Mayfield tells us that the Roman technique of using Pozzualana to make an effective hydraulic cement was lost when 'The Middle Ages witnessed a general decline in the knowledge of cementing materials . . .'.[17] The modern use of hydraulic cements in Britain is customarily traced to the work of John Smeaton, who carried out extensive systematic (one could well say scientific) experiments, triumphantly demonstrating the excellence of his mortar in the construction of the Eddystone Light, completed 1759.[18] Early in the next century, the use of what became known as 'Roman Cement' spread, the names particularly associated with its introduction being those of Joseph Parker and Edgar Dobbs. From an outline of the orthodox history of cements and mortars it would be eminently defensible to assume, as Stephenson and Ritchie-Noakes did, that Steers was faced with the problem of building a dock completely 'in the dry' because he did not have a mortar which would set under water.[19]

Common sense and a knowledge of the general history of engineering suggest that this would not be the case. The very terms 'Middle Ages' or, worse, 'Dark Ages' imply that they were there merely to fill in time between the collapse of Rome and the bursting forth upon the world of the glories of the Renaissance. Are we seriously expected to believe that the great Gothic cathedrals were built by people whose 'lime mortars and workmanship were of poor quality'? If St Benezet built the Pont d'Avignon labouring under such difficulties then he deserved canonization not merely for perseverance in following the instructions of the Angel of the Lord, but for an undoubted Miracle. In fact, these medieval engineers had ready access in monastic libraries to such Roman texts as Vitruvius' *De Architectura* and far from regressing from Roman techniques, they improved upon them.

So it proves. Steers was importing limestone from Halkyn Mountain in North Wales. This is one of the blue lias limes of low chemical purity, containing a fair amount of clay. When, over a century later, Jesse Hartley was constructing the distinctive granite rubble walls described by Sir Robert Rawlinson, the hydraulic mortar which he used was prepared from limestone brought from Halkyn Mountain.[20] For some classes of dock work, some engineers continued to prefer traditional hydraulic lime mortars to Portland cement at least until the end of last century.[21] Steers may have confronted and overcome considerable difficulties, but the lack of an at least passable hydraulic mortar does not seem to have been one of them.

Another difficulty which may be overstated is that of building coffer-dams to enable working in the dry for the excavation of the foundations for the retaining walls and the gate sills. Of course it was no easy task, especially in such a hostile estuary as the Mersey, but neither was it unprecedented. The Exeter Canal, for example, had a lock entering the tidal waters of the Exe in the 1560s, and the first pound locks had been constructed on the Thames in the 1630s.[22] Anyone who has boated on the Thames when it is in flood will know that was not easy either. The foundations for Old London Bridge demanded coffer-dams of considerable size and depth in a none-too-gentle stretch of water. There were already river walls, like the 'New Quay' of 1672, built in the waters of the Mersey well below the level of high water neaps. Neither should we imagine that building coffer-dams soon became a simple matter of routine based on a precise science which accurately predicted their behaviour under working conditions. There were several fatal accidents in Liverpool dock construction works involving coffer-dam failures over 150 years after Steers' first dock, and one in Birkenhead in 1909 very nearly made the bicentenary.[23]

There is one great void in our knowledge of how Steers constructed the dock. Although it was, by later standards, tiny, it still involved huge amounts of manual labour in relation to the size of the town at the time. The amount of spoil removal may have been reduced by using the Pool as a basis for the dock, but a considerable frontage of river wall and a large volume of fill were needed. The construction and removal of coffer-dams and other temporary works involved many hundreds of tons of timber and the retaining walls, although only 24 ft in height, were nevertheless 10 ft thick at the base. The density of the masonrywork is unknown, but the weight of materials needing to be handled would amount very roughly to around 8 tons per linear foot of wall. Where did the men come from who did it? There was, as yet, no established corps of itinerant navvies, so one looks to the employment of men engaged in seasonal trades. The problem is that obvious sources of seasonally available labour, like seafaring, left men available for other work in the winter. We know that even a century later, when there was a much greater accumulated expertise on which to draw, dock construction work in winter not only resulted in high accident rates but in death from exposure and/or hypothermia.[24] The risk of temporary works being damaged or destroyed by rough weather was much higher. We might think that men normally employed in ship-repairing would be available in the summer, when the longer-distance vessels were away for several months. We know, however, that ships were later built alongside and launched into, the Old

Dock, which suggests that such men would be engaged in pretty frenzied activity when the press of vessels at the quays was least.[25]

The contribution of Thomas Steers strictly to the technology of dock-building does not seem to have been very notable. The Old Dock was a rather ill-conceived design, being in bad ground with less-than-perfect foundations. A worse problem was that when Steers was building the dock, he had to divert the stream which flowed into the pool. When, however, the dock was completed, the stream was 'undiverted' into the dock. Its mission in life was to drain the area known as Mosslake Fields, and it ran down the line of what later became Hunter Street and along Whitechapel and Paradise Street. On passage it was used for the disposal of all manner of wastes, liquid and solid and these, together with the natural silt it had always carried, it deposited in the dock.[26] There were no effective dredgers available, so when the silt accumulated to a sufficient degree the dock had to be 'cleansed' by draining it to allow silt to be shovelled out.[27] This was far more than an inconvenience to anyone wishing to use the dock at the time, for it upset the equilibrium which had been established between the ground forces acting on the retaining walls and the effectively static load imposed in the opposite direction by the water. On the one recorded occasion when a wall failure at the Old Dock was of sufficient seriousness to justify detailed enquiry, 'cleansing' was held partly to blame.[28]

The tidal basin and pier which provided short-term berthing and safe access to the dock, were built of stone and seem to have been better constructed than the dock itself. The New Dock was completed after Steers' death by Henry Berry: a small part of its walling is still incorporated in the present Salthouse Dock. It does not appear to have suffered any wall failure for at least the first century of its working life. It is only reasonable to assume that Steers would improve with practice, for although nothing he did was entirely novel, the combination of expertise borrowed from other fields was.

The phenomenal rate at which Liverpool's trade expanded, and the effectiveness with which it competed with older-established rivals such as Bristol has been much published and does not need repetition here.[29] The importance of Steers was that he synthesized the necessary skills of dock construction and passed them on to his successor, that he devised effective means of funding and managing dock construction, and that he demonstrated that, with adequate docks, Liverpool could overcome the natural disadvantages of her location and become a world port.

Vol.I.page 378

J.Ryland del.et sculp

The South West View of Liverpool.

*This 1728 print conveys a fair impression of the Old Dock and its pier – which seems unduly long. Unfortunately it is at variance with the few other views we have. In particular it shows no tidal entrance basin and makes the dock nearly square, when in fact it was roughly twice as long as it was wide.*

### The Tradition Continues

After Steers' death, the next two men to take charge of the engineering of Liverpool Docks were Henry Berry (between 1750 and 1789) and Thomas Morris (1789–99). As already mentioned, Berry had served as Steers' clerk and may therefore be presumed to have been well familiar with his methods of construction and management. Like Steers, he was able to undertake outside work, for the volume of work on the docks was not yet sufficient to require a full-time 'Chief'. One of his outside jobs probably earned him a wider fame than his work in the docks: he was engineer for the construction of the Sankey Navigation, which was the first canal in the world to be built for industrial rather than agricultural or military purposes. The pace of construction of the Liverpool Docks increased significantly during his tenure: three major wet docks (Salthouse, Georges and Kings) were completed, the last being more than double the size of the Old Dock.[30]

Thomas Morris is something of a mystery man. He appears to have

*11*

learned his profession from his father, but unfortunately his father was also called Thomas, which makes it very difficult to establish which works belong to the father and which to the son. Thomas Jnr's tenure was the second shortest of any Liverpool dock engineer until after the Second World War, and he completed just one new dock (Queens) in that time. He left in 1799 under something of a cloud, reputedly because he had asked for an excessive increase of his salary. At 100 guineas per year, his salary was scarcely in the Steers league, but what is perhaps more significant is that when he took up a post as a mere resident engineer under William Jessop in London he was paid the very high (for a resident) salary of £840. Jessop generally being nobody's fool, we may take this as fairly strong evidence of Morris' competence.[31] Against that assumption it must be pointed out that there were retaining wall failures at Queens (as there were also at Kings) and the entrance suffered persistent silting. The silting was occasioned by an elementary error of location. Not far outside the entrance lay the Pluckington Bank, a particularly intractable obstruction to shipping which continued to plague successive dock engineers until the closure of the South Docks in 1972. The cost of dredging was, indeed, a significant factor in that closure. Morris' dock, built before the invention of any effective means of making and maintaining a breach in the Pluckington Bank, never stood a chance of avoiding serious trouble with silt.

For present purposes we need say little more of Messrs Berry and Morris. Each had learned the profession of civil engineering from an existing practitioner. Morris Snr was an assistant to James Brindley. Thanks to Smiles, Brindley is remembered almost exclusively as a canal engineer, but he was also responsible for building docks, albeit small ones, at Liverpool (Duke's Dock) Runcorn and Stourport in addition to his better-known canal construction works.[32] Although his docks were small, they did involve dealing with much deeper (and tidal) water and larger surcharges than were encountered in normal canal work. Morris Jnr therefore had a 'line of descent' from an established civil engineering practitioner just as Berry had. This was the general pattern of the engineering profession during its formative decades, and as the nineteenth century wore on we find that quite often the best engineers were those who had learned from the best men of the previous generation. 'Pedigree' may have counted for almost as much as inherent ability.

## Stage 2: The Involvement of Consultants

The pivotal character is John Foster, appointed in Morris' place in 1799. He was a man of extraordinary abilities. Born the son of a master joiner, he eventually succeeded in establishing a family stranglehold on key jobs in Liverpool. His rise to power began with his success in gaining effective control of the expenditure of very large sums – £150,000 in three years – spent by the Commissioners appointed under the Liverpool Improvement Act of 1785.[33] This money was spent quite effectively for the purposes for which it was intended, for whatever might be said against John Foster (and a lot was, though usually quietly), he was an extremely talented man. The money was also used to place suppliers and contractors under an obligation to Foster and he proceeded to carve out a position of quite extraordinary power in the town. By 1789, he had been appointed Superintendent of the public buildings of the town, giving him power to disburse further patronage, and in 1799 he became Dock Surveyor, on a salary of £300. This is an interesting development: unlike Morris, Foster had no engineering training whatever, yet he was able to command three times Morris' salary. In 1802, John Eyes, the Corporation Surveyor, failed to meet a completely impossible 'forward job plan' and was sacked: his post was consolidated with that of Dock Surveyor, and taken over by Foster. So far as we can tell, Eyes was an honest and competent man manoeuvred out of office as we may presume Morris was.[34]

Foster was thus placed in the position to achieve his objective of establishing a dynasty which would rule the town, not from the Council Chamber, but from offices. His son Thomas was first articled to the firm of Stanistreet & Eden, Solicitors to the Corporation, and then appointed Town Clerk. His son William was appointed first as his assistant on dock works and then as Secretary to the Dock Committee. His son John Jnr was appointed Borough Architect. What Foster had found was an alternative to the Steers method of untying the corporate purse strings. Having found it, he proceeded to enrich himself and his family in a manner we would nowadays consider grossly unethical. We find, for example, that William was still managing the family joinery and contracting business and yet another son, James, was a partner in an iron foundry: neither firm had much difficulty in finding public sector business.

The fact that John Foster was as bent as a corkscrew would eventually have far-reaching effects, but for the moment we must view him in a different light. There is no doubt that he was a man of exceptional ability and versatility, for the dock engineering work carried out under his direction was of a perfectly adequate standard: a remarkable achievement for a man with no professional training. During his tenure the water area of the docks nearly doubled, and a fair amount of modernization of the older docks was also effected. His lack of specialist knowledge, however, led the engineering of the docks into a different path, involving the employment of outside consultants.

At the end of 1799, the Dock Committee had before it an outline design by Thomas Morris for a new dock, considerably larger than any of the existing ones, to be built to the north. Perhaps the reputation of the departed Morris was besmirched by his successor: such things have been known to happen. Perhaps the councillors, remembering the problems at Kings and Queens Docks, doubted the ability of Foster to undertake the design of a project so large, expensive and technically difficult compared with anything he had done before. Whatever the reason, they commissioned a report from William Jessop, perhaps the most distinguished canal engineer of the day. Their commission posed a series of questions, of which two rather telling ones were whether he could recommend an improved form of retaining wall (i.e. one which stayed up) and what he had to say on the subject of silting of entrances. Jessop's report, received on 1 April 1800, contains a great deal of sound common sense. It answers all the questions put, though wisely does not state *how* he would build an improved form of retaining wall, merely that he could. His answer to the silting problem was to do away with tidal basins: the docks should be entered by proper locks from the river, the Pier Heads serving for ships to come to rest and warp themselves into the locks.[35]

These were, however, bad times for trying to raise the money to implement the plan: labour, timber, horses and iron were all rendered unduly expensive by the ongoing French wars. The plan was shelved, and by the time that congestion was getting so acute that action was almost inescapable, it was felt wise to commission a new report, this time by John Rennie.[36] Rennie, like Jessop, was an absolutely top-flight engineer of canals and docks and reported back in 1809 with a scheme generally similar to Jessop's. The main difference was that Rennie employed a tidal entrance basin after

*14*

the manner of previous Liverpool docks, which we can see in retrospect was a mistake: Jessop's lock would have saved a great deal of trouble moving silt around. The exact date at which work on Princes Dock began is not recorded, but was probably late in 1810.

The significance of the engagement of Jessop and Rennie is twofold. It indicates that the lead which Liverpool held in dockbuilding method in the early days of construction had been lost: the most skilled men at the turn of the nineteenth century were those who undertook a variety of dock work in different parts of the country. It also reminds us that although engineering might by now be considered a profession, specialist dock building knowledge was not common property. Published information, at least of a practical kind, was almost non-existent, with the result that even a man of Foster's undoubted talents needed to tap the skills of men who had learned the only way there was – by pupillage. When told how to do it by Rennie, Foster and his men were able to build a dock which is still perfectly serviceable (for anything small enough to get into it) to this day, despite its walls having been subjected to loads far beyond anything either Rennie or Foster could have imagined.

The problem with Foster's regime was that it was absolutely rotten to the core. Leonard Addison, his Superintendent of Works, was removed from office for accepting a massive bribe from the firm of Hetherington & Grindrod, who were grossly overcharging the Dock Committee for stone. As the extent of the overspending at Princes, and the amount of money which was being syphoned out by Foster, his family and his friends, gradually became public knowledge, he became an increasing embarrassment to his political allies and on 27 March 1824 he resigned. He was 65 years old, in poor health and disgustingly rich. Three days earlier, his new Deputy, Jesse Hartley, had started work. After a limbo period as Acting Surveyor, he was formally appointed in November.[37]

## Stage 3: The Development of a Professional Specialism: Hartley, Control and Integration

Like Steers, Berry and Morris before him, Hartley had a practical training, initially as a stonemason, from which he moved into bridgebuilding. In 1826 he was responsible for the structural aspects of the Grosvenor Bridge in

Chester, at the time the largest masonry span in the world. Prior to his appointment in Liverpool he was working as Bridgemaster in Salford. It appears, however, that he had little or no experience of dock building, though he did report on the deepening of Littlehampton Harbour in 1825. The question arises why he, from a field of 14 candidates, was the one chosen. The answer is probably that given unofficially by the *Liverpool Mercury*, that he would be a new broom to sweep away the management methods of the Foster regime.

Under Foster, there existed systems for budgeting, management and materials control which look perfectly good on paper. The problem was that they had never been enforced, because it was not in the interests of the Foster family or anyone else down the line to enforce them.[38] We can find therefore, one category of work on Princes Dock being undertaken simultaneously by direct labour, contract labour and self-employed men, using materials of provenance and ownership just as confused. The entire purpose of the system as operated in practice was to produce confusion in order to make the daily skulduggery hard to detect and almost impossible to prove. Well before this time, the likes of Jessop and Rennie – and Vauban – issued specifications which covered every detail of the work, set out exact responsibilities and formed the basis of a clear and enforceable legal agreement. The Dock Committee's 'Old Agreements Book' survives, but its use was irregular until 1823, when the Audit Commissioners had already got their noses deeply into the business of the Foster clique. Even then, the early entries in the book leave much to be desired in comparison not only with the later agreements in the same book but also with the detailed specifications issued by other engineers. Those produced by John Rennie for works at Grimsby, for example, are models of clarity and enforceability.[39] Some of the work undertaken for Foster was on the basis of scruffy little hand-written tenders and agreements (which survive) written on the early nineteenth-century equivalent of a split beer mat. These give the impression of being informal low-key agreements with self-employed men for such tasks as the shifting of spoil, but the quantities involved, and the frequency with which the same names recur make it clear that some at least of the men with whom agreements were thus casually being made were contractors of some substance. Some work was 'contracted' on the basis of nothing written at all.[40]

Different engineers favoured different methods of control. Telford and Jessop, although they worked together so much, had rather different approaches to the letting of contracts. Telford favoured letting large numbers of small contracts – what one might call a 'divide and rule' approach – while Jessop preferred to let large contracts, often through a single principal contractor. What they agreed on, however, was that everything must be carefully specified and enforceable. On balance, Jessop's may have been the better method, since in the event of non-performance he could simply sue the principal contractor without having to spend time pinning down exactly whose fault the problem was.[41]

It seems clear that the rectification of Foster's deliberately sloppy practices was a key responsibility for the incoming Hartley. He was somewhat circumscribed in that Thomas Foster remained as Town Clerk until 1836 and William as Secretary to the Dock Committee until the following year. Hartley could not, therefore, arbitrarily embargo all firms owned or part-owned by any of the Foster family, which would have been a radical but possibly sensible action. He had instead to overhaul the old system, update it where necessary and, above all, enforce it. To enforce it, more clerical staff and probably also more draughtsmen were necessary, and we find that in the annual accounts for June 1824–June 1825, salaries of officers and clerks are entered at £2,762 16s 5d and wages to 'Assistant Clerks, Measurers, Foremen etc' amounted to £384 10s 10d. By the following June these figures had risen to £6,726 0s 10d and £1,152 12s respectively.[42] One of the surviving reminders of where some of this large additional expenditure went is the small collection of masonry progress drawings in the MD&HB archive.

Under the old regime, the amount of stone delivered was measured in an extremely inaccurate manner and what happened to it after that was anybody's guess. The amount of stone paid for at Princes Dock would have been enough not only to build the dock but also to fill it solid afterwards. The new system may have cost more to operate, but the scale of the losses more than justified the expense of measuring work and producing accurate, highly detailed colour-coded drawings showing what stones were laid on which day. Hartley estimated the cost of his new control measures at about 2.5 per cent of total costs, and they resulted in a significant reduction in the cost per acre of new construction. Because of the accounting irregularities

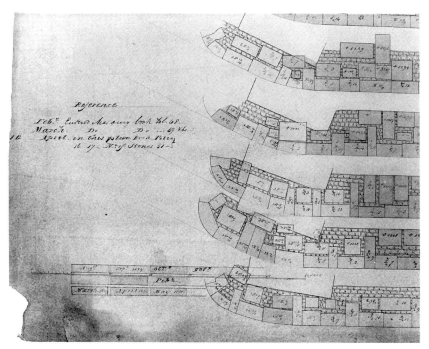

*A detail from one of Jesse Hartley's masonry progress plans (1828).*

under the Foster regime and the changed procedures under Hartley, it is difficult to make exact comparisons from the published accounts of the Trustees. A 'headline figure' does seem to be fairly comparable: according to Baines, the total cost of building Waterloo, Victoria, Trafalgar, Clarence, Clarence Half-Tide, Clarence Graving Dock Basin and the two Clarence Graving Docks, was some £684,669, compared with Princes Dock at £600,000. The combined area of the group that Hartley built was nearly three times that of Princes, and because the individual docks and basins were smaller, there were more walls and gates to the acre. If Baines' figures are even near correct, 2.5 per cent was a small price to pay for such a saving.[43]

That Hartley initially improved the situation a great deal by adopting better practices of specification, tendering and control is beyond reasonable doubt. That was not, however, his preferred long-term solution, and neither was it a significant contribution to the development of dock engineering, since the consultants had been doing it that way for decades. It was, as mentioned above, Hartley's taking of work in-house and building up an integrated dock engineering works, the establishment he called 'The Dock yard', which marks him as a pioneer.

There must have been works compounds constructed for the work on the Old Dock, indeed probably even before that for the quay walls and the pier, but they have left no record. By the time of John Foster, we find that there are temporary site yards (the one at Princes became notorious as the Audit Commissioners found one impropriety after another), but there is also what appears to have been a permanent yard to the west of Salthouse Dock. In 1826, we find the modest sum of £22 8s 3d spent on 'New Dock Yard', followed by £4,264 in 1827 and £1,409 11s 3d in 1828. During this extension of the facilities, the scale of Hartley's operation was already expanding rapidly: the value of 'materials on hand' rose from £5,009 to £8,194 to £15,884. There was a corresponding recruitment drive: wages paid to carpenters rose from £1,302 to £2,534 to £3,940 and to masons from £980 to £1,892 to £2,583. These were still early days, and we must not over-estimate the speed of change, for in 1828 there was still an expenditure of £12,458 9s 2d on assorted contract work for the Surveyor's Department.[44] The process of integration and centralization was well begun.

By 1840, the changes had run a long way. Wages paid to masons and bricklayers were £14,985, while the total expenditure on contracts for masonry, brickwork and slating came to only £1,161. This, however, was to be the crisis year for the Dock Yard: the 'opposition' on the Dock Committee initially succeeded in gaining a resolution which would have virtually abolished the Dock Yard by having all new works put out to contract. But Hartley, despite the fact that he had less overt political influence than most of his predecessors was a forceful and probably an obstinate man: not only did he succeed in getting the decision reversed, but when the site of the Dock Yard was needed for Albert Dock, he was allowed to build a new, bigger and better Dock Yard at Coburg Dock. In 1842, £16,592 was spent, with another £20,949 the following year. In 1843, the wages paid to masons and bricklayers totalled £15,959 and the total spent on contract brickwork, masonry and slating was just £715. In the meantime, Hartley's salary had increased by a third, partly in recognition of his agreeing not to accept any further outside work.[45]

Hartley had, in short, not just established an integrated engineering

*A general view of the Dock Yard in its declining years. The foundry has been demolished, giving much improved access to the boilershop on the left. At the far end is the new gateshed.*

*Jesse Hartley's little stone carrier* Oak, *seen here looking quite respectable in Wellington Dock in 1902, when she was 66 years old.*

establishment providing skills of design and capacity for execution within a wide range of civil and mechanical engineering activities. He had faced attack for inefficiency and extravagance and had inflicted a headlong rout on his critics. The extent of his integration was remarkable: not only had he acquired 'his own' granite quarry in Scotland, he even built his own little ship, the *Oak*, which was registered as built at the Dock Yard, by builder Jesse Hartley, to carry his stone from his quarry to his Dock Yard.[46] She was an expensive little vessel, but she continued to appear in the insurances section of the *Annual Accounts* until 1902: spread over 66 years her cost was probably quite reasonable. Despite the conversion of an old lightvessel into a schooner, at busy times a great deal of chartering was necessary as well. The machinery was in place for the extraordinary outburst of activity which was to turn him into the most prolific and successful dock engineer to date.

The dissemination of dockbuilding expertise from Liverpool, not just in design but in control and execution is not very easy to trace during Hartley's tenure. Although he was a member of the Institution of Civil Engineers from 1825 until his death in 1860, he never contributed to their *Proceedings* even in discussion or correspondence, much less did he present a paper! This may have been because, as Picton stated, he was not particularly eloquent: certainly Picton's statement that Hartley hated giving evidence to parliamentary enquiries seems to stand justified by the nature of some of the evidence Hartley gave.[47] He was more given to making dogmatic statements than to explaining things, and there are times when one feels he was lucky to be facing counsel he was capable of overawing. There is even the possibility that he was deliberately secretive: some of his methods relied on very careful attention to the detail of execution. His retaining walls, for example, were generally rather thinner than current theory suggested they should have been, yet they fell over less often than the general run of walls: he had remarkably few failures. Perhaps he preferred that his competitors did not know why this was. One is tempted to assume that the fact he was a freemason might also have inclined him to keep his secrets, but plenty of other, more communicative, engineers of his generation were masons as well.

There was one group of people to whom he could not avoid telling the secrets, namely his assistants and his pupils. His son, John Bernard Hartley, worked with him from 1846, on the rather vague footing that Jesse's salary rose to £3,125 (and to £3,500 in 1847) and was to include the services of his son. John Bernard was described sometimes as Assistant, sometimes as Deputy and sometimes as Joint Surveyor. He had served his pupillage partly with his father, partly with his father's long-standing friend James Walker, and had worked as a consultant since then. It is generally difficult to separate his work from his father's, but fortunately Jesse was recorded as having nothing to do with the works at Birkenhead, so when we look at those, we know we are looking at John Bernard's work. He appears to have followed his father's methods pretty closely, and given the problems with bad ground which Rendel before him and Lyster after encountered in Birkenhead, it is quite remarkable that none of his walls there is recorded as having failed. When his Alfred Entrance was eventually reconstructed in the mid-1920s, the project ran hideously over budget as the quicksands he and Lyster had conquered gained revenge on their successors.

John Bernard did not publish a lot either, though a paper on 'The Effect of the Worm on Kyanised Timber' clearly indicates that systematic and controlled experiments had been conducted with a view to determining the most suitable material for dock gates. Similarly, short papers on pile driving and on retaining walls for railway cuttings and embankments indicate, albeit slightly enigmatically, the importance of minute attention to the detail execution of inherently quite simple processes, which some might suggest was a large part of the secret of his father's success.[48]

Unfortunately, it is difficult to trace pupils of either of the Hartleys. Pupillage was a personal arrangement, so pupils' premium payments do not occur in the dock accounts, and young men who were occupying junior positions as, for example, drawing office assistants, were lumped together as anonymous 'Assistant Clerks'. In 1848, Assistant Clerks were paid a total of £2,683, at an average of possibly £80 per head (per year).[49] Hidden among them were also men like John Ellacott, who remained in the department from 1847 until his retirement in 1881. Jesse Hartley's personal papers, which might have been more helpful, were destroyed after his death in accordance with the terms of his will, a fact which Ellacott confirmed to the Institution of Civil Engineers.[50]

We can, of course, trace men back to Liverpool rather than forward from it, although such a procedure is something of a 'lucky dip'. There are two outstanding pupils of Jesse Hartley, namely Robert Rawlinson and John Hawkshaw. Both were eventually knighted and elected President of the

Institution of Civil Engineers, and Hartley was the first man to be thus
distinguished by his pupils. Rawlinson became perhaps the most important
figure in what we broadly term municipal engineering, and Hawkshaw
worked all over the world on docks, harbours, railways, bridges and
municipal works. We have already noted that Hawkshaw exported Hartley's
granite rubble masonry technique to Buenos Aires: Rawlinson twice
contributed to discussions at 'The Civils' along the general lines that the
only way to build proper walls was the way his old Chief had done it. When
G.F. Lyster was appointed Engineer-in-Chief to what was by then the Mersey
Docks & Harbour Board, he took up the Hartley method (presumably via
John Ellacott, by then Principal Assistant) and continued to use it for another
20 years. As we shall see in Chapter 5, his pupils are easier to trace than
those of the Hartleys, and they carried Liverpool techniques even further and
wider.

In at least one respect, Hartley could not keep his methods secret even if
he wanted to, and that was in the matter of integration in the Dock Yard,
which was bound to become public knowledge. The first wave of expansion,
on the old site at Trentham Street, pre-dates any comparable set-up in Britain

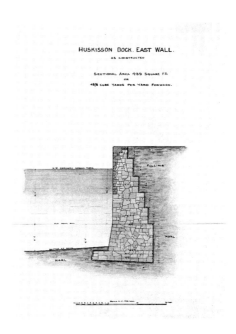

*A fairly typical section of one of Hartley's
later walls. Huskisson Dock was opened
in 1852.*

with the single exception of the Royal Dockyards. As early as 1830, the Edge Hill Works of the Liverpool & Manchester Railway was beginning to follow the Hartley route. It was a route with several termini: Derby, Crewe, Swindon or Doncaster for example. Although such organizations tended eventually to become over-complex and virtually collapse under their own weight – as indeed did Hartley's Dock Yard – at the time they offered the benefit of allowing the Chief and his senior assistants to keep close control of every stage of almost every process, and by concentrating the work in a single establishment to make the turnover large enough to keep top-flight specialist engineers fully occupied and to provide for the training of new members of what had become a specialized branch of the engineering profession.

*What Sort of Men were They?*
The brevity of Ritchie-Noakes' section on the engineers makes it clear just how hard it is to discover anything about the characters or leisure interests of the engineers – a problem on which Smiles remarked 130 or so years ago, saying of Rennie that his life was his work. Among those who were least-known for anything other than their works is John Bernard Hartley, so a brief account of one incident which tells us a little about him as a man is perhaps an excusable digression.[51]

On 6 September 1842, John Bernard married Harriett Say Hall, the daughter of Richard Hall, Gentleman, at Holy Trinity Church, Liverpool. His address at the time of the marriage was Bootle Marsh, indicating that he lived with his father, but not long afterwards he moved to a compact but fashionable house at the end of Mornington Terrace. In 1850, Queen Victoria gave the Royal Assent to a private Act of Parliament to dissolve the marriage. This was an unusual procedure: between 1765 and 1857 (when the law was changed) there were only 276 Divorce Acts passed, eight of them in the year 1850. It was also an extremely expensive procedure: John's legal costs came to over £4,000, despite the fact that the latter part of the case was not contested. We are entitled to ask, therefore, why he should thus attract bad publicity to himself and risk large sums of money. The obvious reason would be that he wished to remarry, as indeed he did, but he appears to have had no such intention at the time.

As mentioned elsewhere in this book, Jesse Hartley was neither fond of, nor very good at, giving evidence before parliamentary committees: when baited by opposing counsel he was given to allowing himself simply to make arrogant *ex cathedra* statements rather than arguing or explaining. As a result, John came increasingly into the frame as conducting parliamentary business for his father, which meant he was often in London for considerable periods. Sometimes Harriett went with him: on 14 March 1846 she wrote to him: 'Of course I should not at all enjoy being in London and you elsewhere, as seeing and being with you will be my greatest Enjoyment (sic). I hope we shall go up, for Two Reasons, on Tuesday; one is I am longing to see you, and "Hope deferred maketh the Heart sick:" . . . I have been thinking with such glee of your meeting me at the station. . . . Your Wife is well and happy and sends her undying Love to her Husband.'

There is no evidence that in the early years of their marriage they were anything other than an affectionate and happy couple, materially well off and both, apparently, physically attractive. What went wrong is partly indicated by Harriett's letter: it was sent not to London, but to Hull, which was where John was. In addition to his responsibilities in Liverpool, he was also Chief on the new improvements at Hull docks, and appears to have had a fairly set routine whereby he spent the week in Liverpool and alternate weekends in Hull. He was also 'Engineer to several other Works'.

In spring 1846, John and Harriett had been in London on parliamentary business, along with his sister Mary and her husband, Henry Forshaw. It was then that they first met James Thomson, Engineer to the Liverpool & Bury Railway, predecessor of the Lancashire & Yorkshire, which was to cross on a viaduct over the new branch of the Leeds & Liverpool Canal which John and his father were constructing down to Stanley Dock. Contact with Thomson became more frequent, and around that time there seemed a change in the warmth of the marriage, but no hint of anything improper. In 1847, John took on yet more work, which involved his spending time in Glasgow, and in July that year a rumour reached his ears that his wife was on the point of eloping with another man. Loyal to the point of simple-mindedness, he made no effort to ascertain whether there might be any truth in the rumour, but set brother-in-law Henry Forshaw, who was a solicitor, to trace it to its source. A Mr Prest was deemed to be guilty, and was persuaded to meet with John at the Waterloo Hotel, where 'Mr Hartley, under my Directions, horsewhipped Mr Prest.' On 17 August, John's friend Thomson, wrote

My dear Hartley,

I only wish to God I had been with you, although from accounts you
needed no help. I stayed last night at our worthy friend Foreshaw's
(sic), who gave me full particulars. I would have run down to the yard
to see you. . . .

Ever most truly yours, in haste,

On 3 October, Mrs Catherine Jones, a housekeeper, rented a house in
Buckingham Terrace, Liverpool in her own name for the use of her master.
He had a number of lady callers, but one of them stayed the night there on
three occasions and was a frequent visitor during the daytime. She was
Harriett Hartley and he was James Thomson. Around Christmas that year,
Harriett ordered Mrs Jones to go to London and to send the furniture to an
interim love-nest in Sackville Street. Mrs Jones continued to work for the
'happy couple' until they moved on to Southsea.

The truth had finally dawned on John in or around September, and a
separation was agreed in November. John agreed to pay Harriett a settlement
of £400 p.a., and then began the long three-stage process of divorce, through
'Doctors Commons' (the Church Court) and the local Sheriff's Court to the
House of Lords. In the Sheriff's Court he gained damages of £4,000 and
costs from Thomson, all of which, and more, he expended on legal services,
and this despite the fact that once the defence discovered that John's lawyers
had found Mrs Jones and her damning evidence, they withdrew their plea.

But somebody else may have known, or had a shrewd suspicion, what was
going on. In 1846, John Ellacott had left the Dock Yard to work as a resident
on the Liverpool section of the Liverpool-Bury Railway. He did not stay
long before returning to the Dock Yard: could it be that with the arrival of
the trusty John Hawkshaw on the job on 25 May 1847 that 'somebody else',
namely Jesse, no longer needed Ellacott as a mole in Thomson's office?

What are we to make of John Hartley from this long and unedifying tale?
The first thing it reveals, with great clarity, is that he was a workaholic.
Whether or not he had early suspicions of what Harriett was up to makes no
difference to our judgement of the man. If he did, then he got someone else
to do his spying for him and carried on working harder than ever. If he did

not, it was presumably because he was too busy to bother to think about what was happening under his nose. In that respect one cannot but feel sorry for him. He made no attempt to conceal the fact that he had neglected Harriett and no attempt to portray her as encouraging the seducer in any way. He did not make any statements which would even be hurtful, much less harmful, to her.

But there is another side to the question: if John was a likeable workaholic loser unfitted to marriage he would not have distracted himself from his engineering efforts for well over two years by pursuing Thomson in the courts and he would certainly have pocketed his damages from the Sheriff's Court rather than 're-investing' them in the Divorce Bill. Hidden inside this superficially kind man there must have been a deep and constant malevolence which demanded the destruction of the reputation of the man who took his wife. Owing to the mid-nineteenth century's disregard for such niceties as the correct spelling of Thomson *vis-à-vis* Thompson, it is difficult to be sure, but the archives at the Institution of Civil Engineers have three James Thompson/Thomsons who were the right age at the right time, two of whom may almost certainly be ruled out: one was a Shropshire ironmaster, and another, the brother of the future Lord Kelvin seems to have been living a life of exemplary probity in Glasgow. In the 1846 membership list there is a James Thompson of 9 Whitehall Place, and in 1851 he is gone, never to be heard of again.

When we think about it, though, it would be surprising if engineers of John Hartley's calibre were entirely amiable and likeable people. They were the winners in a cut-throat world of big-money high-risk projects. If he had not possessed the constancy of purpose he exhibited in pursuing his man, could he have pushed major projects through to completion? Without the ability to switch off thinking about docks for an hour or two while discussing the latest love-nest discovered by his solicitor, he would not have been able to switch between projects in Liverpool, Glasgow and Hull. What did Port Authorities need with nice guys? The engineer was there to do the best possible job at the best possible price, and one way he could achieve that was by ruthless single-mindedness – a characteristic which obituarists might shrink from recording. Yet well within two years he remarried and had two children by his second wife, Frances. His will established a complex trust to protect the interests of the children in the event of her remarrying after his death, suggesting that she was much younger than him. The marriage lasted until his death, so either he had learned his lesson or he had found a wife content to sit around and sew.

That raises the question of Jesse Hartley's personality, a subject open to more speculation than scholarship owing to the paucity of evidence. We may be permitted one deduction from one of the few official documents – there are effectively no personal ones – where he seems to speak from the heart. In 1836, on the eve of the dissolution of the old Council and hence the arrival of a new Dock Committee elected under the Municipal Reform Act, Hartley produced a massive report giving an account of his stewardship of the docks from the time of his appointment to the time of writing. The Committee, who were clearly demob-happy, responded with an admission that in the busy times brought about by arranging their own dissolution, they had not studied it closely, but thanked him most graciously for his loyalty and outstanding achievements, pointing out that while they, the members, would pass into history relatively unnoticed, his works would stand witness to his greatness. Most men would have been pleased.

Hartley was furious: the idea that the members could have neglected to study his report with the minutest care, just because they were being dissolved, was taken not just as evidence of an irresponsible outlook, but a gross personal affront. Perhaps Hartley was expecting a golden handshake, or the presentation of a piece of plate sufficient to sink the *Oak*. Many an engineer of the day might have made such an utterance in a fit of pique, possibly in the course of a slightly drunken after-dinner speech. Gaffes of that kind were not uncommon, but were quickly patched up afterwards. Hartley's case was very different. There survives the manuscript copy from the Dock Yard Office, which was presumably copied from his own draft: having eschewed that opportunity for cooling-off, Hartley went on to have the entire document printed and published.[52] There seem few possible explanations for such an extreme response to what was meant as an extravagant compliment except for his finding it quite incomprehensible that anyone could think anything in life more important than dock engineering.

It may be, then, that John Hartley's neglect of his pretty and vivacious young wife arose in part from an inherited characteristic. Jesse Hartley may well have been an eminently unlikeable man, though his long-standing friendships with men such as James Walker and Albinus Martin suggest otherwise. His excellent working relationship with John Bramley-Moore, Chairman of the Dock Committee 1843–8, resulted in a positive explosion of dock building of a very high standard.[53] Only a little financial *legerdemain* was necessary to show this huge sequence of works as completed within budget despite the extraordinarily difficult circumstances brought about by the Railway Mania. One is reluctantly driven back to Smiles' position, that although one can try to find personal insights, we can really only know these men by their work, which was all that mattered to them.

# 2
# Planning and Decision Making

The engineering of a port was a very large-scale and complex business, and if we view port services as an industry, it was clearly an industry of great national importance. It is a curious fact that neither the people directly involved nor Members of Parliament whose consent was necessary for any but the smallest schemes seem to have realized the implications. There was no institutionalized connection between the planning, financing, construction and operation of ports, no overall conception of their nature and purpose. As a result, they grew up in an even more disorganized manner than had either canals or railways, and as the nineteenth century wore on and the financial stakes became higher, the uncertainties which lay at the heart of the industry were strengthened rather than weakened. It is amazing but true that in a century which spawned repeated enquiries into railways and shipping there was not one which directly investigated the provision of port facilities as a national issue. It was left, therefore, to an assortment of differently constituted bodies to decide for themselves what those basic relationships should be. In the process, they would necessarily come to some implicit view of what ports, or at least their port, was for. The engineers were the key professionals involved, and necessarily played their part in forming the structure of the industry. In the case of Liverpool, the result was a model imitated by many other ports. The relationship between the engineer and his paymasters is therefore an important underlying issue on the wider stage. At the more superficial level it determined whether the money men got a working port for their money or not.

Thomas Steers was in a peculiar position for an engineer through his involvement in all the three main phases of dock construction, namely policy making, design and execution. By the time of John Foster, a considerable mileage of canals and high-quality turnpike roads had been built and it was fairly clearly understood what the relationships between people concerned with the three phases should normally be. In the beginning was the client, which in the case of canals was normally a statutory limited company established under a private Act of Parliament, generally known as an

Enabling Act. The client could, however, be almost any form of body corporate, including a local board of Improvement Commissioners, a municipality or a county council. Exceptionally it might be an individual such as the Duke of Bridgewater or the Marquis of Bute.

The client would only rarely have any specific engineering skills available – again the Duke of Bridgewater seems to be an exception – and would therefore need to obtain the services of a consultant at a very early stage. Since, in the vast majority of cases, the skills of the engineer were needed to provide plans and estimates for obtaining the enabling act, bodies which were not already established had normally to form a provisional committee or similar before the eventual client body officially existed. That was a problem which did not confront a perpetual body like a municipal borough council, but the first steps were otherwise similar. The client had a notion, probably a rather vague one, that benefits would accrue from the construction of a dock, a canal or whatever. The benefits which came to be enumerated in the Bill commonly included the service which would be rendered to the public at large, especially the poor and needy, but in reality, of course, the benefit was almost invariably monetary, whether from anticipated profits from a private venture or from the more general improvement of local business in the case of a municipal venture.

The initial brief to the engineer might be remarkably vague. In the case of a canal company steering committee the members might have only the haziest idea of a feasible route. The brief from the Dock Trustees to William Jessop for the proposed new dock in Liverpool in 1800 is couched in businesslike language, but really says little more than this: we are running out of dock space and we want more; we have had problems with wall failures and silting at the last new docks we built and we expect you to do better; can you, and if so what will it cost?

It is a well-known fact that if you do not ask the right question you will not get the right answer, so the constitution and membership of what we may term the client body is quite important. In the case of an unreformed municipal borough like Liverpool, the chances seem rather high that the wrong questions would be asked. Elections to the Council were a travesty of what we now mean by the word, for the Council was entirely self-electing and, technically, responsible only to itself. For two reasons, this situation in Liverpool did not lead to the dire consequences that the modern observer might expect. The first was the extent and value of the Corporate Estate, which really required professional management – and, in an age when professional local government officers were very few in number, it received it.[1] The second was that although the docks were normally thought of as part of the Corporate Estate, they were, technically, vested in the body known as the Dock Trustees. The Trustees were quite simply the Common Council using different minute books and account books, but there was the vital difference that when they used the Dock Trustees' account book, they were subject to the scrutiny of the body of Audit Commissioners, whose membership they did not control. We do not find, therefore, that the Trustees were desperately bad at building and running docks, as we might expect from the antics of some local authorities at the time.[2] On the contrary, they were actually rather good, and they look particularly good when their work is compared with the efforts of a private company at Hull.

So long as they were dealing with Jessop or Rennie, they would probably manage well, for the next stage in the process was for the consultant to produce a fairly detailed plan and estimate to take to parliament, hopefully returning with an Act which included the authority to borrow a great deal of money. This was where things began to break down in Liverpool, for the intention was to use the consultant only for the preliminaries, the broad-brush work, and then to pay him a retainer to allow Foster to pick his brains a bit from time to time thereafter. A similar arrangement was adopted at Grimsby with equally unsatisfactory results. While in Liverpool the physical side of the work was good and the site management ruinous, in Grimsby there were severe problems in both areas.[3] Such a system placed Foster on two sides of the fence: he was responsible both for most of the detail design and also for the execution. In the normal course of things, Rennie would have put a resident engineer in charge of the work who was responsible for ensuring that the contractors performed satisfactorily. If the client was worried, it was in theory down to Rennie's man, or in serious matters Rennie himself, to take any necessary action up to and including suing the contractor for every penny he had. To protect himself in such situations, the contractor would normally have an engineer of his own, with the result that as a matter of day-to-day practice, many problems would be ironed out before they happened as a result of the mildly confrontational relationship between two fellow-professionals representing different interests.

In the absence of such a relationship, which would also involve a knowing scrutiny of each other's activities, Foster was able to fudge almost anything he wished, so that the only effective scrutiny was that of the Audit Commissioners, who were not engineers and could only intervene when they found serious financial discrepancies, by which time it was too late. The system evolved in the canal-building industry broke down – or was broken – in an exactly analogous way on the Liverpool & Manchester Railway, where George Stephenson was both Principal Engineer and Principal Contractor. There is no evidence that rampant corruption, such as occurred at Princes Dock, was intended or practised there, but a good deal of confusion occurred and wrong decisions were undoubtedly made which caused increased costs. The author makes no apology for citing, as he has cited many times before, the strictures of Thomas Telford on the Stephenson management methods. As so often it is when a system gives trouble, and not before, that someone actually spells out how it is meant to work.[4] James Cropper, who as an Audit Commissioner had been a moving force behind the virtual dismissal of John Foster, was also responsible as a Director of the L&MR for Hartley's involvement on the railway, and it seems likely that this was because he recognized the need for the element of dissent mentioned above.

The system which applied at the time of Jesse Hartley's appointment, where the Surveyor was responsible both for design and for at least part of the execution, was a dangerous one, and the dangers increased as Hartley extended his control through the expansion of his direct workforce described above. Because of the personal power he had amassed, effectively as a Chief Executive, such a system could only work in the presence of a number of favourable circumstances. The engineer had to be of high competence and probably higher integrity, and the body to which he reported had not only to be capable of making wise and well-informed decisions but also of checking that they were in fact correctly implemented. It could not be a body of place-men who yawned briefly and ignorantly through the business of the meeting and agreed everything quickly and unanimously, the sooner to get to the real business of a magnificent free lunch. Neither, on the other hand, should it be a body which would divide on strict party lines. Such a list of requirements looks fairly formidable, even unlikely to be fulfilled, but in fact the Liverpool Dock Estate prospered as never before. Neither the Enquiry of the Municipal Commissioners nor the 'new broom' approach of the new council elected after the passage of the Municipal Reform Act was able to find the faintest whiff of scandal since the appointment of Jesse Hartley. The former body, having been sent out to find examples of abuse and corruption in local government, did what they were told and found some. In the field of dock construction, however, they were reduced to the rather pitiable expedient of picking over the bones of the Princes Dock scandal, by then well-bleached by eleven years of public exposure.[5] Civil engineers would doubtless argue that the real problems of the Dock Estate arose when what they would consider a jumped-up clerk became General Manager.

Unfortunately, changing ideas started to tug, gently at first, at the rug on which the system stood. The first challenge came on the issue of building docks on the Birkenhead side of the river, which was first considered in a report produced by Stevenson, Nimmo and Telford in 1828. The stated intention was to reduce the price of port facilities on the Mersey by introducing a healthy element of competition, but it was an intention which proved hideously misguided. The machinations over land in Birkenhead are well documented elsewhere,[6] so for present purposes it is only necessary to remark that Liverpool's attempts to snuff out the threatened competition were initially successful.

The next attack on the Trustees came on the issue of town dues, resulting in the enormously long and complex 'Bolton Case' of 1833. Counsel recited documents quite literally back to Domesday Book in the effort to prove that the Corporation's treatment of town dues as part of the general revenue was illegal. The attempt was unsuccessful, and the right of the Corporation to do with the town dues exactly as they pleased was reaffirmed.[7] Next came a recrudescence of the Birkenhead problem, with the passage in 1844 of the first Birkenhead Dock Act. This marked the real beginning of an anti-Liverpool campaign by denizens of Wirral which caused them to oppose every Liverpool Dock Act down to and including that of 1873. By 1847, the first little bit of the Birkenhead Dock system was opened, but the money was all gone and bankruptcy was beckoning. There followed a sequence of Birkenhead Dock Acts which attempted to rescue the situation, but succeeded mainly in wasting large amounts of money on parliamentary expenses. It should be remembered that this activity on the Birkenhead side coincided quite deliberately with the huge dock expansion programme under the Liverpool Dock Acts of 1841, 1844 and 1846.

It is possible to make comparisons between the quality of engineering planning and decision-making, as well as finance, on opposite sides of the river in the late 1840s and early '50s. Birkenhead Docks involved a rather odd arrangement where the basic infrastructure was to be provided by the Birkenhead Dock Trust and everything else by the Birkenhead Dock Company. There were dubious cross-financing arrangements between both these bodies, the Chester & Birkenhead Railway Company and the Birkenhead Improvement Commissioners, and there were frequent schisms between a faction led by the Laird family and another led by the Jacksons. Taken together, these factors made the possibility of a good engineering job extremely remote. James Meadows Rendel, the consulting engineer, was twice dismissed, twice replaced by James Abernethy and twice re-instated. Errors of the most elementary kind were made, including the old chestnut of building retaining walls on bad ground because the enclosure of an existing inlet seemed to offer large savings in excavation costs. Test-boring seems to have been unlucky and inadequate. Sod's Law struck as well: having found soft ground where they wanted hard, an area needing to be dredged near the entrance proved to be not clay, as was thought, but rock, causing severe delay and additional expense. The guilty party who allowed the engineers to construct a dock on land which did not belong to the Trust and which they had no powers to purchase has so far escaped undetected. Fortunately, the Commissioners of Woods and Forests, to whom the land belonged, were in a forgiving mood, albeit it at the price of naming Morpeth Dock in honour of the Chief Commissioner.[8]

The Birkenhead Docks up to this point would simply be one of history's little jokes, were it not for the fact that they had already caused problems for Liverpool. It was an ongoing problem of ports throughout the nineteenth century (and beyond) that their customers were never willing to pay a fair price for port services. A fair price required an income sufficient to maintain the docks, service the debts and leave an operating surplus which would provide for obsolescence and the eventual need for replacement.[9] The competition of Birkenhead, pitiable as it was at first, forced Liverpool to reduce its dues, with the result that Hartley and the Sub-Committee of Works had to look for ways of cutting expenditure. Worse, however, was to come. Birkenhead Docks degenerated into such a financial and engineering disaster that there was no possibility of redemption under the existing ownership, with the result that the only possible chance of investors seeing any of their money back lay in the docks being taken over by Liverpool. The 1855 Dock Bill was intended to enable new construction in Liverpool of unprecedented extent, but the objectors from Birkenhead succeeded both in scuppering most of the proposed new docks and in inserting a clause forcing the Liverpool Trustees to take over and complete the Birkenhead Docks. The Trustees were saddled, therefore, with a huge scheme which they neither wanted nor needed and which required many millions of pounds spent to render it usable.[10]

This might have been expected to make the opposition happy, but it did nothing of the kind. There now emerged an alliance between the Great Western Railway, the Birkenhead interest and the Manchester Chamber of Commerce, which attacked Liverpool in evidence before the Select Committee on Local Charges on Shipping,[11] whose investigations were really a revival of the issues raised in the Bolton Case, with claims that the town of Liverpool was milking the revenues of the port for such alleged civic extravagances as the building of St George's Hall. The alliance was both crying out for larger expenditure on the port and seeking to diminish the revenues coming into it. Their eventual success resulted in the establishment of the Mersey Docks & Harbour Board in 1857, as a statutory non-profit-making trust to take over the docks of both Liverpool and Birkenhead.[12]

There were high hopes of the new body, for it seemed that it would end what was portrayed as the parochial control by the Liverpool Council as Trustees and allow a new, elected, body of men representing the users of the port to manage the port solely in the interests of those users. The Act which established it is a most peculiar one: effectively it states that the new Board should continue very much as the old Dock Trustees had done, with basically the same rights and duties (except, obviously, for the application of town dues to general municipal revenue) but with no more specific objective than to operate the port for the common benefit of its customers. It was intended that membership of the Board should be accompanied by a good deal of social cachet, so that the best shipping and business brains in the port would be willing to provide the benefits of their talents without cost. The social cachet was achieved, but the rest, as we shall see, was problematical. That was in part because the fundamental problem, that port users did not want to pay up, was not going away. That, in turn, was because nobody had ever thought of the ports industry – or indeed the transport industry – as a national system, but merely as an assemblage of unconnected opportunities for profit. Profits made by others were normally cause for more jealousy than admiration, with the result that transport generally and ports particularly, were subjected both to chronic underfunding and to spurious duplication of facilities.

To begin with, the changes under the new order were comparatively modest, at least in the field of engineering. Among the membership of the new Board were several of the key members of the old Trustee body, and some of the new men were of high ability and diligence. Just as important, they had more sense than to mess about with the permanent staff, who seem to have been able to continue much as before. Jesse Hartley was now 77 years old: despite that (or possibly because of it) he was still capable of exerting considerable influence on what was now called the Works Committee. We must expect that his powers were declining at such an age, and that a heavy burden fell on John Ellacott, his second-in-command on the Liverpool side and John Bernard Hartley who had taken complete charge in Birkenhead. Nevertheless, the performance of the department remained at the very high levels which had been sustained since the mid-1840s. In particular, the achievement of making an operable system out of the mess left at Birkenhead was remarkable. It may be that the Hartleys continued too long in building ever wider entrances, most notably at Canada Entrance, for vast but shallow paddle-steamers when the age of the narrower but deeper screw-steamer was dawning, but they had become accustomed to a rate of growth of trade which both required and funded the continuous production of new docks. In those circumstances there was always a next time, and the next time would cater for the next need.

Over the next few years, the changes which could have happened suddenly in 1858, began to happen gradually. In 1860, Jesse Hartley retired, and died shortly afterwards. His son, promoted as Chief on the full (enormous) salary of £3,500, retired on grounds of ill-health, in December 1861, after only fifteen months. No conclusive evidence of the nature of John Bernard's illness survives: neuralgia is mentioned as 'his old complaint', but only after he had needed fairly extended absence from work. His retirement to Scotland, where he survived another eight years, coupled with his undertaking a small amount of consultancy work, suggests that a stress-related condition may have been at least part of his trouble. If that is so, then the wisdom of Jesse Hartley in arguing that Birkenhead was simply too much to take on, seems clear.[13]

The post of Chief Engineer to the MD&HB was easily the highest paid salaried engineering post in the country, so it need come as no surprise that when it was advertised it attracted a large number of applicants. The man appointed, George Fosbery Lyster, came from a different mould from any of his predecessors, for the engineering profession had grown enormously in size and changed almost beyond recognition in the process. It was, after all, 21 years since Hartley Jnr had been elected to the 'The Civils' and 36 years since his father had. In that time the Railway Mania had occurred and there had been a rapid increase in such other engineering activities as the supply of water to fast-growing and highly insanitary towns. During the period of Smiles' great engineers, men of practical talents emerged as engineers through developing new skills – new not only to them but to the profession as well. That was not, however strongly sentiment might suggest otherwise, a state of affairs which would continue in mainstream civil engineering. The promising lad would seek pupillage under a well-established and reputable engineer, and in many cases this resulted in a comparatively poor training in actual construction work. A Smeaton, a Telford or a Hartley could adopt a management style, if he so chose, not of 'go and do that' but of 'come and do this'. Frederick Royce is said to have walked around his works listening to the sound of lathes and milling machines, and the man whose machine was not cutting correctly could expect a foul-mouthed rebuke – and a demonstration of how to do it properly, not from the foreman but from the boss. The old generation of civil engineers were much the same. John Bernard Hartley's engineering career had begun in the millwright's shop in the Dock Yard.[14]

In 1846, Commissioner Dowling, of the Liverpool Police had given evidence before the Select Committee on Railway Labourers. When he was asked about the extraordinarily low accident rate suffered by Jesse Hartley's men, he attributed this to the high standard of site supervision by engineers from the Dock Yard, and made it clear that Jesse Hartley himself was in the habit of visiting the works.[15] He is unlikely to have suffered in silence if he saw poor craftsmanship being perpetrated, though such was his reputation as a martinet that anything sub-standard would probably have been well hidden.

Lyster began his career in a very different way. By the time he emerged from a private education, engineers were reaping the social and financial rewards of the triumphs of an earlier generation: not only were they well-paid; they were regarded as gentlemen as well. Robert Stephenson, for example, not only became (according to Smiles) the first millionaire engineer, but was buried in Westminster Abbey. James Meadows Rendel, the man under whom Lyster learned was not quite on that plane, but he was an altogether more exalted man than Andrew Meikle, the millwright under whom John Rennie learned his earliest skills.[16] He was certainly not a man to go boozing with his navvies like Brindley or showing them how to shovel spoil like George Stephenson. The young Lyster began his career surveying railway routes, and of all the work he did in this field only one line seems actually to have been a serious proposal for a railway rather than a scheme for financial manipulation.[17] It cannot have been a professional initiation designed to instil much idealism about harnessing the great sources of power in nature when the benefits were demonstrably to the grubbier kind of financier. What was happening in railway engineering during Lyster's formative years was a change in the realities of the engineer/client relationship whereby the interests of the nominal client – the shareholders – were being subordinated to those of the effective client, namely a small clique of professionals, whether officers or directors, within the company.[18]

At the same time, the Board was beginning to change, and with it the Works Committee. As years passed by, the members of the Board came to have more and more ways of spending their time. Most were leading figures in whatever was their principal business, but all of them had other demands on their time. Some of those demands were in secondary occupations, such as non-executive directorships in insurance and banking. Others were the obligations which came with the social standing necessarily achieved by members of the Board – serving on bodies of the great and the good for charitable or educational institutions, working for religious organizations or officering volunteer battalions. Many were active members of trade associations. Several were local councillors, sometimes serving as mayor or as chairmen of major committees, while a couple even combined the duties of an MP with their numerous other commitments. Some found time for leisure activities and served on committees of sporting clubs, gentlemen's clubs and masonic lodges. Harold Littledale, one of the more engaging and unusual characters, sponsored prize fighters and ran a model farm.[19] Yet he was among the most conscientious members in terms of keeping abreast of the paperwork and trying to check up on the actual performance of the Board's departments. It is probably fair to say that by 1880 not a single member of the Board exhibited the degree of single-mindedness that an engineer like Hartley felt he was entitled to expect.

The Board met at one o'clock each Thursday and meetings rarely lasted less than two hours. We find from the verbatim sequence of *Discussions at the Board* that on what were seen as major issues, speeches of considerable length – several thousand words – were sometimes made. Very few members at any given time were on less than two standing committees: there were 28 members and the number of committee seats varied over the years, but was generally in the vicinity of 80. That meant members being present for at least the early part of two more afternoons per week, and some of the meetings of committees went on much longer than Board meetings. The responsibilities of the Works Committee, to which the Chief Engineer reported, were particularly heavy, so that their meetings could be extremely lengthy. They were responsible for the entire maintenance, modernization, development and construction of the Dock Estate, and in the process they spent sums of money equating to roughly three-quarters of the Board's income from dues. Another problematical committee was Traffic, which could find itself faced with an agenda where the individual items were slight, perhaps trivial, but numbered several dozen, each requiring the reading and consideration of reports and the making of decisions. Their meetings could easily run on to six o'clock. One fragment of evidence suggests that some might have been a little somnolent by then: a small notebook survives which reveals that in June 1870, for example, there was drawn from stock for Board use two dozen bottles of brandy, two dozen claret, and 39 sherry.

The time spent in meetings should have been only the beginning of the commitment. Each member, when first elected, received what was conventionally referred to as 'a bundle of documents'. The 'bundle' was in fact a small packing crate containing among other things, several large bound volumes of Dock Acts, Standing Orders, Board Precedents and the like. It is clear from some of the discussions at the Board and the Standing Committees that at least some members never mastered the contents of their bundles.[20] Even worse was the volume of minutes, reports and other papers which were generated on a daily basis by 28 committee clerks. A member who did his job properly needed to read carefully and with much cross-referencing, through at least 2,000 pages per year. The officers of the Board, Lyster as much as any other, were quite adroit at taking opportunities of concealing pet projects, overspending or other errors in a morass of paper.

It is absolutely clear that the majority of members did not do this. They turned up for the meetings and they discussed the routine business, which was often of remarkable triviality. In the 1870s, claims made against customers for 'damages to the Works' actually went before the Committee: while some of these were serious matters, a high proportion involved the Engineer's Department in repairs costing under £1.[21] What the members of the Works Committee did not do was to fulfil their key role in relation to the Chief Engineer, which was to provide him with wisely and carefully specified briefs and supervise their fulfilment. On the contrary, we can find the Works Committee making decisions of quite breathtaking stupidity. The extremely expensive reconstruction of the Canada Entrance, for example, was completed in 1882 and by 1889 was incapable of passing vessels owned by a company whose principal sat on the Board when it approved the plans. The same gentleman had appeared before the Select Committee of the House of Lords on the 1880 Dock Bill: he gave evidence against a Bill promoted by the Board, and when asked why he had not made his objections within the Board, he replied that he had never seen the Bill before. Not only had he failed to attend, not only had he failed to read the minutes, but he had voluntarily gone to Parliament to given evidence on a subject on which his ignorance could, with charity, be termed total.[22]

Mistakes like that can be seen in two ways, depending on the view one takes of the changing relationship between the Engineer and the members. Hartley and Lyster were not only different in their engineering training, but very different as individuals as well. Lyster was undoubtedly a gentleman engineer, a socializer and a communicator.[23] He handled his Committee pretty adroitly and succeeded in getting away with some fearful errors which one might imagine would have resulted in his eventual dismissal. The only known instance found of his being 'carpeted' related to a piece of trivial bureaucracy involving railway tickets. When he was implicated in a minor scandal over workers in the dock yard doing private jobs for senior staff members, it was the foreman joiner who was demoted and one of his men who was sacked. Lyster, as usual, came up smelling of roses.[24] Hartley, as we have seen, emerges as a dour and uncommunicative man, occasionally downright rude and dogmatic, not very sociable and probably a 'workaholic'. Yet in many ways his relationship with the old Sub-Committee of Works served the Dock Estate better than did Lyster's with the Works Committee.

The relationship, though, goes back to background and training as well. When Hartley began in Liverpool the water area of the docks was only 45 acres, the trade was comparatively small and the complexity of the dock equipment minimal. During his tenure the water area was more than quadrupled, large and complex buildings, a telegraph system, an hydraulic power system and a dock railway were introduced. There was even a brief experiment with electric lighting.[25] In 1824, it was possible for the Engineer to understand every aspect not only of dock construction and equipment, but operation as well, and Hartley fairly clearly did. New technology was introduced gradually and at his pace, so that he was able to master it a bit at a time. He was able, therefore, not only to design a dock, structure, machine or system from a specific brief, but to work up and refine the brief itself. His reports explain the purposes and operations of proposed designs as well the construction and estimated cost. Lyster, on the other hand, came to Liverpool with quite wide and varied experience, particularly in harbour work, but with no directly relevant background in docks or their traffic. Because the estate was now so much larger and more complicated, the chances of his rapidly gaining the depth of knowledge which Hartley had accumulated over decades were minimal. He had to depend on the specialist knowledge of his assistants.

We find, therefore, that one critical stage of planning new works, that where the broad parameters are drawn out and the first outline designs generated was taking place between an increasingly ineffective 'client' – the Works Committee – and an engineer who was not capable of supplying their deficiencies. Astonishing elementary errors could and did result from such a state of affairs: the Waterloo Corn Warehouses, for example, were almost complete when it came to light that floors were not strong enough because the 'client' had been specifying in one unit of measurement and the engineers working in another.[26] It is almost as difficult to imagine that Hartley would make such a mistake as that the Sub-Committee of Works would fail to spot it, or vice versa.

## Working up the Design

Once the initial stage was completed, a set of simple drawings showing the location and leading dimensions of the proposed works was produced. In the case of larger projects, a process of consultation often proved necessary, so that the outline plans, together with an indication of what would eventually form the basis of the Bill were printed and circulated to leading port users and trade associations. There were four main reasons for doing this: to gain a clearer and better-informed idea of the facilities needed and whether the proposal would supply them; to prevent people complaining about them when they were finished and it was too late, to carry out a trawl for potential witnesses to appear before parliamentary committees for obtaining the necessary authority and to try to head off, or find ways of defeating, potential objectors. The first and third of these objectives were normally quite easily achieved, for there was never a shortage of people who wanted to see improvements in the docks, but stopping people complaining after the works were completed was less easy. Unfortunately, matters were rarely as simple as that because, try how he might to avoid it, the Engineer was likely to get caught up in politics, whether of the strictly party nature or otherwise. The prolonged wrangling which took place over building or not building public general warehouses on the quaysides which took place around 1839–40, for example, involved Hartley in a great deal of abortive work, including four different designs for warehouses at Princes Dock which were not, in the event, built.[27] We have already touched upon the problems he encountered with the Dock Yard at about that time, and there had been a good deal of trouble over the semaphore telegraph system which provided communication between Holyhead and Liverpool, with one party wishing at least to run it down, possibly to abandon it, while another wished to improve it. When the 'improvers' eventually won, Hartley had a considerable amount of work in getting the system back to an efficient condition, and many of the signal houses had to be rebuilt. Although some of his schemes got reduced in the interests of economy, in the main Hartley succeeded in gaining authority to build things to the size and standard he considered proper.[28]

Lyster may be thought lucky in not being employed by a body which might divide on party lines. In fact, the board often did divide into predictable groups, sometimes with results just as disruptive to engineering planning as

*The telegraph house at Lysfaen, built in 1841 and now converted into a private residence, but with the name of the Liverpool Dock Trustees still plainly legible.*

those which occurred in the days of the trustees. Probably the most persistent irritation was the Birkenhead lobby, which existed both within and beyond the Board and campaigned for decades in favour of development in Birkenhead rather than in Liverpool. It may seem unfair to describe them as an irritation, but unfortunately there was one fact of port life they would never accept, which was that shipowners and merchants wanted to use docks close to the commercial infrastructure of central Liverpool.[29] The application of cut-price differential dock dues in Birkenhead failed to attract cargoes in high value trades, and for decades Birkenhead unwillingly specialized in low value cargoes like coal, guano, grain and metal ores. The electric telegraph, the telephone and the Mersey Railway first diminished and then overcame the communication problem, but until they did, the Birkenhead lobby wasted the money of the port, the time of the members and the energies of the Board's principal officers. One cannot help but suspect that the real motive of some of those who argued for Birkenhead was that they wanted to use it not for shipping but simply as a tool to force down dues in Liverpool.

*Even a little canal port like Stourport recognized the importance of mercantile activity, and provided its customers with this magnificent* pied-à-terre.

In a sense it is ungracious for a dock historian to make such complaints, for the conflict produced generated a great deal of useful record material. In January 1872, for example, the Board appointed a Special Committee to investigate and report on the state of traffic in the port and the extensions or improvements which might be necessary for continued growth. The procedure adopted was based on that of a parliamentary select committee, calling witnesses representing various trades and interests and questioning them. What emerges is a fascinating picture of the various conflicting interests the Board had to try and serve: just about all they had in common was that they wanted a lot of money spent on new facilities, presenting members with some interesting dilemmas. The shipowners divided according to the size of vessel they used, and would only unite to oppose the interests of merchants, who exhibited a similarly fickle attitude.[30]

The eventual outcome of the enquiries made in 1872 was the 1873 Dock Act, which authorized by far the largest single expansion scheme to date, to the extent of £4.1 million. The Act contained a most peculiar provision, inserted at the insistence of the Birkenhead lobby, that expenditure should be limited to £500,000 per year, so that the scheme, even allowing for nothing going wrong and some adroit manipulation of payment of accounts at year-end, could not possibly be completed in less than seven years. In the event it took nine years to partial opening and Toxteth Dock, the last under the Act, was not completed until 1888. The author has previously argued that these works so signally failed to live up to expectation that they justify consideration as a cause of the overall relative decline of the port. It was not simply that they could not take exceptional ships: as explained below, it was a question of availability for moderate-sized vessels as well.[31] The remodelling of Sandon Dock under the 1891 Act and the extensive works under the 1898 Act, totalling over £5 million, were virtually remedial works to achieve the objectives which had been set out in 1872–3. The fact that Alexandra had, despite its deficiencies, immediately become the top dock in terms of both volume and value indicates that the objectives had correctly defined. The result of needing a second shot at them was, of course, a mountain of debt and an accumulation of obsolete docks whose up-dating kept getting postponed to make way for yet another new large development.

We can begin to understand how things went so hideously wrong between 1872 and 1888. The members of the Board, as we have seen, were not an ideal body of men for making decisions on questions which required the mastery of an enormous amount of detailed technical information. Their Engineer was not an ideal man for providing them with clear, concise reports reducing the decision-making process to a series of relatively simple questions. His railway background gave him a sense of professional dignity when dealing with 'amateurs' which seems at times to cross the dividing line into sheer arrogance. He was under persistent attack by Harold Littledale, renegade Board member and whistle-blower for alleged incompetence, extravagance and even, at times, dishonesty.[32] Many, perhaps most, of Littledale's accusations seem on the balance of historical probability to have been well-founded, but they had the effect of encouraging Lyster to try to keep the Board out of engineering matters – which rendered ineffective one of the key stages in the design process. This, of course, suited many of the members, who did not want to get into detailed consideration of proposals. Lyster, then, was left both with an inadequate brief and an undue amount of freedom in its fulfilment.

Given that the works must take a minimum of seven years, it was impossible to enjoy the latitude the Hartleys had done. Lyster must plan further ahead: he could not simply decide to make the next entrance bigger if events demanded, because next time would be a long way off. Between 1848 and 1859, the widest new entrances to the docks doubled in width to accommodate ever-wider paddle steamers, but they did it in four stages.[33] With the fickleness which we may come to believe characterized shipowners and naval architects, the adoption of the screw steamer caused ships to become narrower and deeper. At the time Lyster was drawing the plans for the 1873 works, this process had been going on for over a decade and the evidence presented to the 1872 Special Committee made it very clear that the customers wanted depth of water. Lyster appears to have recognized this, and often spoke of deep-water entrances for the largest class of vessels, even using the expression 'vessels of exceptional dimensions'.[34] In the light of this, the actual dimensions he planned beggar comprehension, for his Mark 1 Canada Entrance was just three feet deeper on the sill than the Princes Entrance, completed in 1821 for comparatively tiny sailing vessels. Yet there is no possibility that he could be unaware that drafts of over 20 ft were already commonplace and would continue to increase: one of the author's most prized possessions is the set of *Minutes of Proceedings of the Institution of Civil Engineers* which sits in his office on long loan from the Mersey Docks & Harbour Company. It used to repose in a rather grander office, namely that of G.F. Lyster, and he only needed to read the papers on naval architecture published therein. Of course, the fact that the customers tried to force him to build, relatively speaking, on a shoestring did not help, but we must recall that the detail design and quality of construction was superb – and expensive – it was at the higher levels of decision-making that the problem arose. What happened in the years between 1872 and 1883 was much worse than poor engineering or inadequate committee work. It was nothing less than complete system-failure in that critical stage of the dock engineering process which turned a comparatively vague outline for a project into a set of detailed estimates, working drawings and specifications.

This work involved, of course, considerable numbers of the Engineer's staff. In 1873, the salaries of Lyster and his 'Assistants, Clerks, Book-Keepers etc' totalled £6,694, while weekly paid clerks and draughtsmen accounted for another £3,282. The latter group were usually employed on a relatively short-term basis at wages in the region of £2 per week, but also among them were long-term junior clerks and recently-qualified junior engineers. The point for present purposes is simply that it is not unfair to attribute success or failure to the Chief in person. Of that £6,694, Lyster's own salary amounted to £3,500, and William le Mesurier, Chief Assistant Engineer in charge of Birkenhead was paid just £300.[35] Such a huge differential was by no means uncommon in the engineering profession at the time, and it reflects the essential difference in role between the Chief and everybody else. Lyster was not expected to know everything or to do ten times as much work as, say, le Mesurier. He was paid to ensure the department functioned effectively and to take personal responsibility for that effective functioning. This point seems largely to have escaped the members of the Works Committee, who were willing to allow Lyster to come up with all manner of excuses for failures.[36] In the real engineering world outside, excuses did not generally command such a high price.

It must not be thought that either Lyster or the Works Committee was uniquely ineffective. We may call to mind the repeated financial scandals which arose from poor management of the Metropolitan Board of Works. Perhaps a closer parallel, however, was the sad case of Francis Webb, Chief of the London & North Western Railway. He designed a compound locomotive which did not produce the gains in thermal efficiency which he expected. Simple arithmetic and scrutiny of a copy of Rankine's *The Steam Engine and Other Prime Movers*, published for university students some thirty years earlier, would have shown him that the performance he expected required a boiler pressure about six times as high as that employed, far beyond the safe limits of any conventional locomotive boiler at the time. Furthermore, this machine was capable of an amusing party trick: neither its motions nor its two driving axles were coupled, and it was therefore possible for the engine to 'start' with the two axles revolving in opposite directions. What followed was quite remarkable: instead of abandoning an unsuccessful experiment, the company allowed Webb to build nearly two hundred of these absurd machines, leaving his successor with the task not of updating the oldest locomotives in the fleet but of scrapping and replacing all the newest and most expensive ones.[37] Webb may be an unusual case, but the Board of the largest joint-stock company in the country continued for many years to squander its shareholders' money on a locomotive relatively more unsuccessful than even the worst of Lyster's dock designs. At least his failures could be downgraded to smaller vessels or modernized: they did not have to be scrapped.

Towards the end of last century there was a good deal of debate about the best form of organization for ports. The respective merits of control by local authorities, trusts, joint stock companies, of integration with railway companies and of nationalization were all considered at various stages. Because these were essentially financial issues, they are deferred from this chapter to that dealing with dock finances, but the issue which must be examined here is whether engineering in Liverpool was particularly bad under Lyster, or whether all ports, faced with similar problems posed by changes in ships and trade, fared equally badly.

One piece of comparative evidence comes from very close at hand: Birkenhead. Rendel's original intention had been that the main entrance to Birkenhead Docks would be via an enormous tidal basin with a depth of no less than 18 ft below Old Dock Sill. Few engineers at the time thought that it would be possible to prevent such a basin silting up, and since it had not been built by the time the Birkenhead Docks passed into Liverpool's control, it might be expected it would remain unbuilt. Unfortunately there was a contractual liability to the Great Western Railway, who thought it would work and insisted on its being built. At this point, John Hartley decided that there was no possibility the basin would work (in which he was proven right) and he therefore designed a completely new extra entrance to the system. After Hartley's retirement, Lyster completed both entrances. Hartley's design for Alfred Entrance was large and deep enough that it not only surpassed anything Lyster designed in the next thirty years, but also continued in adequate service until the 1920s before it required any significant alteration. If John Hartley could design an adequately deep entrance in 1856, why could Lyster not do so in 1873? He had, after all, actually built Alfred Entrance. But another way of looking at the question is that a joint-stock company with the specific objective of constructing docks had failed ignominiously, and a non-profit trust had succeeded. The problem with Lyster and his Works Committee was probably not a constitutional one. If it had been, the substantial improvements of the 1890s would likely have needed to be preceded by constitutional change. What actually preceded and enabled them were some changes of personnel and a change of attitude.[38]

In considering what went wrong, it is necessary to recognize that it is a mistake to think of the depth of a dock only in terms of the deepest ships it can accommodate. While that was the way in which engineers and their employers tended to boast about their latest and grandest creations, for the ordinary shipowner the length of time when there was, say, 25 ft on the sill was of far more importance than whether the maximum was 30 or 32 ft. Missing the tide meant a wait of, at best, six to eight hours, but if the tide just missed was past the top of the springs (i.e. when each successive high tide was less high than the last) it was possible to be 'neaped' either in or out of dock for up to ten or eleven days. The new North Entrances were nine feet below Old Dock Sill, which gave a depth of about 30 ft on a 32 ft equinoctial spring tide. There were (and are) only about four tides of such height in the year, and the rate of ebb and flow was such that three-quarters of an hour either side of high water took two feet of water off the sills.[39] Given the smaller tidal range of the Humber, John Hartley's Railway Dock and Victoria Dock at Hull (started 1845 and 1846 respectively), with 29 ft 6 in and 27 ft 6 in on ordinary highwater springs would actually provide a greater usable depth over most days of the year and more hours of each day. These docks, be it recalled, were designed before the problem of the screw steamer had arisen at all. Neither was such a degree of 'foresight' – one might simply refer to it as an understanding of the realities of dock engineering – peculiar to the Hartley family. Hawkshaw's Albert Dock (Hull) was begun in 1864: it had its problems, but it gave 23 ft at high water neaps, four feet more than Canada Entrance.[40] Hawkshaw, it might be objected, had worked under Jesse Hartley, but then Lyster had learned his profession under James Meadows Rendel who, whatever his other faults, did not build his entrances too shallow. The comparatively small docks he built for the London North Western Railway at Garston, nearly ten miles upstream from Canada, actually had more water on the sills. The ships using Garston were small by Liverpool standards, but they had the luxury of being able to come and go for a longer time either side of high water.

Despite these difficulties, the large new docks were, in a manner, successful. A proper statistical survey is needed, and is in progress, but a subjective impression may be gained by taking a 'lucky dip' in the Customs Bills of Entry. There are seasonal and cyclical variations in the number of ships in port, but it is exceptional to find ships of over 3,000 tons anywhere

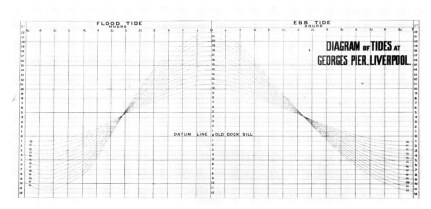

*This tide graph shows the importance of entrance depth in being able to keep entrances open as long as possible: the deeper the sill below ODS the longer any given depth was available. Furthermore, the higher the tide was, the shorter its peak.*

except in Alexandra, and the docks served by the New North Entrances typically contained about 80 per cent of the ships over 2,000 tons. While those larger vessels represented less than 20 per cent of the total number of ships in port, they represented a far larger proportion of dues income: in 1888, for example, Alexandra earned no less than 36 per cent of the dues income for the whole estate. The problem was that the insufficient depth was already becoming becoming apparent in the year in which the works under the 1873 Act were finally completed.

Neither Lyster nor the Works Committee seems to have grasped the importance of the length of time gates could be left open, (if they did, they kept quiet about it) which is remarkable considering their rapid recognition of the time-saving benefits of hydraulically powered entrance gates.[41] As we shall see in later chapters, the system breakdown which had occurred at the stage of moving from an outline to a detail design may well have had causes additional to those mentioned above. What is abundantly clear is that these problems brought about a general level of dissatisfaction among the users of the port which manifested itself in a number of ways, including the campaigns for the Manchester Ship Canal and for the dredging of the Bar. Both of these were harmful to Liverpool in particular, and we may find, in a sense, to the port services industry as a whole.

# 3

# How Good an Investment was Dockbuilding?

It is customary to assume that ports needed to continue to expand and modernize in order to survive financially, but it is an assumption in need of a little testing. With a few special-case exceptions such as single-purpose mineral docks, the truth of Jackson's assertion that the history of ports and docks is that of a continuum of change seems quite clear.[1] Trades and ships changed, and continue to change, quite rapidly and so do the facilities the shipowners and merchants seek from a port authority. That however, is not at all the same as the proposition made by Hyde, that we may judge the overall effectiveness of a port by the amount of money it invested.[2] The reasons for, and the effectiveness of, the investment need to be considered as well.

For the early part of the nineteenth century the changes were of a simple and obvious nature: ships became more numerous and, on average, a little larger. In 1800, 4,746 ships, totalling 450,060 tons – an average of 94.8 tons, paid dues in Liverpool. By 1825, these figures had risen to 10,837 ships, 1,223,820 tons, average 112.9 tons. While aggregated figures like these are not very helpful, we can at least see that the numerical growth was not mainly in the coasting trade, or the average tonnage would have gone down. Dues income had surged ahead from £23,379 to £128,691, a growth rate which, allowing for the implications of the American War of 1812 (which harmed Liverpool's trade, albeit briefly, far more than the Napoleonic Wars) seems extremely impressive.[3] It is, in fact, much less impressive than first sight suggests, for during that time, Princes Dock had been built at a cost of about £650,000, opening in 1821. Now let us be simplistic and suppose, most improbably, that the whole increase in revenue was not only handled in Princes Dock, but was actually new traffic won for the port by the fact of its having invested in building Princes Dock. Let us create what the Dock Trustees did not, a rough balance sheet for Princes Dock.

We cannot, of course, allow the revenue figure for 1800 as a starting point. The last full year before Princes Dock opened produced revenue of £94,412, so our charitable assumptions towards Princes give us marginal earnings of £34,279. The £650,000 which Princes cost was borrowed on bond, typically at a rate of about 3.5 per cent, so that the interest cost of the debt for Princes would be of the order of £22,750 p.a. The actual figure for interest in the 1825 accounts is £28,840, and since Princes was by such a huge margin the most expensive project, as well as the most recent, we may fairly allow our approximate £22,750 for interest to stand. Princes Dock represented just under a quarter of the total water area of the Dock Estate, and the wage and salary costs of the 'central establishment', paying for such things as the Harbourmaster and his men and the Dock Police Establishment totalled £6,919. Let us charge to Princes Dock the modest sum of £1,500. New work at Princes was still proceeding, including the completion of the sheds at a cost of £3,595 and repair works cost £745. The general expenses borne by all the ships using the port included many small items: the largest ones were those for buoys, landmarks, the floating lights and the dredger, and quayside lighting, which totalled £2,183, or say £500 chargeable to Princes. Our wildly optimistic 'profit' on Princes has now shrunk to £4,189, or about 0.6 per cent on capital.

Of course, the Dock Trustees were not supposed to be there to make a profit, so such a small amount was perfectly acceptable. Or it would be, if docks lasted forever and never needed updating or replacing. The date at which Princes became effectively obsolete is open to a good deal of argument because of the practice which the author has previously dubbed 'gravitating', whereby docks gradually slid down from being state-of-the-art in the biggest and most prestigious trades until they ended up stuffed with coasters, which paid lower dues and thus made very little money for a port authority.[4] Certainly fifty years on, when it had had some modernization carried out, it was far past its best, but it was still earning a lot of money – £39,416 in 1875, for example. Only Canada, Huskisson and Waterloo earned more that year. If, therefore, we continue to behave like the unjust steward and make the rather outrageous assumption that Princes would last a century as a useful asset, we must still debit our Princes Dock account with a depreciation cost of £6,500 per annum, which puts the account in deficit.

Now the above may seem rather long-winded, but it is of fundamental importance in the history of dock engineering. Princes Dock was very nearly an optimum case to choose: brand new, large and well-designed and specializing in trades, notably cotton, which were highly profitable and growing at an almost unprecedented rate. Its only problem was that the corruption surrounding its construction had greatly inflated its first cost. Yet, barring a bonanza of a land sale such as that achieved with the infilled site of George's Dock in 1900, it could never approach profitability.[5] What happened next was that pressure mounted for more dock space, resulting in the construction of Canning, Clarence, Brunswick, Waterloo, Victoria and Trafalgar by 1836, almost doubling the water area constructed between 1709 and 1825. This headlong construction was not, of course, funded by paying off old debts, because the revenue scarcely serviced them, much less paid them off. The result was that by 1836, the capital debt of the docks stood at £1,399,477, most of it on bond and most now at 4 per cent. That did not really matter, as the revenue of the estate was increasing faster than the interest cost, though there were still some bondholders around who thought that the trustees should actually pay off their old debts before beginning further construction works. As we have seen, they would have been a long time paying them.

Returning to the proposition at the beginning of this chapter, we find that it becomes necessary to question what bodies like the Dock Trustees built docks for. Even in Liverpool's favourable circumstances of being able to handle, often indeed to control, the comings and goings of highly important trades such as cotton and engineering goods, which lay at the heart of the Industrial Revolution, docks were most unlikely to make a profit unless one simply pretended that the obsolescence problem was not there. Since the Dock Trustees do not appear generally to have been stupid – nor even to have occasionally behaved stupidly in the way that their successor body did – their reasons for investing in docks must lie elsewhere. Either they wanted to build up the trade of Liverpool for the general good of the town, or they wanted to offer port users a service which gave benefits beyond those for which they were prepared to pay an economic price.

In real life these two answers are the same, for almost every form of economic activity in early nineteenth century Liverpool was directly or indirectly dependent upon the port, so that those of life's winners who became Dock Trustees had a direct and personal interest in the increase of trade. Among life's losers there were few, even at the level of scavengers (official or unofficial) or prostitutes, who were not similarly dependent in their lowly way. At the lowest level, Liverpool's paupers were relatively well cared for by the standards of paupers, at least under the Old Poor Law, from poor rates paid largely from the proceeds of shipping and trade. When what one might term epidemic poverty threatened, Liverpool raised a local subscription to pay for extra labourers for dock construction: these men were paid a 'reduced wage' of 10*s* per week – rather more than many in the cotton industry had to live on as a normal wage in such depressed years as 1816.[6] Whatever differences between occupational or social classes there may have been, almost everybody shared an interest in the increase of trade. That put the Dock Engineers in a rather special position compared with their predecessors in, say, canal building, for their works were not expected to show a profit, only to be constructed with a sufficient eye to economy to minimize the constant and inevitable growth of the corporate debt.

After the opening of Waterloo Dock there was a comparative lull in new construction, though substantial work was obviously proceeding in maintenance and modernization works; in 1841, for example, Hartley's stonemasons and bricklayers earned £3,939 in wages and his teams of carpenters and smiths each topped £3,000. Seven docks had four digit sums spent on them. This, however, was the calm before the storm: Hartley was working on the design of Albert Dock and the associated re-modelling of Salthouse, Canning and Canning Half-Tide, and would soon be putting forward his huge scheme for 'New North Works' under the 1844 Dock Act. The main phase of those works was completed with the opening of Stanley, Collingwood, Salisbury, Bramley-Moore and Nelson Docks on 4 August 1848. The accounts for 1849, which still indicate some ancillary work continuing at those docks, show the debt to have risen to £4,036,720, much of it at as much as 5 per cent. This debt was proportionately far more burdensome than that of 1836, for although tonnage had risen from 1, 947,613 to 3,639,146, revenue had stagnated: from £221,994 in 1836 it had risen only to £224,224 by 1848. This was not, however, the result of stagnation in trade, but the reflection of rate cuts in 1836 and 1844, the first a political gesture marking local government reform, the second to try and prevent Birkenhead from succeeding in raising the capital for its proposed dock system.

These cuts sound at first like a serious miscalculation, but were in fact a successful gamble on the part of the Trustees: ten years later the revenue of the port had increased by almost 50 per cent, and Hartley was still building furiously, with his 17 acre Canada Dock under construction at the same time that his son was progressing well with the demanding task of making the 160 acres of Birkenhead Docks function adequately. Of course, the debt was still mounting, but it was sustainable and the port was working as intended, as the engine for growth of the local economy. Even the comparatively poor were getting marginally better off: a prosperous borough had employed the first Medical Officer of Health and the first Borough Engineer in the country, resulting in improvements in such life-and-death matters as water supply and sewerage – though the improvements were from a pretty appalling base-line.[7] The more prosperous sectors of the working class enjoyed wages far higher than in most of the rest of the country, and a very large middle class was fast becoming possessed of the largest concentration of wealth and mercantile power outside London. The evidence is that the apparently risky policy of the Dock Trustees in 'going for growth' was paying handsomely.

The accumulation of capital in Liverpool, especially before the Limited Liability Act extended the benefits of joint-stock financing to most forms of industry and commerce, made it easy to raise loans locally on the traditional bond basis. This was not a specially cheap way of raising money, but it was singularly convenient both for borrower and lender. Deals were done, albeit confirmed later in writing, on the basis of a handshake while walking 'on Change' (i.e. round the flagged area between the Town Hall and the Exchange) or in one of the inns or coffee-houses close by. Just one of these inns, The Lion, at the corner of Moorfields and Tithebarn Street, still retains the evidence of this method of doing business. Glass screens above the bar conceal the customers' faces from the staff, so that in the event of the latter overhearing (which the glass made less likely anyway) some vital transaction, they would probably not be able to identify the parties.

Jesse Hartley did not have to show that his works would make a profit and he did not have to behave like some railways engineers did in order to promote the sale of shares. All he had to do was produce sound designs to fulfil a brief in whose production he had participated and win the agreement of a body which seems mostly to have understood without needing to be reminded too often that it was employing the best dock engineer in the world.

Because people's aspirations vary over time, it is hazardous to try to

*The glass screening over the bar at The Lion, a businessmen's pub near to Exchange Flags.*

express Hartley's salary in present-day terms, and crude cost-of-living indexes are of little help. Bread, for example, would not have absorbed much of his family budget. If we look at the prices of the luxuries which his salary would render affordable, such things as large houses, carriages, works of art, fine old brandy and the like, we might take a rash guess in the vicinity of £250,000 per year. The present Mersey Docks & Harbour Company is a very prosperous undertaking which could perfectly well afford, if it chose, to pay its Chief Engineer that much: it does not so choose, and the Dock Trustees' choice to do so was made for one of two reasons. Perhaps they considered that Hartley's contribution to the success of the port was not only great enough to justify such a salary but also incapable of being fulfilled at less cost by anyone else. The alternative possibility is that they feared that if he left Liverpool his talents, which they clearly regarded as incomparable, would be speedily seized upon by a competitor. The thought of his being engaged to construct an efficient modern port on, say, the site of what later became Avonmouth, might well suffice to make them grit their teeth and pay up. He had an astute understanding of what made a port work, and in addition to his strictly dockbuilding skills he was experienced in such vital matters of the wider port infrastructure as road, railway and telegraph construction. What he had done for them he might do for others.

It is often thought that Hartley was an extravagant engineer, and it is quite understandable that people should have thought this. Many of his works were of quite superfluous durability and far outlasted the uses for which they were intended.[8] With hindsight, we can see that the rate of change in ship design from about 1840 to the end of the century (and beyond) would mean that a dock was unlikely to remain useful for its original purpose for more than about twenty years. Many of Hartley's retaining walls still stand, almost as good as the day they were finished, so it is only natural to assume that they were over-specified and therefore over-costly. His use of granite for boundary walls makes them appear totally indestructible, and therefore, once again, expensive. His mighty warehouses, with walls a metre thick, outlasted their intended trades by a century or so and have survived not only wear and tear, but bombing in the Second World War (Albert, Wapping and Stanley were all hit) and considerable periods of dereliction.[9]

This is a dangerous line of logic to pursue. In the first place, there are other benefits from an over-specified wall than that it should last for 150 years. Virtually every engineer built retaining walls which fell over, some more frequently than others. Hartley's were among the most infrequent fallers, with only two occurrences identified during Hartley's lifetime. The first was at Waterloo, and arose from the unusual cause of Hartley having taken a gamble on founding a wall on rock which turned out to be diagonally bedded. It sheared along the bedding plane, allowing the toe of the wall to slip outwards. Hartley's report on the incident implies, though it does not state, that he had been under pressure to do a cheap job, though he also admits that he should have anticipated the problem. The second was a partial collapse at Brunswick in 1835 which Weir considers was probably prompted by a lowering of the water level, but there seems to be no evidence of the underlying cause.[10] The few later collapses were all connected with new works, when quite abnormal strains were imposed on old walls by such activities as partial demolition and incorporation into temporary works or excavation near their toes. If, as was quite common, failure occurred in the final stages of construction, there would be a certain amount of delay and extra cost, at worst a small number of men might be killed. Failure in service was an altogether different matter: quite regardless of the danger to life and limb, which was considerable, the danger to ships and buildings was acute. Furthermore, the dock in which the failure occurred might well need to be closed to traffic for months, normally with dire effects on revenue. Such consequences were worth spending money to avoid.

The fact that a wall looks as though it will last for ever and actually does last for 150 years does not prove that it was necessarily more expensive than any other wall with which we may choose to compare it. There is the logical possibility that it was simply a better wall, better built of better materials by better masons working under a better engineer. This was certainly the view taken by Hartley's former pupil, Sir Robert Rawlinson. In contribution to a discussion of a paper on the strength of Portland cement, he gave a number of details of Hartley's methods of wall-building which included the following: 'Mr Hartley abandoned the use of ashlar for facing sea and dock walls, and relied upon granite rubble. The red sandstone ashlar cost about 24s to 30s per cubic yard, and the granite facing rubble only from 12s to 15s; red sandstone rubble backing cost about 9s per cubic yard.'[11]

Rawlinson subsequently sent in some further details to the Institution which were published as a footnote to the discussion in which he explains Hartley's method of preparing hydraulic mortar, which he stated cost about 8s to 10s per cubic yard finished at the mortar mill. He gave the proportions for best mortar and for common mortar and stated that random rubble masonry required about one cubic yard of mortar to four of rubble, and then revealed what seems to have been one of Hartley's tricks of his trade: 'Grout is made by diluting the best mortar with water until it will pour evenly over the work. Both rubble masonry and brickwork, when used in dock, sea or river walls, are regularly grouted as the work proceeeds, so as to wet the entire mass, and every stone and every brick is bedded, jointed and covered by grout and mortar, so as to constitute one solid mass.' That is at least part of the secret of why Hartley was able to build his walls rather thinner than contemporary theory suggested they should have been. In terms of cost, therefore, they were both smaller in volume and cheaper per unit volume than was necessary with other techniques. Their only disadvantage was that they required very careful attention to foundation work and piling. The same applies on a smaller scale to Hartley's boundary walls, which appear massive and indestructible, but are actually thinner at the top than the four-course brick walls built by Foster before him and Lyster afterwards.

Lyster continued to build granite rubble retaining walls where he could. This was no doubt partly because he had inherited both a fine team of craftsmen whom it would be expensive to retrain and a quarry supplying good stone at moderate cost. In a number of instances, he ran into difficulties: when he was reconstructing Waterloo and Herculaneum at the same time, the Kirkmabreck quarry could not keep up with his needs, so red sandstone ashlar had to be used. When converting the abortive Low Water Basin at Birkenhead into a conventional dock (Wallasey Dock, completed 1876) Lyster ran short of skilled masons and adopted a system of concrete block construction.[12] He also experimented with mass concrete, notably in the floor of the very troublesome No. 3 Graving Dock, Birkenhead.[13] Despite this willingness to try different methods when he thought it advisable, he continued to use the Hartley method as well. In discussion of a paper he presented as late as 1889, he described the detail of the traditional methods he still used, which were virtually unchanged, and he gave the price of the granite rubble as delivered at $7\frac{1}{2}d$ per cubic foot, or $5s$ $7\frac{1}{2}d$ per cubic yard. The cost of completed masonry in the ordinary run of dock walls was about 18–20$s$ per cubic yard. Lyster tended to use rather larger thickness:height ratios than the Hartleys, and it is interesting that when he was accused of building his walls too thick, one justification he gave for his relatively large sections was that 'they had generally to be backed up very rapidly', which makes clear the importance of the seemingly leisurely, but actually very painstaking, method of back-filling John Hartley had described.[14] There was more to reducing the overall cost of wall-building than the use of cheap stone. As Lyster put it, 'The Kirkmabreck granite work might appear costly at first sight, but it was by no means so considering the circumstances.'

It seems, therefore, that the fundamental wall-building and masonry of the new construction work under Hartley probably could not have been much cheaper, in real terms, than it was. If the accusations of extravagance made against him personally and, by implication, against the Trustees corporately, have any substance at all, it is in the peripherals that we must be reduced to seeking them. By far the largest and most expensive of these peripherals were the huge blocks of warehouses, of which those at Albert, ceremonially opened on 30 July 1846, were the first and the most spectacular. They provided nearly a million square feet of storage space and had cost approximately £375,000 to build, though small amounts of expenditure continued for the first few years after nominal completion. By the standards of the day they were very well equipped, including among other things the first hydraulic lifting appliances that William Armstrong sold outside of Newcastle.[15] Great thought and attention to detail had gone into such apparently minor features of their design as the provision of massive granite quoins on the outside corners where the brickwork was at risk of damage from the protruding iron-bound hubs of cart or wagon wheels. Despite the controversy over the decision to build them and despite their apparent over-specification, they were in fact no less financially sound than most of the rest of the Dock Estate. The highest interest rate on dock bonds in 1849 was 5 per cent, giving an interest cost on the building of the warehouses of around £18,750. The excess of income over ordinary operating expenditure (including wages of £31,578) at Albert was £23,027, so as in the case of Princes Dock, we find a small operating surplus, which would suffice to write off the first cost of the warehouses over about a century. They were, in short, not a genuinely economic proposition, but they were as good as most things in the port, and certainly were not the wanton extravagance they have sometimes been taken for. When Stanley and Wapping Warehouses were completed and in business, they too made a small profit after interest but not taking account of depreciation.

There were, of course, some genuine engineering extravagances on the Dock Estate, and a handful of architectural ones as well. The most obvious example is the Albert Dock Traffic office, with its interesting cast iron portico. There are no bones to be made about this building: it was designed to impress people with the importance of the Dock Trustees, as was the

*The luncheon at the official opening of Albert Dock, 1846.*

Harbourmaster's Office at the north-east corner of Canning Dock. That was only to be expected, it was the normal purpose of such buildings: what is more surprising is that the often dour and frequently parsimonious Hartley seems to have undergone a personality change when he designed pumping stations, accumulator towers and the like. The simple functional style of the Albert Warehouses, the Dock Residences or the Telegraph Houses was cast aside like a glove and a totally over-the-top neo-medieval style took over. The actual requirements of a pumphouse are usually quite simple, relating to being able to hold up the weight of a header tank, support a gantry for lifting bits of machinery in order to repair them, provide a retreat for the drinking of tea by greasers and so on. A sturdy square brick box, such as those A.G. Lyster built for graving dock pumps was perfectly adequate. In slightly flippant defence of Hartley it may be pointed out that there was obviously something about pumping stations which gave engineers a rush of blood to the head, for John Bernard devised a 'renaissance palace' pumping station at Birkenhead, while G.F. Lyster's effort at Langton Graving Docks looked like

*Jesse Hartley's astonishing pumping station at Canada Entrance, built in 1859. Compare this flight of fancy with the Lysfaen telegraph house.*

a fairy-tale illustration of a Bavarian castle. Because these buildings did not produce an income, they could not be financially compared with each other, or with warehouses or sheds.

In the main, the Liverpool dock engineers did not wilfully build in an extravagant manner. Lyster produced some very handsome buildings, but their appeal is often, like Hartley in 'functional mode', mainly a matter of form and proportion, which were mainly governed by mundane engineering or operational considerations. From 1872, Lyster employed John Arthur Berrington as 'Architectural Draughtsman'[16] and from the numerous drawings of his which survive (and which are of superb quality) it is clear that much more attention was given to elaborate detailing in dock residences and the other smaller official buildings in the last quarter of the century than had previously been the case. Some of the large buildings, too, are enhanced with some very good fancy brickwork: since these include the Waterloo Corn Warehouses which were built before the employment of Berrington we may assume that this was a personal liking of Lyster's. Other little touches like fancy iron railings also began to appear, but it would be unfair to mark these down as great extravagances, since their cost was absolutely minuscule in comparison with that of the core work of the department. In at least one case, that of the New River Approaches, completed 1874, we know that the Board, and hence Lyster, were under considerable external pressure to provide some ornamental work to form an attractive as well as convenient approach to the Princes Stage.[17]

## Rising Expectations

As we have seen, the arrival of paddle steamers on the scene created problems for Jesse Hartley in that they got wider with remarkable rapidity. It was fortunate for the Dock Estate that overall tonnages were rising so rapidly that new docks were needed anyway and could be made with wider entrances to accommodate the swelling waistlines of the new vessels, leaving the older docks to the sailing ships and smaller steamers. A new problem arose, however, with the arrival on the scene of the screw steamer. While paddle steamers got wider and longer quite quickly, they did not get much deeper, for the very simple technical reason that their paddle wheels would not work well with a large variation between laden and unladen draft: they would be either insufficiently immersed when the vessel was light, or choking themselves when it was laden down. Not only was the screw propellor much more tolerant of such variations, but other things being equal it generally worked better with a greater immersion.

Some simple arithmetic also favoured building screw steamers deeper. Because the engines were fore and aft in the vessel, they did not need much width, and owners soon realized that the smaller the length:beam ratio of a vessel, the greater the relative amount of unproductive space in the tapered bits at the ends. As Alfred Holt explained, it was the part in the middle that made the money, so ships should have more middle and less end. His adoption of the tandem compound engine, with its short bedplate, worked toward that objective. This realization soon resulted in some very long, narrow ships: by 1870 length:beam ratios of 10:1 were quite common. In order to make a long narrow ship adequately strong to continue to act as a beam when rough seas temporarily removed the buoyancy from either the ends or the middle, it had to be deeper: generally it needed to be roughly as deep as it was wide.[18]

In addition to that, there were legal reasons for building ships deeper. The new system of measuring register tonnage introduced under the Merchant Shipping Act of 1854 enabled shipowners and builders to reduce the register tonnage of a vessel in relation to its gross tonnage. This had the highly unfortunate result for Port Authorities that the gross tonnage, which governed the actual amount of space a vessel occupied in dock, got larger, while the net tonnage, upon which dock dues were charged, got smaller. The formula under the 1854 Act allowed vessels which were deeper in relation to their length and beam to pay less, not more, than the others.[19]

The result was that Hartley's splendidly wide entrances were being approached by vessels which could probably enter two abreast, but which were too deep to pass over the sills except on very favourable tides. It seems odd at first sight that shipowners should be willing to build vessels which could enter existing docks only with some difficulty and risk. Initially they did not: Robert Napier wrote to Hartley in 1836 enquiring whether he had any plans to build entrances as wide as 60 ft, as he was working on the design of some vessels for the Liverpool trade, and this information would 'guide him in his plans'.[20] As it happens, Hartley was able to reply that he was indeed planning such an entrance at Coburg, but at Hull shipowners had to buy according to the sizes of the entrances. The important point, however, is that Napier was building ships to suit docks. As competition between Port Authorities mounted, shipowners could begin to behave differently, because the market for port services was one in which they held all the best bargaining positions. They could always threaten to move their trade somewhere else, whereas a Port Authority's main assets were big holes in the ground, which they could scarcely move or sell secondhand to some other port.

While the screw steamers were getting deeper, sailing ships were doing the same, partly through improved understanding of the structures of hulls, and partly because the best way for them to compete with steam was to maximize the cargo space in relation to the deck space. They could not compete on speed, so they had to compete on cheapness, which meant that the more tons there were down below and the less jolly sailor boys there were aloft, the happier and more frequent the landlubbers' trips to the bank. By the 1850s, exceptional sailing ships were drawing up to 25 ft, and such draughts became relatively common in the 1860s: by the early '70s the biggest sailing ships were already having to lighten themselves by discharging part of their cargo into barges in the river before entering the recently modernized Waterloo Dock.[21]

Even without the shortcomings in design which have been mentioned above, these changes plunged dock engineers into a madcap race to deepen entrances and passages. The scale of the changes can be appreciated by browsing through the MD&HB accounts, where it becomes clear that although new docks were being built, the amount being spent on modernizing old ones, and commonly not very old at that, was rising rapidly. Depth was very expensive to provide for a number of reasons, some simple and obvious, others less so.

The first was the plain foot-tonnage of work which had to be done in raising spoil from greater depths, a particularly important factor in docks which, like nearly all of Liverpool's, were impounded from the river rather than excavated from dry land. In such cases, the dock bottom required little or no excavation, and hence no major spoil raising, for the first 15 ft or so of working depth. To remove the last foot of spoil necessary to achieve 30 ft working depth having started with a notional 15 ft 'free' amounts to nearly

*Widening and deepening a passage was a simple matter – any shipowner could tell you that. It would be safer than telling it to this lot! The photograph dates from c. 1905.*

1,600 cubic yards per superficial acre, weighing anything from half a ton to two tons per cubic yard, lifted through 15 ft. That, however, is not necessarily the end of the matter, for in the earlier days of dock construction it was normal practice to dig out the big hole before the retaining walls were built, which meant that the edges of the hole had to be cut back to about 45° to protect the masons from burial by slippage. Going down a foot more, therefore, meant going outwards a foot further as well, so that an extra volume corresponding to 1 ft depth on the 45° slope for the entire periphery of the dock needed to be excavated.

Next, the deeper the dock, the higher the retaining walls, and the higher they were, the thicker they had to be, increasing both the excavation and spoil-lifting and the amount of masonrywork. In many cases, the greater depth at which the masons were working meant further cost in delivering the stone and mortar to them. The greater the depth at which they were working, the more water got into the workings, bringing the need to instal and run pumps. Because there was always a great deal of rubbish in the bottom of a dock under construction, the apparently primitive chain pump was normally preferred for this duty, being self-priming and capable of very cheap and simple repair if damaged by debris.[22] It suffered, however, from a low mechanical efficiency, so that if we remember that delivery rates running into thousands of gallons/minute could be required, we begin to understand one reason why the Dock Trustees spent over £8,000 on coal in 1848. (When, be it remembered, there were as yet no hydraulic pumping stations to account for large quantities.)[23]

There is always a tendency when considering dock construction to concentrate on digging the hole and buildings walls round it, to become fixated with excavation and masonrywork and to forget the carpenters. During Jesse Hartley's great spasm of construction during the late 1840s, the *Annual Accounts* show the carpenters were always the second largest group of tradesmen after 'masons and bricklayers' (who got listed together) and they normally used over £10,000 worth of timber per year, sometimes exceeding the value of the stone used. When we recall that much of their timber – that used for stagings or for centrings of lightening arches for example, was used several times before being scrapped we can begin to appreciate the magnitude of their work. The deeper the excavation, the deeper the coffer-dams and other protective works needed to keep the excavators and the masons 'in the dry'. The deeper they were, the greater the differential head of water at high tide, and the stronger they had to be. By Lyster's day, the design of coffer-dams had become both a complicated and a precise business: the dam built at Birkenhead the year before his appointment was: '. . . on plan the segment of a circle whose chord was 467 ft, and versed sine 76 ft. The width at the top of the dam was 18 ft, and at the ground line 23 ft. Its extreme height from the toe of the outer row of piles to the top of the dam was 61 ft 6 ins'.[24] It cost £56 per linear foot, total £28,000 and used 80,000 cubic ft, about 1,250 tons, of timber. This was carpentry on a grand scale, and the greater the depth, the grander it got – and the costlier. Lest it be thought that the dam described was over-specified, and thus unduly large and expensive, it may be mentioned that in 1863 it failed, causing a complete wash-out of the works within, which were fortunately fairly near completion, so that the damage was heavy rather than catastrophic.

Increasing depth also brought with it greater strains on gates, which not only meant that the gates themselves had to be larger and stronger, but also that the forces they exerted on their sills were higher. The masonry of passage bottoms and graving docks bottoms was subject to potentially greater groundwater pressures, and there were several instances of 'inverts' (the inverted arches which provided much of the strength of passage bottoms) failing or the occurrence of 'boils' – ingresses of groundwater which lifted and destroyed masonry. Lyster made a bold attempt to avoid this problem with the mass-concrete bottom in Birkenhead No. 3 Graving Dock, but it took several attempts to get it right. Bigger, stronger gates were, naturally heavier to open, and while it was possible, up to a point, to employ bigger, stronger gatemen, the time came when hydraulic gate engines were no longer a luxury. Similarly the penstocks, which controlled water levels in the locks and half-tide docks, became subject to large differential pressures which tended to clamp them to their seatings, again encouraging the application of hydraulic power.[25]

Additional problems came into play when old docks had to be deepened. To begin with, there was no 'free 15 ft': every last cubic foot of spoil had to be raised not to old shore level, but to quayside level. Hundreds of tons of old masonry had to be dug up from sills and passage inverts, much of it, no doubt, still in excellent condition and therefore very difficult to break up. The extreme example of this was Lyster's concrete apron at Canada Entrance: although unsucessful as a means of dispersing silt, and nowhere near deep enough, it survived until after the Second World War, when the Engineer's Department finally tackled the considerable problem of digging it up in order to construct the new Langton Entrance, which opened in 1962.

Much of the work of deepening an existing dock had to be undertaken in a slow and painstaking manner: digging away underneath one of Jesse's 30+ ft high walls in order to underpin it prior to further excavation of the dock bottom must have been quite an anxious task, yet major 'downward extension' of some of the old walls was successfully undertaken by traditional methods. Digging up a passage invert was also a bit worrying: there was always the possibility that it was all that was preventing the retaining walls from slipping inwards. A final problem was that although

Jesse Hartley had customarily produced high quality drawings of virtually everything built, of which a great many survive to this day, the drawings of work by his predecessors were few and unreliable. When Lyster was deepening Princes Half-Tide, for example, he had to have his men begin by surveying and drawing up John Foster's river wall, because neither he nor anyone else had the faintest idea of how sound it was in either design or condition or even what its foundations were.[26]

All these complications for the Engineer arose from the changes in ship technology outlined above which resulted, as one might hope, in a great improvement in the efficiency with which goods were carried by sea. It might, therefore, be expected that shipowners would be not only able but possibly even willing, to pay handsomely for the port facilities which enabled that increased efficiency. Such a suggestion will result in hollow laughter from maritime historians, and, indeed, from anyone who has worked in the shipping industry. There seems to be some measure of agreement among historians that the ocean-going cargo liner of the later part of last century was about three times as efficient in terms of carrying power per registered ton as a contemporary sailing ship, and it is easy to identify specific developments which made dramatic reductions in operating costs. During the 1860s, for example, the thermal efficiency of a set of 'best practice' engines and boilers roughly doubled, enabling reduction in bunker space and in the number of stokers needed. One of the keys to that improved efficiency was the adoption of much higher working pressures, rising from around 20 lb/in$^2$ in 1860 to around 100 lb/in$^2$ in the mid-'70s, and that had the almost incidental effect of reducing the size and weight (per unit power) of engines. Although higher pressures required stronger boilers, the higher engine efficiency which resulted reduced the weight of steam used and hence the evaporative capacity needed, which meant boilers too got smaller and lighter, though not to the same degree as the engines.[27]

The steamship owners did not, of course, boast of enormous profit or benefit from these developments, indeed when we find them giving evidence before Royal Commissions such as those on Unseaworthy Ships and Ship Tonnage Measurement in 1876 and 1881 respectively they present a procession of complaints about the hardness of their lot in life.[28] One is tempted to wonder what strange sense of duty to their fellow men it was which compelled them to engage in such a thankless and unprofitable activity. While many of their complaints can be dismissed as attempts to maintain a status quo which was allowing some unpleasant practices, it is important to realize that ownership of steam vessels was not a licence to print money. It is easy to read the technical literature and be amazed at the speed of technical progress, while forgetting that the result of this in real commercial life was that steamships were very expensive, were becoming more so, and were rendered obsolete long before they were worn out.

The steamship enjoyed the greatest advantages over sail in the liner services, whether passenger or cargo, because of its vastly superior ability to come and go according to a fairly precise timetable. This method of operation opened up new and potentially profitable markets for shipping services, but it did so at the cost of vessels having to leave port when the timetable said they would, whether they were full or not. Because their operating expenses were so high in relation to sail, that meant the need for a fast turn-round in port, to keep all that expensive metal earning money. That, in turn, made them far more vulnerable in times of slack trading: the cost of laying up surplus sailing ship capacity was much lower. The profitability of steam shipping is an area still in need of further research, but it is clear that the majority of companies did well enough that there was never any shortage of newcomers wanting a share of the action, and, of course, the overall growth of the industry speaks for itself.

It may be that shipowners genuinely felt they were living on a knife-edge: be that as it may, they very rarely admitted that they were in a position to pay port charges which would cover the costs of the improvements needed to enable ports to handle their constantly growing high-tech ships. For some owners and at some times, this was probably perfectly true. It was, however, forced on to the ports, partly through their own willingness to compete with each other and partly through the potential threat of what we may term manufactured competition. A final factor which cannot be discounted is that the shipping industry received relatively sympathetic treatment by government: the Merchant Navy's huge pool of skilled mariners of all kinds was seen as an essential reserve in the event of any challenge to the Royal Navy's maintenance of *Pax Britannica*.

In the main the *Annual Accounts* show that the newer and more expensive docks produced much larger revenues than the older ones, indicating that the investment in them was worthwhile from the Board's viewpoint. When

Alexandra recorded its first full year in traffic (1883) it immediately far surpassed the tonnage handled by any other dock, some 22 per cent of the total for the port. But there was more to it than that, for the trades handled at Alexandra were generally among the more profitable ones: receipts at Alexandra that year represented 24 per cent of the total for the port and the proportion continued to rise. Unfortunately, when we look at the wider picture, we find the triumph at Alexandra to be a little misleading, for the corporate debt was still rising. This was, of course, because when the lucrative trades moved into the newer docks, the obsolete and obsolescent docks all moved down a step. The extreme case was Clarence, which in 1883 handled the amazing total of 557,235 tons, or 7 per cent of the tonnage of the whole port, but because nearly all of its traffic was coastal it generated rather less than 2 per cent of the revenue. As the rising debt shows, the funds to upgrade *everything* would never be available, so little obsolete enclaves like Clarence would continue to exist.

If, however, we look at the efficiency of docks from another angle, namely that of tonnage per acre for the year, Clarence at 101,315 makes Alexandra at 37,080 look poor. The Board itself, when considering the need for new accommodation used this as one measure of efficiency, so the question arises once again of just what the Board's investment objectives were: if their objective was simply to move a lot of tonnage then the best way of doing that was by working little old docks highly intensively. It was not, of course, as simple as that, because much of the traffic carried in the little old docks was passing coastwise to or from the large vessels in the newest and most modern docks, and the traffic in Alexandra represented a high proportion of the port's total trade with USA, which traditionally used the largest and most demanding vessels. The two activities were complementary, though it is relatively difficult to find representatives of the trades in question willing to admit that when pressing the Board for improved facilities.[29]

It would be very good to be able to state the Board's objectives and explain why it was that the resources allocated to the Engineer were so loaded in favour of what we may loosely call the glamour trades. For two reasons, these objectives were never specifically stated. The first is explored in *Liverpool Central Docks*, namely that the Board got itself so locked into the consideration of trivia that there was never time at meetings to consider issues of broad policy.[30] The second is that because the terms of their enabling Act were so vague, the Board's policies had always been reactive, though in some cases they did not react very effectively. It does seem, however, that they genuinely saw themselves as a quasi-public service, whose key duty was to please the customers. That being so, the customers most likely to get pleased in any case of conflict were those involved in passenger and cargo liners, or in large and valuable traffics like corn, rather than the operators of Irish cattle boats. Just about the only time the latter got what they wanted was when they were able to force the construction of Princes Jetty on the Board. The way they did it was by objecting to every Bill the Board put forward to improve facilities for large vessels, including the extremely important 1898 Bill, so the exception proves the rule.[31]

## The Question of Investing in Equipment

The criticism was often made of the Board that the equipment of the docks, even the newest and most expensive ones, was poor. A particular source of complaint was the provision of cranes, and it is certainly true that, after Jesse Hartley's rapid adoption of hydraulic hoists at the warehouses, hydraulic cranes did not sprout all over the estate with the rapidity which might have been expected. The question which arises is whether this was brought about by shortage of money, or by short-sightedness or by a sheer incapacity to recognize and provide what the customers wanted.[32]

There is at least a case to be put that it was none of these. Cranes were expensive items: in the 1880s the yardstick cost of a fairly rudimentary hydraulic crane was £100 per ton of capacity, so large or specially clever ones cost well into four digits. Their maintenance was a considerable further commitment: the entry for general purpose hydraulic cranes on the Liverpool side alone normally ran into four digits in the Engineer's Report, before any of the special-purpose ones at places like the High-Level Coal Railway or the 100-ton monster at Langton Graving Docks were taken into account. When the Board looked into the question of craneage, they found that cranes were not a profitable service to provide. This was not altogether surprising, for although it was claimed that the cost of operating hydraulic cranes was only about one eighth that of working handcranes we must always remember, as they did, the dangers of getting swept away by enthusiasm for new technology. Quayside labourers were casual workers, so that the supply could be made to match the workload literally on a daily basis, and winding a handcrane did not require any scarce skills. It might well make better financial sense to use manpower than to have expensive hydraulic machines standing rusting until the new cotton crop came in. Even quite heavy lifts could be undertaken by manpower: incredible though it may seem, the 87 ton crane at Gill Brook Basin (Birkenhead) was originally hand operated, though it did not remain so for long.

As we shall see in Chapter 7, there is a good deal of evidence that the old *modus operandi* of the Liverpool docks was actually quite effective for a long time. It consisted of having only a very narrow quayside, with long clear-span transit sheds behind that and railway tracks behind the sheds. Goods were discharged in a fairly haphazard manner and sorted in the shed. Although some of the old-style sheds had cranes, this system was basically intended to work with ship's tackle, which many shipowners preferred to use anyway, since they considered it cheaper. Even when the new double-storey transit sheds appeared in the 1880s, their roof cranes were intended for working the upper storey only: the lower storey was still worked by ship's tackle. There was also the problem of how high to build cranes: the deeper the ship, the higher it rose out of the water when discharging, which meant that cranes could, and did, get rendered obsolete just as easily as anything else. The important point, however, was that until cargoes started coming and going as large unified consignments, large meaning several railway wagons' worth of identical packages from the same consignor to the same consignee, the hoisting of goods from a ship's hold was not the critical problem. There is, in fact, considerable evidence to the exact contrary, that vessels with powerful steam deckwinches caused chaos, loss and damage to goods by discharging their cargoes quicker than anyone could carry them away or sort them into their consignments.

It was very easy, as a gentleman shipowner or merchant with no understanding of what actually happened on quaysides, to observe that goods were delayed and to assume that lack of craneage was the cause. More craneage would have been an uneconomic investment which would in fact have made the problem worse rather than better. By the time that Lyster defended the old way of doing things as late as 1889,[33] he was probably wrong, for by then direct discharge of larger consignments direct into

*Weighing sugar in a two-storey transit shed. While all these porters were standing around watching, the lumpers were delayed in their work. These methods persisted into the 1960s, though bulk imports began to displace them in the 1950s.*

railway wagons was fairly obviously the way things were going next, but as late as 1900 we can find shipowners speaking out against mechanical quayside cranes and discharge into railway wagons as being slow and ineffective.[34]

If providing general-purpose cranes was a doubtful investment, providing special-purpose facilities could be worse. The pioneer bulk grain-handling plant at Waterloo devised by Armstrong's in collaboration with Lyster was a fairly unsatisfactory piece of engineering. But let us set that aside: for present purposes we should remember that the high cost of being the pioneer was incurred because the Liverpool corn trade said that bulk was the coming thing and that Liverpool had better be in there at the start. They made a lot of noise and the Board believed them. When the costly new warehouses were opened, with their novel machinery, they immediately required the addition of extra general-purpose hydraulic hoists because over two-thirds of the grain was arriving in bags.[35] Through incidents like this, the Board was driven to the position, which its successor body maintains, that special-purpose equipment should be the responsibility of the user.

One can find simple, clear-cut, instances of a failure to invest in relatively inexpensive items of equipment where considerable savings would result. The Board was, in the main, parsimonious about lighting in sheds and on quaysides, when it is obvious that the cheapest way to improve the throughput of a dock in the winter is to provide some floodlights. The surprise which was evinced when floodlighting belatedly provided at the High Level Coal Railway had exactly that effect, suggests a lack of thought and an unwillingness to listen to practical advice from those at ground level. These cases are, however, comparatively unusual, and an apparent refusal to keep up to date by installing high-tech equipment is often based on caution rather than ignorance. It may be significant that, as we shall see, criticism of the port's equipment often came from those with more than one interest.

Because the Board's objectives were vague, and because the costs and benefits of some of their investments are difficult or impossible to quantify, the question posed in this chapter would require the analysis of vast quantities of statistics to answer it with certainty. It is suggested that, on the basis of an admittedly superficial examination of the evidence, both the Trustees and the Board pitched their level of engineering investment about right. It was in the implementation of the investment programme that things began to go wrong later in the century.

# 4

# **The Problem of Competition**

It is one of the underlying axioms of capitalism that, other things being equal, competition will result in goods or services being provided in the manner preferred by the customer when he exercises choice between competing suppliers. In the case of port services it was far more complicated than that, not least because the qualities sought by the customers were complicated by the fact that the customers fell into various 'interest groups', each seeking different attributes in their ideal provider of port services. Their demands involved all of the departments of a Port Authority to a greater or lesser degree – that, in theory at least, is why the departments existed.

The Harbourmaster's Department, for example, was responsible for the operation of the dock entrances, and at busy times when the high tides were on their way down from spring to neap, the skill and judgement of dockmasters or piermasters could save or waste days for a captain, by succeeeding or not succeeding in working the maximum possible number of vessels through an entrance on a particular tide. The consequences of their getting it wrong, which could include a ship getting stranded in dock, earning nothing, were a serious matter for steamship owners whose profits depended on keeping their expensive investment working all the time. It was not uncommon for ships, whether sail or steam, to be damaged, sometimes seriously, by attempting to enter or leave the docks when the depth was insufficient or the weather unsuitable, which put the cargo as well as the ship at risk.[1] The Traffic Manager's Department also had a vital role to play in the speed of turn-round of vessels through ensuring the expeditious dispatch or arrival of goods from or to the quayside. This was a matter of importance to the merchants as well as the shipowners, for getting goods in and out at the right time was part of the service for which they were paid by their customers.

The place where all the demands converged, however, was in the Engineer's Department. When an assistant traffic manager was beaten around the head with a rolled-up *Journal of Commerce* because goods were piled up in the rain or standing in pools of muddy water (apparently a common reason for being rude to ATMs) he passed the problem up the management line. If, instead, the complainant had sent one of the hundreds of stroppy letters received each year, the end result would be the same: if the complaint was judged by the Chief Traffic Manager to be of any substance, it went before the Docks & Quays Committee, and they, if they thought it of any substance, passed it to the Works Committee. It may be remarked in passing that the Docks & Quays Committee, functionally sandwiched as it was between the Marine Committee (to which the Harbourmaster reported), the Traffic Committee and the Works Committee, was occasionally accused of an undue enthusiasm for off-loading responsibility in either direction. None the less, if shed accommodation was insufficient, the surface of the quayside was deficient or the drains were blocked, if, in fact, any physical cause of the problem could be identified, then the Engineer would be required to report on it, giving an estimated cost for his preferred solution. The Works Committee would then consider the report and make a recommendation to the Board, which would determine the action to be taken. In minor matters they usually rubber-stamped the Committee recommendation with a minimum of fuss, but the procedure was a cumbersome one, normally occupying a couple of weeks. In theory it was not necessary for minor jobs, which were supposed to be carried out on the authority of the Engineer, and Hartley cheerfully carried out quite substantial repair works in that way. The Board, however, became steadily more bureaucratic until the 1890s, and the rivalries which grew up between departments also made Lyster anxious to watch his back. The Secretary's Department was particularly given to issuing officious instructions as part of its 50-year campaign to wrest control from the Engineer's Department.[2] One result was that the full procedure got invoked for tasks of ever-decreasing importance, such as clearing the downspouts of the valley gutters of transit sheds – one of the favourite sources of those pools of water about which the customers complained.

Taken in conjunction with the crucial position the Engineer held in relation to new construction and to the larger modernization schemes, these smaller responsibilities meant that customer satisfaction all along the line, regardless of whether the customer was a shipowner or a merchant, large or small, in sail or in steam, in corn or in cotton, was in some way dependent on the Engineer's Department. It was in recognition of that fact that in the mid-1840s the Dock Trustees had paid Hartley as much as the next three highest-paid officers, namely the Secretary, Treasurer and Solicitor, put together. When Miles Kirk Burton was employed as the first 'Chief Executive' under the title of General Manager & Secretary, his salary was less than half that of the Engineer-in-Chief.[3] The spending of the Engineer's Department was enormous: virtually all the capital went into major works, and the revenue expenditure on 'general repairs, maintenance and improvements', together with the 'official charges' (the relatively small costs from Lyster's office which were not apportioned to particular jobs) ran at some six times the level of the next-highest spending department, the Harbourmaster's. In 1883, for example, Lyster's *revenue* expenditure was £198,968. This was partly a reflection of the fact that Liverpool was the greatest cargo-liner port in the world, but it was also partly a reason.

When the users of port services made their decisions which port to use, there were some factors which were outside of the control of the port authority. These might include the location of the port, the effectiveness or otherwise of the inland transport connections or the skills of the local mercantile community. Of the factors which were within the authority's control, all hinged on the Engineer, placing him in the front line of the competitive battle for traffic. In many cases this was, like the competition itself, entirely fair and reasonable. There were, however, instances of the engineers at Liverpool, as elsewhere, being forced into expenditure which varied between unnecessary and downright harmful, in the interests of competition which held little or no benefit for anybody in the long term.

It has long been recognized by historians that the building of railways in Britain under free competition was a foolish and wasteful process resulting in much duplication of effort and the adoption of inferior routes because rival groups of promoters could not sink their differences. It was recognized at the time as well: Robert Stephenson, for example, spoke out against duplication of competing routes, and there were regular spasms of public repugnance at railway financial policies which caused recurrent suggestions in, for example, the early 1840s and the mid 1860s, that railways should be nationalized.[4] For much of last century, a similar concern about wasteful competition arose in the ports industry, though the inherently local nature of existing port administration meant that the idea of nationalization did not attract much attention. We have already considered the case of Birkenhead, a port brought into being by the idea that Liverpool was expensive only because it held a local monopoly and that it must be possible to provide the services cheaper. It was claimed, and believed, that Birkenhead would charge no dock dues or town dues, (both payable on the ships) but only tonnage dues on the goods the ships carried. Perhaps it would, but the question arises of what was in a name. The simple fact was that even in hypothetical optimum circumstances, such as building a dock system which worked at a price which had about the same number of digits as the estimate, Birkenhead would have needed to charge roughly the same amount that Liverpool did for a given ship and cargo. There really was no kind dock fairy to wave her wand and provide expensive facilities for nothing.

The really interesting thing about Birkenhead Docks, however, is that when they had been completed, 160 acres of them, with deeper entrances than at Liverpool, the traffic did not go there. As we have seen, the traffic Birkenhead attracted compared unfavourably both with old and with new docks on the Liverpool side. Yet by 1880, the Board had been forced to invest very nearly £6,000,000 in Birkenhead since 1858, more than on the more extensive and incomparably more productive Liverpool Docks.[5] In short, the investment at Birkenhead was entirely uneconomic compared with additional construction at Liverpool, and the reason for that was that it was berths at Liverpool that the customers wanted. We are, therefore, driven to the conclusion that the earlier protestations in favour of Birkenhead were merely a bargaining ploy to force Liverpool to cut its dues. Had the port been left to invest in the obvious and sensible manner, by looking at what worked best and doing more of that, the result would have been lower overall costs for everyone, including the agitators. In 1878, for example, the Annual Accounts show the interest cost of Birkenhead Docks was running at over £250,000 per year against an income of £72,295. The deficit corresponded to almost 3 per cent of total dues income for the whole of the port.

The engineers could not win. John Hartley was faced with the prospect of completing a large and expensive system with an entrance he knew would not work, and which would therefore leave millions of pounds worth of new docks unused, earning nothing. His highly superior additional entrance at Alfred was better and deeper than anything on the Liverpool side.[6] Instead of causing the deepest ships to move across to Birkenhead, the Alfred Entrance served the Birkenhead lobby as a reason for continued opposition to investment in Liverpool, on the grounds that it was unnecessary until Birkenhead was working to full capacity. Later, Alfred became the basis for demands that the entrances on the Liverpool side should be made as good as it was. One place where these demands were entered was in the evidence given before the various Select Committees on the three Manchester Ship Canal Bills.

The Manchester Ship Canal as built was a great feat of engineering, though perhaps not quite as epoch-making as its first historian, Sir Bosdin Leech, would have us believe.[7] It is also a good example of the way in which the supposed benefits of competition and the supposed iniquities of monopoly could be so trumpeted around as to result in the construction of a major work of civil engineering which was neither necessary nor financially sound. Because, in the event, it succeeded, we are tempted to view its promoters as wise and far-sighted. When the canal eventually became profitable, its success depended largely on developments like Trafford Park and Stanlow oil refineries which were completely unforeseen at the time of its promotion. One might even bring the story up-to-date by remarking that the fortunes of the company over the last few years have had more to do with property development than shipping.

The fact is that when Liverpool men said of the scheme that it could not be built within budget, that investors would have more sense than to put up the money for it and that if it did somehow get built, it would trade at a loss, they were right on all three counts. The final cost was some three times the first estimate and the capital was raised only by massive aid from Manchester City Council amounting to £5m between 1892–4. Revenue proved insufficient to meet the interest costs, and arrears mounted, despite the fact that the Corporation paid over another £1 million in revenue direct from the rates between 1896 and 1904. In the latter year, another crisis arose: despite the subsidies, arrears of interest were now approaching £2 million, necessitating a complex and anxious capital reorganization in which the Corporation obligingly allowed newly created stock to take precedence over its own.[8] Finally, to get some traffic on the canal, the Corporation played an active role in the establishment of Manchester Liners.

The traditional view of all this, following Bosdin Leech, is that the canal was a bold venture confronting the entrenched vested interests of the wicked shipping conference men in Liverpool. The fact of the matter is that dozens of witnesses had filled large volumes of Minutes of Evidence about how inefficient the Port of Liverpool was, how it was making iniquitous profits which it salted away in things like the Sinking Fund and the Unappropriated Revenue Account, and how a much better service could be provided for far less money at Manchester, via the canal. What then happened was that first the promoters and later the operators discovered that building and running a port was not quite the piece of cake they had thought. They learned the hard lesson familiar to many a retired boxer or footballer who thought that anyone who was suitably skilled and experienced at drinking beer could make a nice living out of running a pub. How lucky the Ship Canal promoters were to be able to learn it at the expense of the ratepayers of Manchester.[9]

The message to port users was clear: that there was no reason why port facilities need achieve a return on their capital, and that if you can let a project fall deep enough into the mire, someone will rescue it. The result was the development of a dependency culture in which the shipowning industry and its customers sought, largely successfully, to gain the use of hugely expensive capital assets without paying a fair price for them. The arguments they used are exactly those we might expect: shipping is a highly competitive business and if we are saddled with high port charges the nasty foreigners will take our trade and then there will not be enough naval reservists to defend Our Island Home. This was the same sort of argument that had been used in defence of the democratic right to send men to sea in coffin-ships free of government interference, and it bore a family resemblance to the explanations by millowners of an earlier generation of the disaster which would befall the nation if children were allowed to work less than twelve hours a day.[10] It conveniently neglected to notice that foreign tonnage using British ports was increasing, suggesting that port charges were not driving trade away.

Municipally subsidized competition in the port industry was not necessarily an inherently evil thing: some corporations, like Bristol, had been doing it for decades, and it may be argued that the general benefits to the population of a port community made it worth providing some inducement to shipowners.[11] But that, of course, was not how the system was meant to work. Subject to a few exceptions like Bristol, anything big enough to be called a port (rather than a single dock or harbour) was normally administered in one of three ways: by a non-profit-making trust like the MD&HB, by private dock companies like those in London, or as an ancillary activity by railway or canal companies. The assumption in all these cases was that the operation of a port would pay its way. (Although in real life railway companies tended to cheat by using railway revenues to subsidize port operations) The introduction of supposedly competing facilities, which were in fact entirely non-competitive, made life very difficult for those port authorities which attempted to continue to play the game by the rules as they were generally understood at the time. Whatever its other faults, the Board viewed its reputation for financial soundness as extremely important, and the idea of rendering the port insolvent, as happened at Birkenhead and Manchester, would not have been entertained for a moment. The supposed rules of the game were that ports raised capital to invest in their fabric and levied charges in a competitive market to cover those costs. Liverpool was trying to play fair when other ports were receiving public or other subsidies, which was bound to create problems, and those problems often ended up, for the reasons mentioned above, on the desk of the Chief Engineer. Even the enormous resources available in Liverpool were severely strained by this disparity between theory and practice in which customers could buck market pressures and suppliers could not.

One piece of public subsidy provided Lyster and his successors with a particularly unpleasant problem. For some years, passenger liners had been getting deeper at a greater rate than other types of vessel, and the fastest, deepest and most expensive of them were those which plied the north Atlantic. In 1885, the US government paid for the artificial deepening of the channel into New York, which allowed shipowners, having got deeper water at one end of the voyage, to start a Dutch auction for deeper water at the other. In Liverpool, the consequences of this act of governmental generosity on the other side of the Atlantic were to cause major financial difficulties and engage the two Lysters in an engineering equivalent of the Vietnam war in which the commitment of ever-greater resources seemed to serve only to make either victory or an honourable withdrawal more difficult to achieve.

## The Liverpool Bar

About 15 miles out from the old docks close to the centre of Liverpool, lay a sandy underwater ridge called the Liverpool Bar, which had been known for as long as men had sailed in and out of the Mersey. In the early days of the port it had not been a problem, because even at the lowest low water of the year it rarely had less than 10 ft over it. As ships became bigger, and as people began to make surveys and draw charts of the channels in the mouth of the Mersey, disturbing facts about the bar came to the attention of the Dock Trustees. The first was that the slope of the sides of the bar was steeper than the normal angle of repose of the sand of which it was made up, and the second was that it not only gained or lost height from time to time, but that it moved bodily landwards or seawards as well. It was not necessary to understand a lot of science to realize that here was some kind of dynamic system, but what made it behave as it did was far beyond the frontiers of anyone's science until well into this century, which made the bar a particularly frightening thing. What might it do next? Could Liverpool end up like Chester with a completely silted-up river? Are we doing anything which might cause it to grow? Can we improve the situation? Nobody knew, despite a number of surveys, including those by Francis Giles in 1820 and Captain Denham in 1833. Denham it was who first attempted to alter the condition of the bar by making a breach in it using an implement resembling a harrow. His reasoning was that quite a small reduction of the height of the bar at a chosen point would cause the ebb to flow faster at that point, thus enlarging the breach. It was a tempting idea, and one which others would take up with enthusiasm, but it was wrong.[12]

As mentioned above, the hugely expensive works under the 1873 Act were formally opened in 1882, and gradually completed over the next six years. Although the works were to prove a bitter disappointment in relation to the promise held out, they were nevertheless a considerable extension of the available space for larger vessels. The customers of the port, exhibiting as usual the gratitude and temperance of a three-year-old in a toyshop, immediately started agitating for the dredging away of the bar. What use, after all, was it to have those expensive new docks if the ships could not get to them at a wide range of states of the tide? It has to be admitted that the lack of depth at Canada Entrance, and hence the short time for which it could be kept open on each tide, provided a measure of justification for some of the cries of 'Gimme, Gimme'. The initial reaction of the Board was 'Thou knowest not, my child, what thou dost ask' followed by a stout refusal, based on Lyster's recommendation, to do anything of the kind. The customers now began a campaign of letter-writing in newspapers and journals as well as directly to the Board. They held meetings and they gave evidence to the Ship Canal Select Committees, alleging indolence on the part of the Board.[13] Much was made of the investment in the Ship Canal, rather less of the fact that the investment made in Liverpool and Birkenhead Docks not only corresponded to building a Ship Canal about every fifteen years, but made provision for obsolescence as well – a provision conspicuous by its absence in the accounts of the Ship Canal Company. The customers were, in fact, going to scream and scream 'til they made themselves sick.

The tales of ships and cargoes lost, of waste and delay and of the excellence of other ports which had dredged away their bars, proliferated, helped along by engineers like Russell Aitken who thought that, through Lyster's unwillingness to act, they might gain a fee or two. It is even possible that since Lyster was nearing retiring age, they thought they might get his delightfully well-paid job. Aitken was by no means alone, but was probably the most indefatigable writer of letters to the Board and the press. None of the examples he gave of successful dredging-away of bars was a valid precedent for the situation in the Mersey, and when he claimed that the Tyne bar had been removed entirely by dredging we are forced to assume that he was attempting to mislead, for the removal of the Tyne bar had also involved the construction of quite extensive training walls.[14]

Lyster has never seemed an endearing character, and one of his less endearing traits was that he could often be dogmatic to the point of arrogance. This was no doubt, at least in part, a defence mechanism against what he saw as interference in his professsional field by amateurs. It still makes it all the more surprising that he should have advised strongly against doing anything with the bar on the grounds not only that it was unlikely to succeed, but that it was terribly dangerous to interfere. He willingly admitted that he did not understand the forces which sustained the bar, rather implying that any of his contemporaries who claimed they did were (at best) misguided. There were four quite distinct theories about the formation and maintenance of bars, differing in such fundamentals as whether the material forming them came downstream or from the seabed. What Lyster clearly did know was that the forces involved were very large, and that monkeying about with a natural system one did not fully understand was extremely unwise. He was entirely right, for the risk being run was that in attempting to gain a little extra profit for the users of a small number of large ships he might spend a great deal of money on work which would effectively close the port to anything bigger than a trawler. Such a thing was not to be lightly embarked upon.

Eventually, under the continuing pressure of complaints from customers and the dubious claims of engineers that removal of the bar was a simple task, the Board caved in and authorized Lyster to begin the experimental use of a sand-pump dredger at the bar. Lyster engaged dogmatic mode, and announced his opinion that if you dredged 10,000 tons of sand from the bar, another 10,000 tons would take its place. Speaking at the Institution of Civil Engineers, he stated that he thought the experiment was unlikely to 'approach the results which some people expected from it', and he told the Board bluntly that he would, of course, accept their instruction to dredge 'without, therefore, departing from the opinion which I have all along held and expressed as to the futility of dredging experiments'.[15]

The experiment began in September 1890, using one of two steam hopper barges fitted up with sand pumps intended to be capable of raising 8,000 tons of sand per day. There were technical problems, followed by legal wranglings, with the other impromptu 'dredger' which resulted in it not starting work until the following May. By July 1893, the total dredged was close to 2,500,000 tons, giving a depth of 18 ft at LWST, which seemed quite an impressive result. The dredgers had, however, raised three times the weight of sand which should have been necessary to effect that degree of deepening. The Mersey Conservancy was delighted, and encouraged the Board to persevere: this they did, building the largest suction-dredger in the world, *Brancker*, which was capable of filling its 3,000 ton hoppers in 45 minutes and emptying them in less than ten. By 1899, no less than 41 million tons had been dredged, at a remarkably low unit cost.[16]

It is at this point we realize the nature of what the Board had taken on, for of that 41 million tons, not much more than half (22.5 million tons) had actually been raised from the bar: the rest had come from the main channel, which was beginning to shift and form shoals. In short, the fears of Lyster

Snr were being justified. Lyster Jnr now applied that characteristically Victorian engineering maxim 'if at first you don't succeed, get a bigger steam engine on the job'. *Brancker* had already been joined by sister ship *G.B. Crowe*, and in 1905 the *Coronation* toppled them from their perch as the largest dredgers in the world. Only briefly though, as the aptly named *Leviathan*, of 10,000 tons began work in 1909. Capable of raising that weight of sand in 50 minutes, and dropping it in ten, her pumping engines would have driven a respectable ocean-going ship, and her propulsion engines another one. In *Leviathan*'s first year, over 12 million tons were dredged, about two-thirds of it from the channels. The visible annual cost was around £50,000, but that rather hid the capital expenditure: *Leviathan*, for example, cost just over £100,000.[17]

The finances of the Board had been looking doubtful during the 1890s, and positively perilous during the years 1901–5. Given the continuing level of investment demanded in the docks themselves, including £5 million for the works under the Acts of 1891–8 and a putative £12 million for the new dock to the north which would eventually be named Gladstone, this

Coronation, *by now only the second largest dredger in the world, at work in the river, c. 1910.*

*1:48 scale builder's model of the* Leviathan, *dating from 1909, showing the arrangement of the suctions.*

expenditure on the bar was absolutely the last thing either the Board or its Engineer needed. But there was worse to come, for although Lyster Jnr had originally been of the opinion that the bar could be significantly reduced by dredging alone, it was now becoming increasingly clear that the more you dredged, the more you needed to dredge. The dredging had indeed provided more depth over the bar, but the effect of that had been to increase the speed of the ebb through the main channel, eroding the sandbanks to either side and setting up a textbook meander pattern.[18] The channel, the lifeline of the port, was getting narrower and crookeder directly as a result of the misguided expenditure of huge amounts of money and effort.

It is with the question of fixed works – revetments or training walls – that the sad comparison with the Vietnam War becomes apparent. Lyster had always insisted they were not necessary, a commitment which they did not need to make. When he was forced to back down, he found himself on a logistical treadmill where everything got bigger and more expensive with every step he took.

The obvious starting point was Taylor's Bank, for it seemed clear that the main problem, the growth of Askew Spit, was caused by the deposition of material eroded from Taylor's Bank, and the decision was taken, in 1906, to revet Taylor's Bank. Quite why the Board decided to approve Lyster's proposal that this be undertaken as direct works by his department is not clear: they had no experience of such work, they were not equipped for it and they did not have a suitable supply of stone. Thus there began the process of acquiring a quarry at Dinorben (north Anglesey), dredging a channel to it, building a jetty at it, building cottages for the quarrymen and arranging for the management of the Welsh end of the project, which even included some administrative difficulties in transferring funds to pay the wages, Dinorben being rather out in the sticks.[19] As one would expect in what was clearly an unlucky project, the more vulnerable stages of this preliminary work, notably dredging the channel in a rather exposed position, were assailed by some of the foulest weather on record: on 22–3 February 1908, for example, the dredger crew came close to mutiny during a gale which lasted 17 hours with average hourly velocities up to 73 mph and gusts to over 100 mph. Not until April 1909 was the first cargo of Dinorben stone shipped out. It is probably coincidence, but it was during this delay that the White Star Line showed its appreciation of the efforts being made to comply with its earlier requests by transferring its express passenger liners from Liverpool to Southampton.

The actual process of building a revetment was so simple that it sounds to a layman as though it would never work. It consisted merely of dumping large quantities of limestone from hopper barges at positions along the line of the revetment which had been marked for them by a buoy tender. Irregular lumps of limestone of the right size (usually between 100 and 150lb) would gradually settle and interlock to form the underwater equivalent of a drystone wall. The reader will readily recognize that it was not really as easy as that. A drystone waller is generally reckoned to be a skilled man, but he has the considerable advantages of being able to see what he is doing and of being able to stand still to do it, rather than working from a barge which is moving up and down, often by several feet. Lyster's team learned as they went along, and really got very good at it eventually. In particular, they discovered that it was better for the hoppers to steam slowly along the line – 'running dumping' – rather than to come to a halt and dump on a specific spot. The new method proved to be easier because the hoppers were better under control when they had steerage way and a higher proportion of the stone therefore landed in the right place. The work was completed in November the following year: the revetment was some 13,000 ft long and had involved the quarrying, transport and dumping of 235,000 tons of limestone. Now, with the supply of replacement sand cut off, the mighty *Leviathan* could hoover up Askew Spit and carry it away.[20]

So she could have done, had it not been for the truth of Lyster Snr's remark about another 10,000 tons taking its place. In children's cartoons, when the Roadrunner erects a door in the middle of a desert, the Coyote stops and knocks at it instead of simply going round it. The tides of the Mersey showed no such consideration for Lyster's revetment: denied sand from the previous location, they went round it and collected sand from beyond its ends. In 1914, *Leviathan* alone removed 5.3 million tons of sand, and the channel was still deteriorating. It was not until the 1930s that understanding of what was going on in the channels, aided by the use of effective experimental models, reached the point where a final solution, involving the construction of extensive training walls in the Crosby Channel, could be achieved.

Taken entirely in isolation, this was engineering nonsense. It was also nonsense in policy-making terms, for in 1912, when Lyster was dredging 16,524,850 tons of sand, the Board was frantically seeking economies at the humblest levels of operation. A special committee formed for that purpose was reduced to issuing the Stationmaster at Riverside with a new uniform every twelve months instead of every eight as previously. One lucky member of Lyster's department was called upon to report on what saving might be effected by painting the water pipes in the gentlemen's urinal at Riverside Station instead of keeping them polished.[21] This was not an organization which could afford to divert tens of thousands of pounds a year (£71,063 in 1912, for example) into an abortive project. It may not be a coincidence that Lyster retired that year at the age of 60, not apparently through exhaustion or sickness, since we find him working for the port of Bombay, as well as serving as President of the Institution, shortly afterwards.

The pressure on the Board was appalling. The tonnage of the largest North Atlantic liners had more than doubled in the last ten years, and new monsters to dwarf *Lusitania* and *Mauretania* were building: *Aquitania* and her great rival *Imperator* would both be over 50,000 tons. These vessels took enormous marginal horsepowers to find the last knot or two of their top speeds, so that a twelve-hour delay waiting for a tide equated to the waste of several hundred tons of coal which had been burned to shorten the passage time by that much.[22] The desire of their owners that they should not be delayed is understandable. The results of their actions were, however, wasteful and harmful. Cunard, for example, deliberately used both

*The new Sandon Entrance in 1903, an effective stop-gap which could just about handle* Lusitania, *but not* Titanic *or* Aquitania.

Queenstown and Fishguard as bargaining pawns in their efforts to get better facilities in Liverpool. They did not, as is sometimes thought, use Fishguard only for setting down mail: on 10 April 1911 a storm prevented the *Mauretania* from landing 500 passengers there.[23] The result was that both the Cork Harbour Commissioners and the Great Western Railway wasted resources on facilities which Cunard neither wanted nor needed for any purpose except to make Liverpool waste further resources in competition. Sadly, the press became unwitting allies, when, for example, they printed stories about how Milford Haven was attempting to become a transatlantic passenger terminal.[24]

The passenger liners had refined to new heights the art of decreasing their NRT in relation to their GRT, thus reducing the amount they paid to Port Authorities while at the same time increasing the demands they made on them. In the case of *Mauretania*, the NRT was about 22 per cent of the GRT. Now it may be thought it would eventually dawn on somebody that port facilities have somehow to be paid for one day. In 1911, so far from this being the case, the Post Office suggested in evidence on a Bill promoted by the Port of Bristol that ships carrying mails should be exempt from port dues. This generous concession was being offered to shipowners following the withdrawal of the old mail subsidy system. Since the expression 'whether under contract or not' was included, the effect would have been to allow any large passenger ship to avoid payment altogether.[25] It is an extraordinary illustration of the widely held belief that ports did not have to be paid for.

The end result of all these pressures was to put a number of ports, including Liverpool and Bristol, into a position where few major developments were possible. When the Liverpool South Docks closed in 1972, the more modern-looking parts were eminently recognizable as the system left at the end of the programme of works under the 1898 Act. The rest of the south system had already been obsolete in 1898 and had remained largely untouched. From Princes Dock northwards to Wellington the situation was a little better, thanks to the windfall in 1928 of the sale of Clarence Dock to the City Council for a power station. The proceeds of the sale, together with government 'work-making' grants allowed the heavy remodelling of Trafalgar Dock to form a good modern coasting faciltity. The now-useless Canada Entrance was closed during the 1930s, only re-opening for the exigencies of war-time operation when anything which worked at all, however badly, was desperately needed. Birkenhead was similarly starved of funds, with only three major projects this century.

The effect of all this has been to make the port industry of the first half of this century seem backward-looking and unenterprising. The dock engineers similarly appear to be have evolved into little grey men: tied to their dreary new scientific and mathematical methods and largely office-bound, they make the Hartleys and the Lysters seem not only the giants of the profession but men of inspiration whose like we shall not see again. Perhaps the Hartleys and the Lysters really were giants, but they enjoyed a huge advantage which was denied to their successors. They worked in the era before the port industry had finally been financially crippled by the long-standing and almost universal supposition that somewhere there was a good dock fairy who would pay for everything.

# 5

# The Staff in the Dock Yard and their Work

## *Dramatis Personae*

It is usually difficult to discover exactly who did what in a large civil engineering establishment: because the results of mistakes could be catastrophic, the Chief was expected to see and approve everything and to put his name on it. When reports were written, perhaps recording successful completion, perhaps explaining away delay or over-spending, it was the Chief's name at the bottom. When papers were read at the Institution giving an account of works undertaken, it was rare for the author to give any details of who was responsible for what, or exactly how the administrative system worked. As mentioned elsewhere, it was often only when accidents, scandals or litigation occurred that anybody bothered to record how the system was meant to work in order to show how it had come to fail. This was presumably because in normal circumstances everybody knew that needed to, so nobody bothered to write it down.

It was mainly for the acceptance of responsibility for all the rest of his team that the Chief was paid several times as much as his principal assistants. Very few of the thousands of drawings in the MD&HB collection, for example, have any indication of who actually drew them if the Chief did not. Some documents mention the names of draughtsmen and assistant engineers, leaving us to wonder who this chap was and what he did, while others do not even lead us that far. During the controversy over the elevation of Lyster Jnr, for example, we find passing mention of his having taken a step up the ladder when a 'Mr Blandy' left. Who Blandy was, where he came from, what he did and why he left are questions on which we are left to speculate. Nor are these trivial questions: engineering training, for example, was the subject of prolonged debate and soul-searching both within and outside the profession at the time. It has since been one of the issues in the long-running and incredibly voluminous historical debate about Britain's industrial decline, and it would be fair to say that there is still some controversy among engineers as to the relative merits of academic and in-service training. Knowing what kind of training engineers in a major establishment like the dock yard had undergone or were undergoing helps place the dock yard in the broader context, and may even add a little to our knowledge of the wider picture.

Whatever the rights and wrongs of the 'decline controversy', one activity in which Britain remained highly competitive was civil engineering, with the result that British firms undertook contracts all over the world. Furthermore, Britain exported the administrative machinery of the MD&HB to several major colonial (and other) ports and thus created an overseas demand for in-house dock engineers. Since the Liverpool Dock Yard was the largest specialist establishment of its kind in the world, it is to be expected that men who had worked or trained there would be found in places like Bombay or Rangoon, and also that young men from such places might wish to serve a pupillage in Liverpool. Historians have readily given credit to such institutions as the Ecole de Ponts et Chaussées both for developing engineering skills and for disseminating them. If any similar claim could be advanced for the Liverpool Dock Yard fulfilling an analogous role in the field of dock engineering, we need to find out whether, among the little-known band of subordinates gathered under the two Hartleys and the two Lysters, such transfers actually took place. We also need to consider whether the skills of the Dock Yard were disseminated to any significant degree through any other means, such as publication of books or papers.

Another difficulty which arises in studying the dock engineers is that of trying to envisage what really happened in the department. Since the Chief was increasingly office-bound and responsible for increasingly broad oversight of increasingly diverse activities, most of the day-to-day responsibilities which Hartley was able to discharge in his early days, when everything was very small-scale, had to be delegated. If we are to form any impression of the effectiveness of the department as this process advanced, then it is obviously helpful to have some idea of the training, skills and experience of those to whom the work was delegated. As suggested in the case of John Bernard Hartley and his failed marriage, it is very difficult to form any picture of the engineers as people, but if we can start to put names to particular aspects of the work then at least we have a marginally better chance of understanding the inner processes by which docks were designed and built.

At the time of Hartley's appointment the engineering establishment was very small. We know that Hartley was a good draughtsman. The fact that he had to take examples of his drawing to interview when he applied for the job suggests that his predecessors were not. This would hardly be surprising, for the tiny number of earlier drawings in the collection are of middling-to-poor quality, and good quality engineering drawing was a fairly esoteric art at the time. It is also quite possible, as Weir suggests, that some pre-Hartley drawings were removed to protect the guilty.[1]

The earliest of the surviving drawings bearing Hartley's signature are therefore reasonably likely to have been his own work, but one must question whether that situation persisted for very long: the system of detailed progress drawings he instituted as a site management and materials control tool would surely have taken too much of his time and we must expect that he would seek to delegate: in 1829 we find William Anderton being paid £175 p.a. as a draughtsman. There was also a Surveying Clerk named George Thornton, who left the following year, and it is just conceivable that he was young enough to be the same George Thornton who worked on Lyttleton Harbour Works, Canterbury, New Zealand, in the late 1870s.[2] Unfortunately, the term 'clerk' was used both in its modern sense of someone to deal with the routine paperwork and in the older sense meaning an assistant, making it very difficult to trace the men who worked under Hartley in his early days. As the Dock Yard establishment got bigger, matters became even more difficult when 'Assistant Clerks' began to appear in the *Annual Accounts*, with an aggregated sum debited for their pay, leaving us ignorant of who they were, what they did, how long they stayed or even how much they earned.

Another difficulty arises in the shape of the small membership of the Institution of Civil Engineers: later in the century almost anyone with any credibility as a professional engineer would be a member.[3] If they kept up their membership until they died, which many did, then we will find a memoir published in the *Minutes of Proceedings*, but even if they did not, it is normally possible to find their candidate circulars, effectively a nomination paper for membership or for transfer from one class to another. These give at least some useful information, including where the subject was trained. Many nomination papers provide a much more useful piece of information by stating that the nominee had held a specific responsibility on a project. A.F. BLANDY, a pupil of Lyster's, of whom more later, is one such for whom we have no memoir, but his transfer from Associate to Member status in 1867 gives a fair idea of his activities.[4] In the early part of Hartley's tenure, membership seems to have been confined to Hartley himself and a few of the young high-flyers.

As a result, we know the names of only a few of the large number of men who worked with Hartley during his 36 years' service, and of some of those we know very little more. ENFIELD FLETCHER, for example, was a pupil of Jesse's who started on the docks, then worked for Jesse on his 'private job' on the Manchester, Bolton & Bury Railway and then moved on to work for James Walker on the Selby & Hull Railway. Walker was an extremely distinguished engineer and a long-standing friend and admirer of the talents of Hartley, having been one of his sponsors when he was elected to the Institution in 1825.[5]

The two men – apart from John Bernard Hartley – upon whom Hartley's claim to fame as a trainer of young engineers and a disseminator of techniques must chiefly rest were each with him for comparatively short times, but each rose to the very top of the profession and both implicitly or explicitly acknowledged their debt to him.

SIR JOHN HAWKSHAW was born in Yorkshire in 1811, and spent the first few years of his career working under Charles Fowler. He then became 'before he was twenty years old' an assistant to Alexander Nimmo, well-known to port historians as one of the co-authors with Telford of the original (1828) plan for a dock system on the Wirral peninsula. Nimmo was a man of many parts, and was involved in early railway surveys, including the first scheme for a route from Liverpool to Leeds. He also worked on the Manchester, Bolton & Bury, which is probably where his young assistant first met Jesse Hartley. Nimmo died in 1832, and Hawkshaw repeated the mistake of both Richard Trevithick and Robert Stephenson by going to seek his fortune in the metal mines of South America. Like them, he found it a lawless and disease-ridden place, and returned to England in poor health. The faint suspicion occurs that, like Trevithick, he may have returned penniless, making a job in the Dock Yard, within easy walking distance of where his ship docked, a particularly attractive proposition. From Liverpool he moved on to Hartley's friend James Walker, and from there he took charge of the works of the Manchester, Bolton & Bury. His successful completion of the line was obviously a factor in his transfer, in August 1838, from associate to full membership of the Institution.

His career took him into virtually every branch of engineering and to every continent: if it is intended to claim that his relatively short time with Hartley influenced his future career, and that he disseminated techniques from the Liverpool Dock Yard, it is necessary next to show some evidence of Hartley's influence. That evidence forms one of the stranger stories in the history of dock building, mentioned in passing in the Introduction above. In 1883, as one of the doyens of the profession, he was approached to design a dock system for Buenos Aires. Clearly he was too old to play any very active part in directing construction, but he did produce a design in 1884, which was carried into effect by the younger members of the firm of Sir John Hawkshaw, Son & Hayter, the detailed survey work being carried out by Hawkshaw Jnr and James Dobson. The docks exhibit a quite extraordinary design feature: there are retaining walls built of granite rubble with granite ashlar quoins, copings, etc, in the Hartley manner. Now as we have seen, the Hartley method was cheap as he applied it, with his own tightly integrated set-up and his teams of skilled men. There was no suitable granite to be had in Argentina, so the rubble was imported from Uruguay and the ashlar from Cornwall. Clearly that was not cheap, which must mean that an engineer as accomplished as Hawkshaw thought the Hartley technique good enough to justify carrying stone a quarter of the way round the world.[6]

To attempt to write a full curriculum vitae of Hawkshaw would be an extremely long and not terribly rewarding venture, but a brief summary of the key points might not be out of place. During the remainder of the 1840s, after he left the dock yard, he worked on a large number of railway projects, including the Liverpool & Bury line. In 1850 he established himself in practice in Great George Street, Westminster, where he practised for 38 years. He continued with railway work, including work on the forebears of the London Underground and in Russia, India and the West Indies. He was involved as a 'second opinion' on the Suez Canal, reported on the difficulties of building the Panama Canal, and built the Amsterdam Ship Canal. In the field of ports and harbours, he worked at or advised on works at Holyhead, Alderney, Dover, Folkestone, Belfast, Aberdeen, Greenock, Wick, seven Brazilian harbours, Hull Docks, East & West India Docks, Penarth, Fleetwood, Maryport, Granville Dock (Dover) and Greenock. He also worked on river control schemes and sewage disposal. He served on numerous government committees and one Royal Commission. In addition to being President of the Institution in 1862–3, he was also President of the British Association in 1875. He was, in short, one of the most versatile and prolific engineers of the century, a man whose considerable influence on the profession is perhaps best summarized by the fact that his contributions to the *Minutes of Proceedings* of the Institution run to six pages of entries in the index volume.[7]

No less distinguished was SIR ROBERT RAWLINSON. Born in Bristol in 1810, Rawlinson began his engineering career at an early age, helping in his father's business as a contractor and millwright, and joined Hartley's staff in 1831 working as a draughtsman and in that critical role of 'measurer of masonry'. He probably also worked for a while as a mason. He remained for five years, by the end of which time he was reputedly one of Hartley's most valued assistants. Certainly his subsequent career suggests he might well have been. He next went to work on the London & Birmingham Railway for Robert Stephenson, then returned to Liverpool as Assistant Corporation Surveyor, 1840–3.

From there he moved, on Hartley's recommendation, to be Engineer to the Bridgewater Trustees, no mean post for a man in his early thirties. It was during this time that he solved the structural problem of the huge brick arch ceiling of St George's Hall which the architect had conceived but could not build. In 1848, however, his career took a diferent turn, when he was appointed an Inspector under the Public Health Act of that year. He served on several Royal Commissions on sewage disposal, river pollution and similar issues, was sent to the Crimea (where he was wounded) to advise on the improvement of field sanitation, and then was appointed Chief Engineering Inspector to the Local Government Board and Parliamentary Secretary to the Poor Law Board. He was knighted in 1883 and elected President of the Institution in 1894. He died in 1898.[8]

From the above outline it will be clear that Rawlinson became more an engineering adviser than a working engineer. He never forgot his roots in the practical stonemasonry of the Liverpool Dock yard: twice when retaining wall technique was discussed in the Institution he participated at some length, explaining the superiority of the methods of Hartley. He attempted to gather material about Hartley for the Institution Library, but was thwarted by Hartley's insistence in his will that his personal papers be burned. The Institution Archives still hold the letter from John Ellacott, Hartley's assistant, confirming that John Bernard Hartley performed this last duty. The latter part of Chapter 1, above, may indicate a possible reason. The only item Rawlinson was able to acquire was a small pocket-book of Hartley's in which he recorded some of the work on which he helped his father as a boy. This was stolen from the Institution many years ago, but turned up again later and was 'rescued' by the then Merseyside County Museums. Of greater interest than the book itself is the letter from Sir Robert, dated 22 July 1889 which had been trimmed down and pasted into the book. It includes this description of Jesse Hartley: '. . . may be considered the greatest stonemason England or any other country, ancient or modern, has produced.'[9]

JOHN ELLACOTT was the sort of man every Chief liked to have in the background. Born in Devon in 1811, he first served his time as a carpenter under his father, who was a Plymouth builder. In 1834 he went to London to widen his education and experience, and worked with a number of builders and architects. He then became articled to a land surveyor and practised as such in Plymouth in 1841–2, but business was poor and he had to seek comparatively humble employment as a draughtsman in the Dock Yard. He was promoted to be Head Draughtsman, but in 1846 went to be District Engineer for the building of a section of the Liverpool & Bury Railway. After less than a year he returned to the Dock Yard asking for, and getting, his old job back. Cured of itchy feet, or mission completed, as the case may be, he remained there until his retirement in 1881.[10]

His very wide experience during his travels made him an extremely useful man, and he made his way up the hierarchy, rising to Chief Assistant in 1860. The following year he served as Acting Chief during the illness of J.B. Hartley, but failed to secure the Chief's post when Hartley was forced to retire. He remained as Lyster's right-hand man for the Liverpool side of the Dock Estate. He was elected a full member of the Institution in 1866, and his paper on the Birkenhead Low-Water Basin, cited elsewhere in this book, earned him a Telford Medal and a Telford Premium.

It is virtually impossible to point to anything on the Dock Estate and say of it that it was certainly the work of Ellacott, yet, if his obituarist is to be believed there were few, if any, works undertaken on the Liverpool side between 1860 and 1881 in which he did not play some part. He appears to have been one of those invaluable men who were willing to grind out the detail work leaving those below him in the hierarchy free actually to go and get things built and those above free to concentrate on the broader issues for which they were paid. His surveying and mathematical skills led to his services being sought by other departments of the Board, especially where sensitive negotiations over land were involved. He died in 1894, after a long career of exemplary loyalty which saw phenomenal change and growth in the Dock Estate.

Just such another was WILLIAM LE MESURIER, who was born in Guernsey in 1839, and articled to G.F. Lyster during his time as Chief at St. Peter Port, remaining with him from 1856–9. He then went to London for a couple of years, and on his return was appointed Assistant Engineer at St Peter Port, serving as Resident from 1861 to 1865. On 28 September 1865 he was appointed Resident Engineer for Birkenhead at a salary of £300. In 1881, he was promoted to take charge of the Birkenhead Dock Yard as Principal Assistant to the Engineer, and in 1883 he was elected a full member of the Institution.[11]

In September 1890, Lyster Snr gained the permission of the Board to engage in a form of semi-retirement by passing some of his responsibilities on to Lyster Jnr. This was a blatant 'fix' effectively to appoint Lyster Jnr as Chief-Designate, a position to which le Mesurier, with his long experience of some of the Estate's most problematical works, might legitimately have hoped to succeed. When Lyster Jnr was finally and formally appointed as Chief in 1897, le Mesurier was given the substantial *douceur* of a salary increase to £1,500.[12]

He did not produce any publications of any substance, confining himself to a couple of minor contributions to discussions at the Institution, both on unhappy subjects. He had been involved with the unsuccessful scheme to sluice silt away from under the Floating Stage, and when this failed, resort was had to 'scrapers' – a harrow-type device dragged below the stage, which also failed. The other subject on which he appeared briefly in print was refrigeration machinery: the initial installation at the Birkenhead Foreign Animals Wharf was not at all effective, a state of affairs only partly attributable to the youth of the refrigeration industry.[13]

Le Mesurier is an even more shadowy character than Ellacott. His services were obviously highly valued, for while Birkenhead might in some ways be considered a poisoned chalice, his position in charge of the dock yard there involved some measure of autonomy and is therefore indicative of a high level of trust. He retired in May 1910.

Given the close personal connections and loyalties which characterised nineteeth century engineering, it would be surprising if we found no sign of a 'Guernsey Mafia' following on Lyster's arrival. In fact, only one other Channel Islander seems to have followed him, namely WILLIAM JANVRIN DU PORT, born at St Peter Port in 1834 and articled to Lyster during his time there. After a spell on the Marseilles & Toulon Railway, he returned to Guernsey where he was placed in charge in succession to Lyster. He then moved to Birkenhead as, according to his obituarist, 'Resident for the Birkenhead works'. The MD&HB records state that William Duport (they obviously did not hold with these Frenchified spellings) was employed from 8 January 1863 as 'Chief Assistant in the Birkenhead Office of the Engineer', at a salary of £300. With such a title and salary he was presumably directly under Ellacott. He resigned on 28 July 1865, and his post went to le Mesurier in the following September.[14]

After he left Birkenhead, he was appointed Engineer-in-Chief for the construction of the Tajong-Pagar docks (Singapore), and following their completion he was appointed Government Engineer-in-Charge of the new harbour works at Alexandria. Since he had done all his formal learning with G.F. Lyster, most of it before he came to Liverpool, it may seem that he could have taken little knowledge away away from the Dock Yard to spread around Egypt or the Far East. He would, however, inevitably have worked with one man from whom he could not have failed to learn a good deal, namely JOHN MILLAR, the Principal Foreman of Works, who was responsible for the general superintendence of all maintenance, repair and construction work 'excluding masonry' anywhere on the estate. Millar was not, strictly speaking, an engineer, but he was clearly one of the most important men on the Estate. In an age when in many fields blue collar and white collar workers were becoming more widely separated in social origins, recruitment, training, career prospects and pay, Millar was paid £600 p.a., twice as much as du Port, twice as much as the Head Draughtsman and the same nominal amount as Ellacott. In reality he was paid slightly more, as he had a Board residence with free 'taxes, coals and gas', which perk was usually given a book value of about £50 p.a. Yet this man did not come of a 'good family' and he was not an engineer: he was first hired by Jesse Hartley as a millwright in 1825 at a wage of 28*s* per week, and it was not until 1846 that he was appointed Principal Foreman, at the generous salary of £450. This was £75 more than the long-serving Gilbert Cummins, Hartley's Chief Clerk.[15]

Millar appears never to have gained any formal qualification beyond being a time-served millwright, but after 35 years with Hartley he must have been one of the most accomplished practical men in port construction anywhere. If it is a recurrent theme that both Hartley and Lyster appear to have been able to retain the long-term loyalty of some able men, we must also consider the converse, that to rise to such a position under a man as demanding as Hartley, Millar must have been very good indeed. Du Port was clearly a bright young man to earn Sir John Fowler's recommendation for a post of such importance as that at Alexandria at the age of only 36, and perhaps we may be permitted to guess that he had learned a lot about site management and practical matters from Jesse's old foreman.

ADAM BLANDY was articled to Lyster from 1858 to 1862, and then worked as an assistant engineer 'in charge of works' for a further three years. What these works were we have no way of telling, but the pressure at the time was on the Birkenhead side, reflected in much higher expenditure there than in Liverpool. He then went to work as a resident on the Aberystwyth & Welsh Coast Railway, after which he worked as a resident at Millwall Docks under John Fowler. In 1873 he rejoined the Dock Yard in Liverpool and was described as Chief Assistant in Charge of Dock Works, though again we cannot identify anything specifically as his work. In 1876 he was elected a full Member of the Institution, and in 1879 he presented quite an important paper on dock gates, cited in Chapter 7, below, but soon afterwards he was forced to resign through ill-health, and appears not to have worked as an engineer again.[16]

One man whose work we have little difficulty in identifying is JOHN

ARTHUR BERRINGTON (1851–1934) who was employed as an architectural draughtsman in 1873, initially on a weekly wage of 30*s*. This was, of course, the time of the largest construction programme to date, and Lyster was regularly hiring in extra engineering staff on weekly wages because he was allowed to do that without having to seek authority from the Works Committee as he had to for anyone employed on a salary. Berrington remained on wages (which gradually climbed to 90*s* per week) until 1891, when he was at last placed on the Established List at a salary of £250. Many of Lyster's buildings, though not wildly extravagant, had excellent brickwork detailing coupled with bits of fancy stone and/or terracotta work, and the superb surviving drawings of these details were executed by Berrington. Since he was at one stage paid more than the Head Draughtsman and as much as a junior qualified engineer we may reasonably assume that he not only drew the enhancements, but designed them as well. In 1916, when he was due to retire, he was asked to stay on until the end of the War, as the Drawing Office had been so depleted by military service that experienced men were needed to train the 'Lady Tracers' who were helping the war effort by doing men's jobs. He was finally superannuated on 12 June 1919, having answered to the same job title for 46 years! One cannot but feel some sympathy with him in later life, as the successive waves of financial stringency made it impossible for the Board to afford to build the things he so obviously loved to draw and the aggressive ugliness of ferro-concrete began to displace brick and stone from the estate.[17]

The career of WILLIAM BRODIE is a classic example of the way a man could start at the bottom of the departmental ladder and spend his life gradually climbing it. Born in 1854, he was appointed at the age of 16 to the strangely-titled post of 'Youth in Drawing Office' at the modest wage of 3*s* per week. Like Berrington, he was destined to remain on weekly pay a long time – promotion in 1884 'to take charge of the Drawing Office' at the substantial wage of 95*s* per week was not, of itself, the entree to the charmed circle of the Established List to which he was finally added as Chief Draughtsman in 1889, at a salary of £300 p.a. Not until 1911 was he appointed 'An Assistant Engineer', following the retirement of le Mesurier, despite having been admitted an Associate Member of the Institution so long ago as 1899. Promotion now came rapidly: in 1896, his salary, after 23 years with the Board, was still only £300. By 1919 it had risen successively to

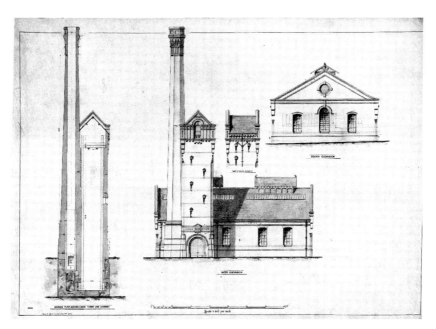

*Two examples of Berrington's work, a general arrangement (above) and a detail view of the hydraulic pumping station at Brunswick, 1889 (below). The originals are coloured, but even in black and white the superb quality of his drawing is readily apparent.*

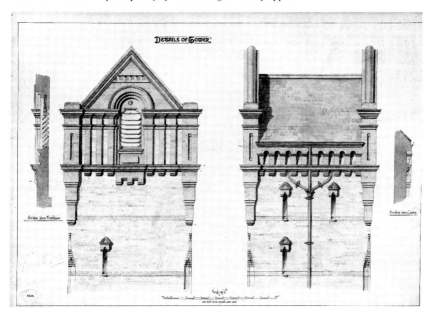

£450, £700, £1,000 and finally £1,500. Given that the Chief's salary in 1919 was still no greater than Lyster's had been when Brodie started, something seems a little unbalanced there, and there must be a suspicion that Lyster Snr took a dislike to him and held him back. It seems strange that he should make such sudden progress, beginning with a substantial rise in the year that Lyster Snr finally retired. Certainly Brodie's younger brother, who had followed him into the department, in 1875, had much the more distinguished career of the two, which might not be entirely unconnected with the fact that he left the Dock Yard and Lyster's pupillage after four years.[18]

William went on to be elected a full member in 1914, and his candidate circular at the Institution refers to him as an 'indoor assistant' before giving a long list of the major works to which he had made some significant contribution, including administrative work connected with the employment of from 4,000 to 11,000 men.

JOHN A. BRODIE was born in Shropshire in 1858 and spent his pupillage under Lyster 1875–9, before winning a Whitworth Scholarship and a Cannings Scholarship to read Mathematics at Owens College, Manchester. He spent three years in the drawing office of Sir Joseph Whitworth, before holding a temporary post in the Liverpool Borough Engineer's Department. The years accounted for by his obituarist do not add up: at the least his time at Owens College must have been concurrent with his time at Whitworth's. He then went to work on 'harbour works near Bilbao', though the substantial official history of the Port of Bilbao does not make it clear what works these were.[19] In 1884 he returned to Liverpool and was appointed a general engineering assistant, rising by 1898 to be City Engineer. (Liverpool received its City Charter in 1880.) He remained in that post until 1926, spanning the period in which some of the largest and most striking works of municipal engineering were effected, including the massive expansion of electricity generation and the electric tramway system. A huge programme of slum clearance and of municipal building was implemented, much of the latter enabled to spread into the suburbs by the tramways, and, later, by arterial avenues and boulevards which are adequately spacious for the traffic of the 1990s. Despite his involvement with the golden age of tramway construction, he was quick to realize the potential of road vehicles after the Great War and was among the first proponents of the East Lancashire Road. Taken together, these developments have caused him to be remembered as much as a town planner as an engineer.[20]

When municipal discontent with the policies of the MD&HB reached boiling point round 1905–6, the suggestion was made that new docks for the coasting trade should be built by the city. It may have been no coincidence that the City Fathers had as their Engineer a man who had begun his professional life on dock construction.[21]

His resignation in 1926 was occasioned by his appointment jointly with Sir Basil Mott as Consulting Engineer for the Mersey Road Tunnel, which was completed in 1934, the year of his death. He accumulated many honours in a long and distinguished career, including the Presidencies of both the Civils and the Municipals. In Liverpool he will always be respected for a different contribution to the progress of mankind, for in 1890 he invented the football goal net.

Probably the best known of all the subordinates in the Dock Yard was BRYSSON CUNNINGHAM, born in 1868, appointed as draughtsman at 30s per week in 1890. Unusually, he was not articled to 'The Chief', but to Fielden Sutcliffe, another member of the department. He had started attending engineering lectures at University College, Liverpool, the previous year and carried on with his (obviously part-time) studies, graduating B. Eng. in 1895, and in the same year he was elected an Associate of the Institution, in which election his sponsors included Professor Hele-Shaw and John Brodie. After qualifying, he was engaged as Assistant to Sutcliffe, who was serving as Superintendent of New Works. The achievements recited for his transfer to full membership in 1914 mention various heavy works, but then state that from 1902 he was mainly working in the Dock Yard, which suggests that the 'heavy works' may have been the improvements to Wellington and Sandon Docks, including the very large new river entrance, completed that year. He then apparently became the departmental specialist in estimating and was placed in charge of all the parliamentary work, in which position he was still engaged when he resigned in 1908 in order to move to London, where, he rightly assumed, the recent establishment of the Port of London Authority would provide better career prospects.

Cunningham is not famous for any of the above, nor particularly for anything he did at the PLA. His fame rests on the production of a number of books which became standard texts for anyone with a professional interest in docks. By no means all of what he wrote would be regarded as beyond criticism by modern dock engineers, and it may be argued that it is unwise to provide 'cookery books' of engineering when the works are usually on a multi-million pound scale, but they served generations of engineering students in the past and port historians find them useful now. Probably only L.F. Vernon-Harcourt's books could be claimed to have even comparable influence, so that in one sense Cunningham is the Dock Yard's greatest disseminator.[22]

Another disseminator was C. GRAHAM SMITH, who was born in 1851, and was in articles in mechanical engineering at Neilson & Co of Glasgow before spending six months under John Fowler on the Metropolitan Railway. He was then articled (yet again!) to Lyster in 1870. In 1872 he left to work on a number of railway projects, and then in Fowler's office, returning to the Dock Yard in 1874 to become Resident for the restoration of the Liverpool Stage (after its destruction by fire in that year) and the construction of the stage and piers for the Foreign Animals Wharf. In 1877 he worked on the preliminary plans for the Overhead Railway. There followed a short spell in private practice before he was appointed Engineer to the Port Commissioners of Rangoon. In 1883 he left that post in poor health and under something of a cloud and died the following year.[23] A brief career, and not an especially noteworthy one, though two papers he wrote while a student member of the Institution earned him Miller Prizes, and one, on the Birkenhead Stage was considered worthy of publication in the *Minutes of Proceedings*, a relatively unusual honour for a student's work. His contemporaries seem unanimous in regarding him as of outstanding ability before his illness and premature demise.

In 1875, along with five other pupils of Lyster's, he founded the Liverpool Engineering Students' Society, with the over-ambitious intention of the members presenting weekly papers. The following year, meetings were reduced to a fortnightly frequency and the word 'students' was deleted from the title: membership increased to 51. By the time the first volume of *Transactions* was published in 1881 the membership was 97 and already included some distinguished engineers – such as the President that year, Alfred Holt. Some of the papers were given by significant authorities, such as E.B. Ellington on the hydraulic power system of Hull. By 1903, there were 417 full members and 63 associates. When we look at the member's list, we realize the significance of what Smith and his colleagues did. There are, of course, men from the Liverpool Dock Yard there, including A.G.

Lyster himself and there are ex-Dock Yard men like Wilfrid Boult now subscribing from other parts of the country. There are important figures like John Brodie, and his predecessor, H.P. Boulnois, J.A.F. Aspinall, Chief Engineer of the Lancashire & Yorkshire Railway and Professor Hele-Shaw. But there are also engineers from the Bombay Port Trust, the Harbour Works, Colombo, and Bristol Docks, and some well-known consultants specializing in dock and harbour works, such as A.C. Hurtzig. The Society was a worthwhile organ for the communication of expertise in port engineering.[24] Of course it would be easy to over-estimate its importance in that respect, for there are also plenty of railway engineers, naval architects, marine and municipal engineers to be found in the list of members, but we may see in the Liverpool Engineering Society a little further evidence for the importance of the dock yard – and of the subordinate engineers employed there.

Not many of the Dock Yard men became academics, although A.G. Lyster was Associate Professor in Port Engineering at the University of Liverpool. There is one very notable exception, however, in the shape of HUGH TAYLOR BOVEY, articled to Lyster in 1873 and appointed an Assistant Engineer in 1875. In 1878 he was appointed to the Chair in Civil Engineering and Applied Mechanics at McGill University and in 1909 returned to Britain as Rector of Imperial College London. By then, the main letters after his name were MA, DCL, LLD, FRS, MICE, MIMechE.[25]

Another of the founder-members of the Engineering Society was WILLIAM SQUIRE, who was born in Bombay in 1854. After serving his time under Lyster he was retained as an Assistant Engineer until 1879. He was then employed briefly at Hull Docks before becoming Chief Assistant at Bombay in 1881. He was promoted Chief Engineer in 1892, and, returning to England in 1898 worked in private practice with Sir John Wolfe Barry for a short while before being appointed Engineer of Bristol Docks, where he was involved in major developments at Avonmouth.

Other young men from the Dock Yard went to work abroad. Two rather sad cases were ISAAC RIDGEWAY and MAJOR ERIC STUART DOUGALL, VC, MC. Ridgeway was a pupil of Lyster Jnr, then briefly an Assistant Engineer, then in 1910, appointed Resident Engineer to the Wallasey Embankment Commissioners (to which body Lyster was also Chief). In the following year he became Chief Assistant to the Engineer for the Fremantle Graving Dock and in 1913 District Engineer for the Queensland Coast. He volunteered to join the Australian Army, and was killed at Gallipoli in 1915. Dougall was also a pupil of Lyster Jnr, and on completion secured an Assistant's post with the Bombay Port Trust, where, after three years he was taken on to the permanent staff. In 1916 he applied for, and was granted, leave of absence to return to Britain to join the Army and was commissioned into the Royal Field Artillery. A short military career of the utmost distinction ended when he was killed in action on 14 April 1918.[26]

GERALD FITZGIBBON was born in 1857, and is unusual among the Liverpool dock engineers in having received a specialist technical education overseas. (It was a cause of widespread concern at the time that English universities offered no specialist engineering education and no alternative form of higher education to supply that deficiency had been introduced. Those seeking such a course of study had to apply to Scottish or continental universities.) He was articled to Lyster in 1879, and on completion of his articles served briefly as an Assistant Engineer on New Works before going to work on Alexandra Dock, Hull, under James Abernethy. Between 1887 and 1894 he worked on the Manchester Ship Canal and then went into private practice, working on a number of dock and harbour schemes including Heysham. Despite this deplorable record of serving competitors, if not downright enemies, of the Port of Liverpool, his application for transfer to full membership of the Institution in 1897 was sponsored by Lyster Jnr and le Mesurier.[27]

FIELDEN SUTCLIFFE was yet another of those who profited from the employment boom brought about by the works under the 1873 Act. Born in 1844, he started as a draughtsman on 10s per week and took only tentative steps up the ladder until 1874, when he was appointed General Superintendent of New Works, North. Like several of his contemporaries, he remained on weekly wages as a matter of adminstrative convenience, but at 100s per week was in fact better paid than many of the lowlier salaried employees on the Established List. In 1891, he finally made it onto the list as Superintendent of New Works at a salary of £350 p.a. He was superannuated in 1909, having worked through the whole of the period of most frenetic activity in the history of the Estate.[28]

Just one volume survives of the daily record of the taking-on of manual workers in the Engineer's Department, covering the period from July

1892 to November 1894. It is tantalizingly labelled '22'. From this, it is clear that Sutcliffe was largely or entirely responsible for hiring and firing of men on the new works since the majority of the entries relate to men taken on by him, often labourers in batches of a couple of dozen, but he took on skilled men as well: on 23 July 1892, for example, he took on 25 labourers, one shipwright, one engineman, two firemen and three masons. Each week's entries were initialled by Lyster Jnr. Labourers were rarely under 21 or over 40 years of age, were almost always paid 3s 6d per day and their names were entered in the book in no particular order, suggesting that they may have been recruited from a grapevine which fulfilled the function of the dock labourers' hiring stands in a marginally more genteel manner.[29]

WILFRED S. BOULT was another of the same generation, and was an early, though not a founder, member of the Engineering Society. He worked on the reconstruction of the Landing Stage after its destruction by fire in 1874, but would probably only merit a brief mention here were it not for another chance survival, which is a large notebook he kept during the latter stages of his pupillage. Some of the information in it is readily, and perhaps more reliably, available from other sources, but it is rich in informal jottings about how things were costed, how to draw up specifications and estimates, how much a horse could pull and how much a man could shovel.[30]

## What did Assistant Engineers do all day?

If we merge the personal information above with the more general information in Chapter 2, we can begin to understand how works were actually planned, organized and controlled in the time of G.F. Lyster. Because we have even fewer shreds of evidence from Hartley's time it is harder to establish what happened in real life in the office and on site, but it is probably fairly safe to assume that the procedures were broadly similar, although smaller in scale.

Let us begin at the point where the Board has recognized a problem, whether of insufficient area of dock available or the inadequacy of the facilities for new and larger ships. The first stage, carried out by the members themselves, assisted by the secretary, was to try to quantify the problem, to find out exactly what the customers wanted and then to find the minimum with which they might be satisfied. The most exhaustive exercise of this kind was the Enquiry the members organized leading up to the Bill for the 1873 Act, but it must be remembered that such procedures had in any case to be re-enacted before the parliamentary Select Committee which would expect to see evidence which both established the need for the proposed works and demonstrated that there was no acceptable cheaper alternative. Other principal officers of the Board, especially the Harbourmaster and the Chief Traffic Manager, had an important part to play at this stage in providing detailed statistical information on such matters as how many vessels used particular docks, what trades they were in, what tonnage of goods per water acre and per linear yard of quayside was passing through, what measure of congestion and delay occurred.

Once the Board had established to its own satisfaction that major expenditure was inescapable, the question was passed to the Works Committee to produce proposals to solve the problems. Formally, what then happened was that they posed simple and formalized questions to the Engineer, upon which he was instructed to report back. In practice it is clear that informal liaison took place, as one particular irregularity shows us. Harold Littledale, the dissident member of the Works Committee who hounded Lyster unmercifully (albeit probably justifiably), wanted to find out about the 'scrapers' which were being constructed in an attempt to solve the problem of silt under the George's Stage. He therefore went to the dock yard with a view to asking Lyster, but when he found neither Lyster nor any of his senior assistants present, he spoke with a foreman involved in the construction of the 'scrapers', making uncomplimentary remarks about Mr Lyster in the process. For this he was severely and rightly censured, but it is clear that what caused offence was his approaching 'other ranks': no suggestion at all was made that he should not have gone to the dock yard to speak to Lyster or his senior assistants.[31] It seems, therefore that there was no reason why individual members should not discuss proposals informally, and it would be most surprising if the more conscientious ones did not. As amateurs, they would find it hard to make useful contributions to discussion if they were not able to ask questions outside the formal proceedings of the committee rooms.

The end result of this phase of the project was that the Engineer had a fairly clear idea in general terms of what was wanted: location, number of berths, depth of vessels using them, principal traffics and so on. It is at this stage that the rest of his staff began to get involved. A rough survey of the site, including level-taking and core-sampling had to be made, which was a cold, wet and unpleasant job and therefore tended to be delegated to the lowest reliable level, normally a fairly junior Assistant Engineer not long 'out of his time'.[32] This was not always a wise way of going about things: there were instances, notably at Birkenhead, where docks might well have been better built in a completely different place, had the preliminary survey successfully identified just how bad the ground was on the site actually chosen. By combining information from the outline brief with that brought back from the survey, it was possible to start on the critical task of estimating.

The levels taken on site would enable the line of any new river walling required to be determined. A balance had to be struck between seeking the maximum depth of water over the sills of the completed work and the spiralling cost of construction when the walls went below the level of low-water spring tides. The older docks had been so designed that their river walls could be constructed by tidal working 'in the dry' at spring tides, but the increasing depths demanded from the 1850s onwards meant that caissons and coffer-dams became the rule rather than the exception. As with the excavation of the docks themselves, the cost varied approximately as the cube of the depth. Other things being equal, the line of the wall would follow the line at which the necessary depth of water could be achieved with the minimum amount of excavation below LWST. Among the other things which might not be equal was the load-bearing capability of the ground and the depth at which rock could be found: from the core samples taken it was necessary to work out what piling would be required, and a balance was then struck between minimizing excavation and protection works on the one hand and piling on the other. We know that some of the Assistant Engineers ('indoor assistants') specialized in staying in their nice warm office working out just such problems as these.[33]

In general terms, Hartley built his retaining walls comparatively thin, resulting in a high ground pressure requiring thorough and extensive piling, while Lyster tended to the view that it was better to build the walls with lower ground pressures and save on the piling. Both were valid approaches so long as either the pressures were correctly calculated or the Engineer was extremely skilled and experienced in empirical 'craft method' – which scientific engineers would dismiss as merely educated guesswork.

One of the advantages the staff in the Dock Yard enjoyed was that the Dock Estate was never free from heavy construction or re-construction works of one kind or another. This meant that it was always a simple matter to find out the actual and up-to-date cost of a particular class of work, because somebody in the office was bound to have had something comparable done quite recently. It also helped in the adoption of an empirical approach, for it needed to be based not on the wisdom of one man but on the accumulated experience of many. From looking at drawings of retaining walls built in Lyster's time, it appears that both methods may have been in use, for some drawings show calculations and others do not. More to the point, there are plenty of drawings which do not show the necessary construction lines for making the calculations. One is tempted to suppose that the older men still used the rules of thumb they had learned with Hartley, while the younger men used the 'new methods', but since the assistants are not identified on the drawings, we can really only guess. In making such a guess we must remember that Ellacott, one of the older men, was noted for his mathematical skills, as John Bernard Hartley had been.

The next stage of the process was to determine the overall shape of the new dock: based on a proposed position for the river wall and the landward boundary of the Estate, the shape, size and alignment needed to provide the required berths could be drawn out fairly simply. Information from the core sampling needed to be fed in, in case there were particular parts of the proposed site where it would be notably easier or harder to form a sound foundation for the walls or for any problematic features like graving docks, whose bottoms were vulnerable to groundwater pressure and whose blocks (on which the ships rested) required particularly sound foundations. These issues were resolved by junior engineers working on the detail and then passing their proposals up the line, eventually to Lyster. In the outside world, any qualified engineer was expected to be able to turn his hand to every aspect of a project. In the Dock Yard, because of the constant flow of work we know some of the staff became expert in particular aspects, as Blandy was on gates and sills, while others got on with working out quantities and costs.

These were the essential preliminaries to estimating the cost. Jesse

Hartley, especially in his earlier years, paid a great deal of attention to estimating, and in a number of cases achieved the seemingly impossible of completing a project within budget. As time went on, things got rather laxer, and parts of his 1844–8 programme, for example went quite badly over budget, though the global figure at the end was reasonable. This programme illustrates the pitfalls which may await even the wary: when the estimates were prepared (possibly by John Bernard) the Railway Mania had yet to get going properly. When it did, the costs of labour, construction materials and credit rocketed. It was only the collapse of the Mania that enabled the sums to come out more or less right at the end. Under Lyster, matters deteriorated further, and one reason for this can be deduced from Boult's notebook and from the Commonplace Books. Both documents contain all sorts of useful little yardsticks for estimating costs. Actual costs of double track swing bridges and dock gates are recorded, and then worked out at a cost per foot width of opening. Prices of broad categories of masonry are worked out per cubic foot. We even find a figure for complete docks, £20,000 per acre. It may be thought that there was a certain laxity creeping in, and that exact site circumstances may sometimes have been less than fully considered. For reasons that never clearly emerge, apparently similar classes of work actually cost quite different amounts on different projects, even those being carried out at the same time. Even so, we may be unprepared for the cavalier attitude which was sometimes adopted. Under the 1898 Act, Brunswick Dock was to be deepened. Ritchie-Noakes correctly records that it was deepened to 20 ft below ODS and that the work was largely completed by 1905. The actual instruction from the Works Committee to the Engineer did not specify a depth, but a cost, of £160,000. The sums were done for deepening to 21ft 6in below ODS, but the answer came out wrong, namely £166,813. Written underneath that figure are the immortal words 'For deepening dock to 21ft 0in below ODS called £160,000.'[34] Curiously, and subject to the usual reservations about the accuracy of the accounting system, the work seems to have been carried out within budget. It remains, however, a classic example of how not to estimate.

It will readily be recognized that the last few paragaphs have thrown a great many variables up in the air. These, in their turn, could generate others through a financial knock-on effect, wasting time and money and probably demoralizing staff as well. The High Level Coal Railway at Wellington and

Bramley-Moore and the question of how to operate it and whether or not to extend it, suggest that the Board did not really have a clear policy towards the coal trade. Did they wish to encourage it as a major trade in its own right, or merely as a service for bunkering the ships engaged in other trades more profitable to the board?[35] The question of aborted projects also arises, and is considered below: the present purpose is simply to indicate that the work of the Engineer could be both complicated and soured by what one might term window shopping, as well as plain old indecision, on the part of his employers.

The most difficult task so far now beckoned, which was to unite all the separate threads and to produce a report which presented members with a limited number of straightforward choices to make. While the initial pulling-together would begin at the level of Ellacott or Le Mesurier, the finished product was Lyster's. It is clear from his performances in the Works Committee and his evidence before parliamentary Select Committees that he was a lucid and persuasive talker, alert, tough and resilient under cross-examination. The few pictures of him which survive indicate that he was an impressive-looking man. The written reports he presented have the same tone: confident, authoritative and garnished, rather in the manner of Jeeves, with a subtle blend of professional arrogance and deference to the client. He really was very good at that, indeed possibly too good, for he sometimes managed to convince people that he should go ahead with schemes which might have been better forgotten.

The action now remained with Lyster for some time, as he played the leading role in presenting the scheme to the Works Committee, to the full Board and eventually to parliament. But while he was being the front man, work in the office continued. As each successive hurdle was crossed, effort intensified, as evidenced by the growth in the number of wage-earning staff in the office *before* the 1873 Act was passed. The reader may care to look again at the 'potted biographies' of Lyster's assistants given above and note how many of them were there when the works under that Act were being planned. In the process, a possible cause of some of the inadequacies of the 1873 works emerges. In relation to the size, scope and variety of the works, it was a very young team, rich probably in talent and certainly in ideas, but with only two really experienced men, namely Ellacott and Blandy, among those involved.

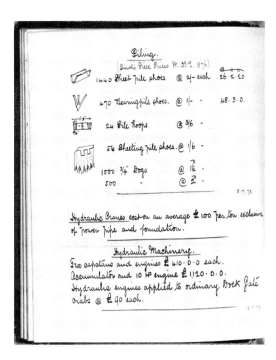

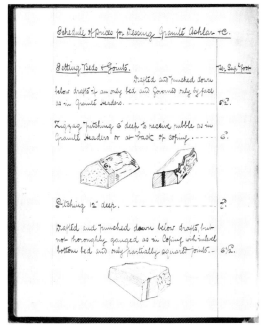

*Pages from Wilfred Boult's 1876
notebook giving the cost of iron
shoes and hoops for wooden piles
(above) and yardstick costs for
masonrywork (left).*

It was at this stage that the first major opportunities for serious embarrassment began to arise. This was when more detailed survey work on the site could reveal hitherto unsuspected problems – as in railway surveying, there was often something nasty, like a pocket of quicksand, which the core sample missed by just six inches first time round. A delightful drawing survives to illustrate the principle. It is a piling progress plan for the construction of Princes Jetty, which shows the intended positions of the piles and their actual positions as driven: the discrepancies are numerous.[36]

The question also arose of the balance to be struck between direct and contract works: although estimates were needed in growing degrees of refinement from the earliest stages of the Engineer's involvement onwards, the choice of contractor, or the decision to use direct labour, might well have a considerable effect on the actual cost of the completed job and it was essential to keep track of costs as closely as possible while the work was proceeding. Any qualified engineer was expected to be familiar with the procedures for drawing up specifications and receiving tenders, and long before the Act was obtained, young men would be writing what they hoped

*Core sampling in progress at Sandon, probably in 1908.*

were watertight specifications for the supply of materials or services. Unfortunately, specifications had, by this date, become such a matter of routine that standard clauses were simply copied out from previous ones. Little thought seems to have been given to the specific difficulties which might emerge in particular cases and the almost invariable insistence on 'materials of the highest quality' soon became meaningless. As a result, it was possible for contracts to go very badly wrong through the failure not just to foresee difficulties but even to attempt to do so. If practice makes perfect, familiarity breeds contempt.

The choice between contract and direct works could be a fairly simple one. Certain activities, such as overall design of the works, design and construction of coffer-dams or other protective works, control of water regimes and the specialized aspects of construction would almost invariably be undertaken in house. The straightforward excavation work, together with simple construction work of minor buildings, was very likely to be contracted out. But from the statement that the number of men employed under William Brodie's administrative responsibility reached 11,000 we can deduce that on some jobs much or all of the excavation was by direct labour as well.[37] The last stage of the project, when the Act had been gained and before work began on site, was to pull together the various tenders and specifications, for Lyster to decide what course he thought best and then to send the issue into the committee machinery of the board. When they decided, then work could begin.

## A Sad Little Epilogue: The Problem of Aborted Projects

There were, however, occasions when work never began at all, so that all the effort described in the latter part of this chapter went to waste. Sometimes this was a blessed relief, certainly in retrospect and possibly recognized as such at the time. One such was the project for carrying the Board's private telegraph wires over rather than under the Mersey. Now this might sound such an obviously stupid idea as to gain no credence at all in the early 1860s, when submarine cables were already a well-established technique. In fact, the Board's new electric telegraph, which replaced the old optical telegraph system extending from Anglesey along the North Wales coast to Liverpool,

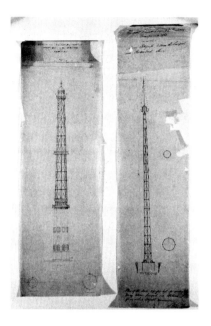

*Two alternative designs (1861–2) for supporting the proposed overhead cross-river telegraph cable.*

had had an unhappy time with its cables under the estuaries of both the Dee and the Mersey. Concern was, perhaps justifiably, felt that under the Mersey was a bad place for a cable owing to the risk of it being damaged by anchors or dredgers. The new telegraph was installed by the Universal Private Telegraph Company, but there was no possible way that the Board could delegate, to them or to anyone else, the design of such a potential hazard to shipping as an overhead cable across the river. In order to provide a safe clearance for sailing vessels at high water while allowing for considerable sag in a cable span of over half a mile, the 'poles' had to be some 260 ft high, and considerable work was undertaken in the department to calculate the forces acting on the proposed structure and to design wrought iron lattice towers, to be sited at Princes Dock and at Alfred Entrance, of adequate strength. Because of their exceptional prominence, their aesthetic treatment was important as well, and two different designs survive: there were probably several more which were considered within the confines of the department.[38]

In 1860, a correspondent using the pseudonym 'An Old Operative', said to have been Jesse Hartley, had floated the idea in the local press that a high-level Mersey Bridge above The Sloyne would be highly beneficial: one of its many advantages would be that it could carry telegraph cables.[39] The construction of the towers was delayed literally for years owing to contractual difficulties between the Board and two different telegraph companies, and by the time that work could begin the obvious and sensible course, implemented in 1869, was to follow the route of what were by then the public cables, via Runcorn and Queensferry.

One of the features of the works under the 1873 Act was that there was to be at least one hydraulic lifting dock.[40] These huge machines were a well-known and moderately well-established substitute for graving docks, and were considered particularly appropriate for brief inspection or minor repairs to larger vessels. Vessels were floated over the iron platform of the lift, which then rose vertically, bringing the ship out of the water. The ones proposed for Liverpool were to be 500 ft long and 60 ft wide with a lifting capacity of 6,000 tons. They were to be constructed by Messrs Standfield & Clark, who were the market leaders in both hydraulic and floating docks. It might seem, therefore, that the Engineer need waste little time on what was effectively a 'design and build' contract. This was not, of course, the case: when, on 26 April 1878, the Works Committee agreed that the question be postponed *sine die* the implications went far beyond the £750 which the Board eventually agreed to pay to Standfield & Clark for their wasted efforts. The lift or lifts were to have been placed in the middle of one or more of the new branch docks, and clearly their enormous weight, even before a ship was lifted, would need some pretty clever foundation work. This, together with the considerable hydraulic supply needed, had to be worked out for the parliamentary estimates. The reason for abandoning the project is not stated, but the in-house design work which had gone into it was written off, only to be repeated in a different guise when the graving dock capacity proved insufficient without the aid of the lifting docks.[41]

There had long been ideas of building docks further inland, and one of these plans featured in Lyster's original 1872 scheme for the 1873 Act. It provided two new docks east of the Dock Road, one on either side of Sandhills Lane, with passages from Huskisson No. 2 to the Northern Dock and from Sandon to the Southern: there was also a passage between the two new docks. Their total water area was just over 21 acres, and access was by 60 ft passages with a depth of 6 ft 6 in below ODS.[42] We can see with

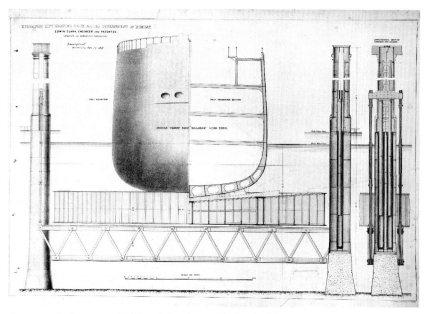

*One example from a small folio of drawings of hydraulic lifting docks supplied to Lyster by Standfield and Clark in 1876.*

hindsight that such a niggardly depth would be insufficient for large vessels. It was just 8 inches deeper than Stanley Dock, whose use was already dwindling through the combination of insufficient depth with the inconvenience caused by operating a movable bride on the perennially crowded Dock Road. The proposal was quietly removed during the drafting of the Bill, and it was fortunate indeed that it was, for it was an obvious white elephant. Once again, however, a good deal of work had gone into producing plans for a scheme which, although comparatively minor by Liverpool standards, exceeded the total water area of many a small port of the day.

These examples of wasted time and effort are all taken from the Board's own waste-paper basket, into which they had been voluntarily, and probably wisely, thrown. The work which was wasted through unsuccessful applications to parliament was of a completely different extent. The Act of 1844 had been one of the great landmarks in the extension and improvement of the Liverpool Docks, and the bill of 1855 would have been another, had it passed.[43] It included what eventually became Canada Basin and Canada Dock, with its 100 ft entrance, but there was also a huge dock of no less than 52 acres to the north of the basin. Two docks on the inland side of the Dock Road totalled almost 29 acres, and connecting these with the proto-Canada Dock was a 9 acre dock with five graving docks, two of them 100 ft wide. In addition, there was a new connection to the Leeds & Liverpool Canal and an extensive system of long narrow docks between the Canal and the main docks, built with wide quay margins right across the line of the Dock Road. The road ceased to exist, and was replaced by up-grading an existing minor road further inland. The 'canal docks' were not mere boat docks, for their access was by 60 ft passages, quite a generous width for sailing vessels or the screw steamers which were beginning to force themselves on Hartley's notice.

In addition to these works, extensive new quayside warehouses were proposed at, among others, Waterloo, Princes and Brunswick Docks. This was truly a grandiose scheme intended to set the port further ahead of its competitors for perhaps another 20 years: with a total water area of over 100 acres it would have made a substantial port in its own right. Once again, it is a blessing that it failed, for it exhibited at least three failures of foresight in relation to remaining in the front rank for 20 years. The first is the well-known change in the shape of ships, so that huge widths became unnecessary but ever-greater depths were needed. The second was that, although it was moving in the right direction by having a greater quay length: water area ratio and wider quay margins, only the canal docks were as narrow as docks could usefully be, providing space for quayside berthing both sides with only enough space for vessels to come and go down the middle. Finally, the warehouse-building side of the scheme did not recognize that the relative importance of quayside warehousing was likely to decline as extensions to Britain's free trade policies resulted in the reduction and simplification of import duties. Jesse Hartley was getting old, but Canada Dock as built showed some important innovations, so the shortcoming probably arose from a failure even on the part of shipowners and builders (who were, of course, consulted as part of the design process) to foresee the extent of the changes which were just beginning. It should also be remembered that much of the work for the 1855 bill was likely done by John Bernard Hartley, at that stage still working directly with his father prior to his taking charge of Birkenhead.

The reason the proposals were reduced to a fraction of their previous extent had nothing to do with their merit: they were scuppered in parliament by the 'Birkenhead lobby', who insisted that the priority for expenditure by the Liverpool Dock Trustees should be the completion of the unwanted and unused Birkenhead Docks. This was hailed as a great victory in Birkenhead, but in 1872 the modest bit of Hartley's last great scheme which did get built, totalling less than 30 acres, was earning some 63 per cent more revenue than the entire 160 acres of Birkenhead Docks.[44]

It is impossible to discover the cost of producing a huge scheme like this, or, indeed, of a smaller one in 1858, which also failed, to build a reduced version of the proposed 52-acre dock together with a smaller dock and three graving docks, again to the north of Canada Basin. The design was not taken down to a very fine level of detail, but it is revealing to discover that in the 1890s the Board became concerned about the moral aspects of owning

*Excavation at Queens Branch No. 1 in February 1899. One of the few photographs showing an engineer on site. The letter 'A' which has been written on the negative keys the position to a drawing.*

public houses in which they suspected all manner of ungentlemanly activities took place.[45] The reason the Board owned public houses was that they had bought them in the 1850s in order to demolish them for the building of the aborted inland docks. This indicates that planning in the Engineer's Office had been going on with some confidence, which in turn suggests that a good deal of detailed surveying had already been done when the project was scrapped.

The temptation with aborted projects is always to assume they were stupid ideas that just drifted inconsequentially across history's stage. Sometimes they were stupid enough to be amusing. This must not blind us to the fact that engineers have always designed things which did not get built, and that at one or two stages in the history of the Liverpool docks there was probably more engineer's work going into those than into the projects which came to fruition. The ones which did get built posed an enormous challenge to the younger men of the department, the ones who were now destined to spend some years getting cold, wet and muddy. It was to the likes of Fielden Sutcliffe that the responsibility fell for ensuring that what got built bore some resemblance to what had been drawn.

# 6
# After the Silver Spade:
# Sitework and Site Management
# in the Late Nineteenth Century

The MD&HB archive contains several dozen of the old photographs of dock construction in progress of which a selection appears in this book. When one makes the obvious comparison with the well-known published collections of photographs of the Manchester Ship Canal or the Great Central Railway under construction, the Liverpool photographs seem to show scenes of absolute and total chaos.[1] Now we know that on some occasions this is probably an accurate impression, but the photographs of, for example, the Brunswick reconstruction of 1900–8 look no more orderly than others and those works seem to have proceeded pretty much according to plan.

*A general view of the (very orderly) Manchester Ship Canal works at Frodsham Marsh.*

*Laying iron culverts in 1902, probably at Brunswick Entrance. A health and safety inspector's nightmare, with tools, materials and rubbish to trip over at every step. Notice especially the broken ladder which no one has got round to throwing out.*

What these photographs should actually tell us is that the sitework of dock construction was of much greater complexity than was common in linear engineering works like canals or railways, especially when it was not being carried out on the muddy equivalent of a 'green field site'. This complexity arose from the diversity of the different operations involved: demolition of old works; excavation to a number of different levels in different places; the establishment of spoil removal and material delivery systems to serve each level; the control of groundwater or leakage water from the protection works; staging and other heavy carpentry; laying of pipework and culverts; masonrywork. Later in the programme, the mechanical elements such as gate engines and balance paddles, not to mention the gates themselves, added to the variety.

It was not uncommon to find a hundred or more men per acre at work during hours of daylight. In abormal circumstances, it could be far more. One of the great problems was the short time available for tidal working, and from 1878 onwards, electric arc floodlights were introduced to facilitate working on night as well as daytime tides. Lyster gave evidence before the Select Committee which enquired into Schemes by Local Authorities for Lighting by Electricity[2] and explained that on some tides less than two hours' work was possible, though in favourable circumstances it could be as much as four. This necessitated the employment of 300–400 men on the tidal works at Canada Basin. Even in the description of the process by the urbane Lyster, we can deduce something of the confusion – and the hardship – of such works. One of the merits of electric lighting was that previous attempts at night tide working had relied on 'open tripod grates with cannel coal' and tin 'duck' lamps which burned some pretty vile oil. The result was that men working down holes as deep as 20 ft below LWST were 'frequently obliged to leave their work to get breath and to clear their lungs'. This was not only bad for productivity but also for quality control: if the smoke in the workings was that thick, then the supervisors could not see with any certainty whether work was being done correctly or not. To this was added the smoke of the various steam engines driving the pumps and other machinery.

The lighting plant consisted of two Gramme dynamos driven by an 8hp steam engine and supplying two Serrin arc lamps of some 6,000 candlepower each – a truly amazing amount of light at a time when the incandescent gas mantle was still to be invented. It was so powerful that at first they did not even bother to apply reflectors to the lamps. The result, according to Lyster was that the work proceeded both faster and better, and allowed the supervisors to ensure that all was as it should be. (This was, of course, especially important where foundation works using hydraulic mortar were being laid: everybody abandoned the works as the tide rose, and by the time it fell again a multitude of sins could be hidden, if not for ever then at least until the new work failed and had to be dug up again.) The *status quo ante*, with its smoke, fire, noise and chaos must have resembled a fanciful vision of hell – a hell with the added torment that everything had to be sorted out by the time the tide returned.

The number of items of steam plant – pile drivers, locomotives hauling materials and spoil, cranes of various sizes, excavating machines, winches, 'travellers' for lifting spoil wagons, and finally the pumps, ran into dozens

*One of the Gramme-type dynamos and Serrin arc-lamps which Lyster used for site illumination in the late 1870s, now in the collection of Merseyside Maritime Museum.*

on larger projects.[3] How, one wonders, could an engineer picture what was going to happen when, and thus in which sequence events should be planned to occur?

The answer seems generally to have been fairly badly. Although the day-by-day records of what happened on site do not survive, the occasional disasters or irregularities which occurred bring out the details of what was meant to happen. Periodically, the Engineer's Department was criticized for excessive bureaucracy and it appears that in the late '80s approximately 100 assorted books and ledgers were being kept. Since 1868, there had been a record kept which was known as the 'Total Cost of Works' ledger, which is the only one to survive complete, and it tells us, for each of a number of types of work in each area of the Dock Estate, what money the Engineer's Department spent in each of three categories: wages, supplies and contract services. This should, in theory, enable us to work out approximately how well or badly things were going on the ground. If, for example, we found a sudden increase in the cost of blacksmiths' work in repairs to picks, cutting shovels and masons' tools at Canada Entrance in 1876 we would be justified in assuming that the deepening work going on there had run into some unexpected rock. These documents would merit some detailed analysis, but there is, unfortunately, evidence to call their reliability into question from the start. That comes from what the Board's cataloguing system for its documents often engagingly filed under 'I' – for irregularities.

The first cause for concern comes from the trifling incident mentioned in passing in Chapter 2. A retired employee of the Board made the allegation that it was common practice for work to be undertaken in the dock yard for the private benefit of G.F. Lyster and various other senior staff. This was a serious matter in ethical and managerial terms, for of course if 'the bosses' were seen to be profiting from an impropriety of this kind, everyone else in the Engineer's Department would regard it as *carte blanche* for any pilferage or undertaking of 'foreigners' they thought they could get away with. What was trifling about it was its scale in relation to the overall throughput of work in the department. For present purposes, its significance lies elsewhere. The Board decided that it could not or should not hush up the allegation, and asked the Board of Trade to send in an impartial auditor, who reported that Lyster and the others had paid for the work done privately for them, but that they had not paid what seemed to him to be a reasonable price for the work involved. A joiner was dismissed and a foreman joiner reduced to the ranks for failing adequately to record the work which had been done.[4]

Now it may well be that we are looking at a whitewash which set out to penalize the lowly as atonement for a small but insidious bit of corruption by highly-paid and trusted officers. Such things happened. Alternatively, workmen may have been using the Board's resources in an attempt to curry favour in an organization which had very long (albeit steep and narrow) promotion ladders. That is not what matters: what matters is that the auditor found that time spent and materials used were not being correctly recorded. Under the Total Cost of Works system it was difficult, if not impossible, to 'lose' time and materials from the record altogether. That means that if the joiner making, say, a quick-assembly gazebo kit for Le Mesurier's garden, did not book all his time and the materials to the said gazebo, he must necessarily have been booking them to something else. That meant that the something else, whatever it might be, was recorded as costing more than it actually did.When estimates were being prepared and decisions were being made for future joinery work, the falsified record would be part of the corpus of precedent on which they were based, with obvious potential for making wrong estimates or decisions.

The story of John Lynch has been told before.[5] A part of it must be recapitulated here to show that the recording of information in the Engineer's Department could be so bad that incidents like the joinery 'scandal', together with their undesirable consequences, were capable of almost infinite proliferation. John Lynch was a travelling timekeeper in the Engineer's Department. The timekeepers' duty was to visit every location where men of the Engineer's Department were working, twice a day, and record the hours worked by each man. The information was first gathered in a pocket notebook, from which it was transcribed on to a time sheet in the Timekeepers' Office, then on to a pay sheet in the Check Office. On one occasion Lynch made a mistake by booking hours worked by a man who was not there: to conceal the fact that he had actually been sitting in the pub inventing the information to go in his pocket book off the top of his head, he let things ride and went and drew the man's wages, purely to avoid detection. This proved so easy that he repeated the procedure, and within a year he was working the 'fictitious employees racket' to the extent of some 35 pay packets per week. It was only when he was moved to a different section that his misdeeds came to light and he was arrested. This does at least prove that not all the other travelling timekeepers were working the same racket (unless they were doing it much better) but his hand-written confession and his evidence at his trial contain allegations of appalling inefficiency at each stage of the fairly complex process of calculating and paying wages.

For present purposes, the key points are these. It was not shown in the trial that Lynch's negligence in filling up his pocket book with what one can only term fiction was unique, or even all that unusual. Nor was it shown that his allegations that it was frequent practice to alter time sheets, or that some of the office staff were habitually drunk on duty or that his crime had been greatly facilitated by the amazing slackness of the entire system, were untrue. The total sum he obtained was over £3,500, which would correspond very roughly with about 2,000 man/weeks of work. (He dealt mainly with skilled men working on floating plant at quite high wages). Incredible though it may seem, it was *not* the loss of that considerable amount of work which led to Lynch's detection. We are forced to conclude that the information fed into the managerial system in the Engineer's Department could be wildly inaccurate. However good the system might look on paper, lots of paper, the old computing maxim applied: 'garbage in, garbage out'.

It may also be worth briefly mentioning the 'aftermath' of the Lynch case, which hinged mainly on attempts to recover the money. (Lynch, being far from stupid, had squirrelled what remained of the proceeds after a fairly extravagant lifestyle in trust funds from which the Board were unable to recover any significant sum.) In 1903, a man named Thorpe was quietly dismissed from the Check Office. Lynch's evidence contains the reason: 'Thorpe was one of the boozy men: I have seen him . . .'. The same year, it needed Mr Hughes to spell out the importance of the case in a Board meeting: it was not, he said, a case for expressing moral outrage at what Lynch had done. He made damning comments on the management and administration 'from the highest official in the Engineer's Department to the humblest'.[6] It is clear that up to that point, the attention of members had been focused on the expensive efforts of the Solicitor's Department to recover a smallish amount of money mainly for purposes of revenge.[7] The idea that there were important lessons to be learned from the case only dawned a little later.

Further examples could be given of minor failures of the system which had wider implications for the management of works. When, therefore, an Assistant Engineer invited tenders for a specific piece of work, the precedents from which he worked could be extremely inaccurate. This was bad enough when it led to mistakes in estimating or a misguided decision to avoid a particular technique because it had proved very time-expensive on the last occasion it was used. It could lead to far worse, as the important lawsuit of Eckersley, Godfrey and Liddelow v The Mersey Docks & Harbour Board shows.[8]

We must at this stage recollect the photographs of chaotic scenes with which this chapter began. Somebody on the engineering staff needed to be possessed of one particular remarkable attribute. There is a famous remark of Elgar's, when asked how he composed his music: 'It is in the air all

*The new Canada Half-tide under construction, 1875–6. The heavy masonrywork in the foreground is the intake for the silt-sluicing system which was supposed to keep the tidal basin clear.*

around me and all I do is write it down.' Elgar and a number of other composers who combined unusual technical skills with their artistic ability could write out sounds they heard in their heads by working their way down the staves of a full score rather than by writing the 'tune' across the page and adding the other parts one or two at a time. It was a somewhat analogous talent which was required in the man in overall control of a dock construction site. Many of the operations which took place were capable of interfering with the progress of the others, and in extreme cases there was potential for disaster. There were, for example, repeated inundations of the New North Works under the 1873 Act,[9] and one of the many misfortunes which befell Eckersley et al. was an inundation during construction of the Canada Branch Dock.[10] The most frequent, if less dramatic, difficulty which arose was the moving of spoil. The engineer in charge needed to be able to envisage complex sequences of spoil removal and schedule them in such a way that spoil from one part of the job did not prevent progress on another.

*Modernization works at Trafalgar in about 1930. Clarence has vanished and the power station is in commission. A careful look at the activities going on here makes the complexity of work programming very clear.*

He also needed to ensure that such things as the laying of sluicing culverts did not put the temporary railway tracks used for removing spoil from another part of the works out of action at a time when they were urgently required.

In short, he needed to have an overall vision of work proceeding smoothly to its conclusion, with all the multifarious activities coming together at the right time. To expect that he would be able to achieve that when his knowledge of how long things actually took was jeopardized by the activities of such as Lynch and the denizens of the Check Office is rather like expecting Elgar to compose the coda of his First Symphony without being allowed to specify the lengths, but only the pitch, of the notes. The chances of it emerging as a triumphal re-statement of the 'great tune' of the first movement would be about the same as those of poor Fielden Sutcliffe as he tried frantically to keep all his 'players' on the same page of the score.

That is why most major works ran over schedule, and of course running over schedule almost automatically meant running over budget. While work executed by contractors was commonly anchored to a job price, work undertaken directly by the department involved large numbers of extra, often casual, labourers. An 'extra labourer' was one not on the permanent payroll, but the permanent men were comparatively few in number, suggesting that there were many 'regular casual workers' just as there were plenty of staff in the offices who were not on the Established List. Given that it was possible to find literally thousands of extra labourers working at one time on a major project such as the Sandon Entrance and Half-Tide remodelling, the price of miscalculation could run to possibly £1,000 per day in extra labourers' wages alone, before even considering the smaller army of skilled men or the cost of the plant. The larger machines, such as a railway locomotive or a steam navvy cost over £2 per day before paying their crews or supplying their coal.[11] Because these machines were expensive, they were in limited supply, so that any delay on one site would have a knock-on effect on another as either the machinery was unavailable when required or it became necessary to throw money at the problem to obtain extra machinery from outside at short notice.

It is by no means unknown for people like civil engineers working in the field to have only a limited respect for those of their colleagues who deal with administrative matters, and one assumes that the relatively young men who were out on site in the continuum of activity a century ago may well have felt much the same. As we have seen, they had plenty of justification for doing so. There was another organizational problem too, in which they were probably not blameless. The staff structure under Lyster was, or appears to have been, very 'flat' with just one man we would now call Deputy Chief Engineer between him and a large number of Assistant Engineers. There seems to have been no clear differentiation between them except for their specified duties. They were also expected to work closely with Principal Foremen in the mould of John Millar, who were nearly always 'commissioned from the ranks': older men with no formal qualifications except a PhD from the school of hard knocks, but with decades of experience of what did and did not work.[12] They were not necessarily the easiest colleagues for a young engineer until he had earned their respect. The fact that they were on the permanent salaried establishment and he was on a weekly wage of much less, even before taking into account the free house Principal Foremen usually got, probably made the winning of respect harder, unless the older man took a paternal interest in 'looking after' the younger.

This is no doubt one of the reasons why Eckersley et al. were enraged, frustrated and run around in circles by contradictory instructions from different members of the engineering staff. Reverting to Fielden Sutcliffe and the musical analogy, the rostrum should only be big enough for one. It emphatically must not accommodate the leader, the principal viola and everyone else who thinks they have, or should have, some authority. That way chaos lies.

What, then, was the role of the Chief in all this? First, it must be reiterated that the reason the Chief was paid several times as much as his Principal Assistant and about 15–20 times as much as a young Assistant Engineer, was not that he did many times as much work or did it many times as well. It was not even because there were certain engineering tasks which only he could perform.He was paid for two principal duties of which the first was to act as a focus for all the multifarious activities of the department and make sure that they fitted neatly together. The second was closely linked, which was the acceptance of responsibility for everything which happened in the department.

In the 'good old days', the scale of operations was such that Jesse Hartley was able to get out on site, albeit relatively infrequently, and ensure that things were being done to his satisfaction. John Millar, Principal Foreman of Works, had an amazingly wide brief which he appears to have been able to discharge perfectly adequately. We should, therefore, pause to consider the scale of operations under Lyster through the medium of a glance at an example of the published Engineer's Report, chosen to represent an only moderately busy year.

The report for 1881 is, like that for every year, only a very concise summary of what had happened, but it still runs to 57 pages. Despite the completion of Langton and its graving docks, the Canada Entrance and the partial opening of the huge Alexandra Dock the previous year, it records the expenditure of £664,935. A contractor was excavating 'Dock F' (Hornby) and work was continuing to complete Alexandra: sheds, railway lines, road surfaces and a movable bridge were all in hand. There were major works proceeding at Georges Pierhead, and at Toxteth, Harrington and

*Raising the principals of one of the sheds at Alexandra, 1881. The travelling derrick employed was known as the* Giraffe.

Herculaneum Docks. On the Birkenhead side, the railway sidings and coaling berths at Cavendish Wharf were nearing completion. Every dock in the system received some attention, even if only in minor matters like repairs to shed roofs, and of course the various mud counter-measures – dredging, sluicing and 'scuttling' continued every year throughout the estate.

These are the things we would expect to find: there are also dozens of little entries for 'Alterations and Repairs &c.' to the Dock Office, and to several other offices and miscellaneous buildings like the Workmen's Dining Hall; repairing lighthouses; 'establishing telephonic communication'. Anything which related to matters technical in any way whatever, throughout the extensive property and operations of the board would, one year or another, appear in the Engineer's Reports. The payroll for the office establishment even included one George Biddle, trained as a surveyor, employed as 'Steward of the Estate'. His duties were not, as one might

*The heavy lift crane at East Coburg in 1891, with some of Lyster's maintenance men in action. Photographs of commonplace scenes like this are rare, but there were hundreds of men doing such things.*

imagine, confined to keeping watch over the physical state of Board property not in the direct use of the Board, but 'to look after all Property and matters concerned with Rentals, Occupations &c.'[13]

In 1881, the salaried staff in the Engineer's Department numbered 18, but as we know from chapter 5, this conceals those who were paid weekly wages for jobs which one would normally expect to be salaried, including senior time-served draughtsmen and young but fully qualified engineers. The amount of wages paid to 'Clerks and Draughtsmen' that year was £3,677, and the highest wage paid, to qualified engineers, seems to have been £5 per week. Draughtsmen were mostly paid less than £3 10s and juniors often under £2. Unfortunately the records, and the accounts, are so compiled as to make it impossible to put an exact number on such jobs, and probably deliberately thus compiled, or so Littledale alleged. It is fairly clear, however, that we are looking at not less than another 25 staff.

It is absolutely clear that no Chief, however remarkable his talents, could make any significant design input to more than a tiny fraction of the work undertaken in such a large department in any particular year. There was no reason, in a large establishment, why he should. A.G. Lyster, for example, was a bright young man who was enthusiastic and soon became knowledgeable on matters electrical and hence came to deal with them. There was no point in his father having anything directly to do with the nitty-gritty of electric lighting for night-time tidal working at the Canada Tidal Basin beyond authorizing the expenditure on it and collecting the credit if it was a success (which it was) or producing the excuses if it were not. When giving evidence before the Select Committee, Lyster mentioned that reflectors were being tried on the Serrin lamps, but he had had no detailed report of their performance. Things like that were, quite properly, delegated. The ability to support a team of in-house specialists was one of the great benefits of a large establishment like the dock yard.

Lyster's responsibilities as Chief were fundamentally altered from Hartley's by these changes in the nature of the department. He now needed the ability to absorb and retain simultaneously the minimal particulars of a huge variety of projects large and small, to prioritize and synchronize them and to act as a facilitator to those who were doing the actual designing and constructing. He needed to exert a fatherly authority over a large number of assistants, some of whom were undoubtedly rather pushy young men of very high talent and promise but comparatively little experience or achievement. The original, hopelessly over-ambitious, objectives of the Liverpool Engineering Society clearly suggest a bunch of bright and enthusiastic young men who wanted to mend the world. They needed unambiguous statements of what their organizational position, their powers and their responsibilities were. If they received anything of the kind, no trace of it survives. It is clear from the way in which plans were subject to major alteration during the execution of projects that Lyster changed his mind on key issues such as the depths of extensive structures like the New North Entrance and the Toxteth and Harrington Docks.[14] Because Lyster personally could not have more than a general overview of the problems, the most likely reason for such changes of heart is that he had changed sides in internal conflicts between his assistants.

Even the quality of his overview is open to question both in breadth and depth. In 1896, he read a paper to the Liverpool Meeting of the British Association, and in the Commonplace Book for that year we find a tabular statement of the authorities for the various statements of fact in his paper. The hand is definitely not his, indicating that the maximum contribution he could have made to the writing of 'his' paper giving an overview of his work as Chief was to sketch out the general framework before handing it on for someone in the department to write the paper. (It should in fairness perhaps be interpolated at this point that Lyster was now 74 years of age and was really Chief in name only.)[15] In the Commonplace Book for 1872, we find, most unusually, a copy of an internal report which has the author's name on it. The report is on the methods of manufacturing hydraulic lime mortar employed on the estate and agrees in general principles with the methods described by Sir Robert Rawlinson. It is quite detailed, running to four pages, and was written by C. Graham Smith on Lyster's instructions.

One is gradually forced to the conclusion that Lyster had, willingly or unwillingly, amassed such a heterogeneous collection of responsibilities as to drive him almost entirely into the role of 'front man' for an organization which may well have been too ponderous to be adequately controlled by any one man. It certainly does not seem to have been adequately controlled by Lyster, with the result that the men at the drawing boards or out in the field were not getting the support and guidance that they should have done. In the circumstances it is scarcely surprising that mistakes were made.

## Work on Site

By the time of the major constructions under the 1873 Act, methods of working on site had changed somewhat from the well-known methods employed during Hartley's last and biggest developments from 1844–59.[16] They had not, however, been revolutionized in the manner we are sometimes led to believe. It is true that the larger amounts of spoil being moved and the greater depths from which they had to emerge led to a growing adoption of steam power in various forms, but it is easy to forget that human sweat was still a cheap fuel. In terms of contractors' prices, that is to say including an on-cost, a small steam crane cost double the price of a horse, cart and driver – before allowing for the wages of the crane's driver and fireman. If the crane were being operated by direct labour, its daily coal and water alone cost more than the wages of two extra labourers.[17] It was, therefore, important for engineers to think carefully before bringing in a lot of high-tech machinery, because in some circumstances it was neither the quickest nor the cheapest way of doing the job. Rankine's famous textbook *The Steam Engine and Other Prime Movers*, used by generations of pupil and student engineers, continued to include sections on optimizing the application of muscle-power (whether equine or human) for the whole of the period with which this book is concerned. Wilfred Boult's notebook contains a number of little *aides-mémoires* on the capabilities of navvies and horses, written in 1876. The excavation in tidal working described by Lyster was all done by hand for a different reason: it was not worth installing and then removing plant in the short time available between tides.[18]

Some machines seem to have established themselves as clear improvements on the older methods of working. The steam traveller, an overhead gantry crane whose gantry strides out over the side of an excavation seemed to be one of them. Railway tipping wagons filled with spoil were brought under it on temporary tracks in the dock bottom and then raised to ground level and placed on temporary or permanent rails connected

*Steam travellers in action on the building of Langton Graving Docks, c. 1877.*

to the main line of the dock railway for removal to the tipping site. The erection of travellers is often mentioned in reports as one of the key preliminary works. The same machine could, of course, lower materials to the dock bottom, including the considerable amounts of coal (and sometimes water in bowsers) which the various steam machines down below needed. On average, the machines used about three tons of coal each per working day, and it is interesting to note in passing that, by the time it had got to the machine's tank, the water they used commonly cost more than the coal. But travellers did not become universal: we find railed inclines with winding engines in use hauling wagons of spoil out of excavations in the 1890s in much the same manner as when John Foster first employed one in 1811. An intriguing photograph survives showing a balance hoist used for spoil raising: for part of the time coal and water for the machines would provide a downward load, and at other times stone and mortar for the masons, but organizing the flow of upwards and downwards goods must have been a considerable extra headache. The wagons used look too large to be counterbalanced by men. It does appear, however, that the legendarily dangerous barrow-run had disappeared: the calculations of Boult, and those in the Commonplace Books are alike in not mentioning how many foot-tons per day a horse could shift at a barrow-run: the notes are about how many men it took to fill wagons and the cost of moving wagons through different distances, both vertically and horizontally.

As late as 1874, the Institution of Civil Engineers published an abstract of a paper giving details of comparative costs of different methods of spoil-raising on the construction of the Sirhind Canal in India.[19] This was a work of considerable size, having a surface width of 200 ft. The authors give as a datum the cost of the traditional 'coolie and basket' method, which at daily wages of 6d for '1st Class men' down to 4d for boys, worked out at 3.24d per cubic yard. The traditional English navvy method using the barrow run was found ineffective as the men were not strong enough. Another method, which had the highest theoretical efficiency in the textbooks, was some form of counterbalance device, like that invented by Coignet. This involved navvies climbing a ladder from the excavation and then using their own weight to hoist the spoil. Unfortunately, the coolies were not heavy enough to raise a worthwhile load. Each of the different applications of winding plant tried appeared to reduce the unit cost of spoil raising, but the calculations do not include the capital costs of the equipment. The almost infinite variations of 'lift and lead' – the height through which spoil had to be raised and the distance to the tipping point – make the figures even more suspect. In short, it seems that at the time Lyster's men were embarking on the New North Works, the cheapest and most effective way of lifting and removing spoil was still open to some argument.

Similar considerations apply to the 'cutting'. There had been experiments with steam excavating machines since the early 1840s, particularly in America, where labour costs were comparatively high. The steam navvy as a practical machine for dock construction in Britain seems to have arrived with the employment of an early Ruston & Proctor machine at West Hartlepool Docks in 1877–8. Only a year earlier, the steam navvy had been at a very tentative stage of development, in which mechanical problems frequently arose from components insufficiently strong for work which was extremely demanding compared with that of the steam crane from which the navvy was descended. Progress in eliminating these teething troubles was very rapid, and the Hartlepool machine worked from November 1877 to mid-February 1878 without any stoppage for repairs. The manufacturers claimed at the time that the machine was the equivalent of up to 60 men and that it would normally save its own cost of £1,150 in six months' steady work.[20]

In reality, the picture was less favourable. The early machines could only work when resting on six sturdy screw jacks, and they could only slew their load by 180°. They worked at a 'face' of up to about 25 ft height, in the same way navvies normally did. Because the cutting was performed in an upward arc of the bucket, it was difficult to avoid leaving substantial curved 'gullets' on the bottom, which had to be removed by hand by up to four 'gullet trimmers' before the machine could be advanced for another cut. The pivoted motion of the jib meant that the working face was curved, so production of a deep square hole also required handwork by up to four 'slope trimmers'. The machine itself required a crew of no less than seven men, of whom only the stoker and the pumper (of boiler feed water) were paid less than navvies. The manufacturers claimed that the worse the ground, the greater the saving from the use of the machine: this was true, but was their tactful way of explaining that in easy ground the spoil tended to collapse from the face before it was cut, leaving heaps of material at the bottom of

*A Ruston steam navvy at work on the Manchester Ship Canal. But notice there are eleven men, four of them shovelling, a horse and a boy in addition to the footplate crew of the machine.*

the face which the machine was ill-adapted to tidy up. In the circumstances, it is not surprising that the Liverpool dock engineers did not show a great or an early enthusiasm for this particular form of mechanization.

During the mid-1870s, Lyster was attacked by Littledale for not knowing how many men he employed. As a partial response, to disarm similar criticism in the future, Lyster started to give brief details in his annual reports of the men and plant employed on the New North Works. What we find confirms the view that there were reservations about mechanizing the excavation work. In 1876, for example, 'The Contractor for the Excavations employs in his work about 1,200 men, 15 locomotives, two steam cranes, one steam hoist and about 300 wagons. The number of men on the Works in the employ of the Dock Board is about 900.' The following year the pace was increasing, with 1,551 board men and 1,200 contractors' men, the latter now using 500 wagons, but there were still only three steam cranes. The clear implication is that the 2,850,000 cubic yards of spoil excavated up to

*The multiple levels in this view of Canada Graving Dock in 1898 correspond to the depth of cut of the steam navvy, and have been utilized to provide reasonable gradients for spoil removal by rail.*

that time had been cut by hand, and most of it shovelled by hand into wagons and hauled up inclines by the locomotives. In 1878 the total volume of spoil raised was over 4,000,000 cubic yards, and there is no mention of any additional machinery. Even in 1891, by which time steam navvies were well-established in use, it appears that there was only one in service on the fairly large excavations for the Canada Branch Dock.[21]

Much has been made of the use of steam navvies in the construction of the Manchester Ship Canal, probably because people remember the splendid photographs of them published in Sir Bosdin Leech's famous book. We should remember that the Ship Canal also employed something approaching 20,000 human navvies, and the employment which would thus be created in a time of recession was one of the subsidiary reasons advanced for undertaking the construction of the canal.

Another application of machinery which we might expect to find growing and spreading, especially after the development of the 'trench' technique, described below, is the excavation of a small part only of the total depth, followed by letting in the water and removing the rest with bucket-ladder dredgers. This method was extensively employed in the construction of the Suez Canal, and seems to offer many advantages, including the ability to use boats as a more effective way of removing spoil than wagons. The only reference before the turn of the century, however, which makes specific mention of dredging is in the controversy which arose over the failure of a coffer-dam at Birkenhead, which was alleged to be Lyster's fault in that he insisted on too much spoil being removed 'in the dry' (thus undermining the coffer-dam) exactly in order to minimize the need for dredging after the water was let in.[22] There were several objections, in general terms, to the use of bucket ladder dredgers in the 1860s and '70s which we may assume Lyster considered to outweigh their advantages. Their mechanical efficiency was low, as anyone who has heard the clanking and grinding of a surviving specimen will readily understand, and the energy which made that noise was, of course, busily wearing out the machinery. A considerable foot-tonnage of water was repeatedly lifted along with the spoil, and while on the one hand light sand tended to fall out of the buckets before it was lifted, a good sticky clay stayed in the buckets and simply went round and round with them. There was also an administrative objection, that the straightforward excavation work was normally put out to contract and the clearer the lines of demarcation between the contractor and Lyster's in-house work, the better. Finally, we must remember that in the New North Works, Lyster employed substantial concrete bottoms in most of the docks, which provided a strong incentive to keep the works dry until completion. Not until the construction of Brocklebank Branch Dock (completed 1908) do we find that 'The work of excavating the body of the dock, a small portion of which was done by hand, is being completed by powerful dredgers.'[23]

The basic techniques of traditional navvying may have changed comparatively little, but the sequence of operations saw one important, though not universally applied, change. Such pictorial evidence as we have of early dock construction indicates that the job was tackled in what seems to be the logical order of events, that is to say that a large hole was dug and retaining walls were then built round the edges. The specification for Canada Branch Dock, which has survived as part of the documentation of the dispute with Eckersley, Godfrey and Liddelow, describes an entirely different method. A large trench was dug by the excavation contractor and its sides secured by sheet piling and 'walings' (horizontal tying of the piles). The in-house teams then installed such bearing piles as the test borings had indicated were necessary and timber 'cribwork' as the foundation for the masonry which followed on top. (Though in some cases the walls were directly founded on rock.)

After a due delay for the mortar to gain strength, the back-filling behind the wall could begin. This was a critical process, as John Hartley had indicated in his paper to the Institution in 1841 and Lyster acknowledged in his paper of 1889.[24] If the back-filling were done with undue haste or in over-large increments, two undesirable consequences were possible. The first was that the fill might not consolidate properly, leading to settling of the quay surface under surcharge loads when put into service. The second, much more serious, was that the fill would impose an overturning load on the wall before the mortar was fully cured, resulting in distortion or even collapse of the masonry. For that reason, whatever the degree of mechanization in other parts of the work, back-filling long remained a wheelbarrow job. It is also important to remember that hydraulic lime mortar continued to gain strength for as much as a year, so that in works where it was employed the imposition of severe loads at an early stage was particularly undesirable.

In order to keep the different activities proceeding as constantly as possible, walls were constructed from one end to the other, so that towards one end of the wall the cutters would be digging out the trench and the carpenters lining it, behind them came the pile-drivers and more carpenters constructing the cribwork, behind them the masons, working at progressively higher levels and behind them the labourers doing the back-filling. The paving or other quay surfacing was usually left undone for as long as the engineer dared in order that any settling of the backfill would occur before rather than after he had laid the surfacing. If the wall were to have 'relieving arches' then a team of bricklayers would be working between the masons and the backfillers. Because the foundations were usually below the water table and certainly below the level at which any leakage from protective works would infallibly reach them, it was necessary to have a temporary drainage system in the trench, feeding into a sump emptied by a steam-driven pump.

*Massed pile drivers in action as part of the Tranmere Bay development in 1906.*

The pumps long continued to be chain pumps which passed boards on loops of chain up a wooden conduit. Despite their crude appearance, and the fact that the clearance between the boards and the housing was measured in eighths of an inch, these could achieve an efficiency of about 60 per cent provided they were run at the optimum speed for the particular size of pump in question. (This speed was surprisingly high – rarely less than 500 ft per minute.) The volumes they pumped were surprisingly high as well: one experiment in 1876 for example, shows an engine of 40 horsepower raising over 1,800 gallons per minute (equivalent in volume to the output of two large modern fire engines) from a depth of 36 ft.[25] In return for their losses, they offered great advantages. If they pumped the sump dry they neither harmed themselves nor lost suction, and would immediately start to lift again as soon as there was water there. Second, they were virtually immune from getting clogged with mud. Third, if some substantial foreign body found its way in, the worst it could do was break a wooden board or two, and these

*A chain pump of the type normally used for draining the works: crude but effective.*

were both cheap and simple to replace. Fourth, they could work happily from the top of a hole in the ground, rather than having to be installed down it. The chain pump was a good example of the retention of what we now call an 'appropriate technology', and the sinking of wells and installation of chain pumps continues to be mentioned in the Engineer's Reports into the 1890s, after which A.G. Lyster's more succinct style of report-writing deprives us of such details.

The exact date at which the trenching technique was introduced does not seem to have been recorded, but the first specific mention of it is in the Engineer's Report for 1891, and implies that it was a new method. Certainly progress reports before this time normally give the impression that the excavation preceded the masonrywork, and reports after that time mention trench working, so we may assume that the Canada Branch Works of 1891 quite possibly were its first application. It should have been a highly successful technique, appearing to maintain a deployment of labour which

*147*

kept each group out of the way of the others. In practice, as we know from the innumerable delays which occurred on the works, it also had the disadvantage of making the different groups of workers inter-dependent. If the cutters were feeling a little fragile for a day or two after the Feast of St Patrick, or a cartload of nails for the carpenters at Herculaneum got sent to the carpenters at Huskisson by mistake, the whole process ground to a very expensive halt.

What we may term the flow-line system also required very careful attention to the innumerable ancillary jobs which were going on either in the dock yard or in the site compound. Sharpening piles, for example, was a simple task, but such was the size and hardness of the timber used that, according to Wilfred Boult's notebook a skilled carpenter could sharpen only eight Baltic Pine piles in his ten-hour working day. Boult does not give a figure for the greenheart piles then already well established, but such is the hardness and oiliness of greenheart that they would take several times as long. Keeping a supply of piles ready for use required careful matching of

*Demolition of the walls between Brunswick Graving Docks and the former Union Dock to form the new Brunswick–Toxteth Passage, c. 1900. Although this is a comparatively small job, there is a large area required as a stockyard for concrete blocks and other materials.*

workrates. Similarly, the masons who were bedding the stones needed to be carefully synchronized with those preparing them. Rubble backing was not a problem but pieces which had to be carefully prepared to an only reasonable standard of accuracy and finish could easily take a skilled man an hour or more per square foot of finished surface. The shoddiest grade of coping stone – that with only partially squared joints and an unlevel bottom bedding face – took about the same, so that a large coping stone would take between two and three days to prepare. Then there were the long granite headers which tied the facing to the rubble backing: they were cut with zigzag sides and preparing the sides alone took about four hours. These things had to be there, ready for the masons who were going to lay them.[26]

As mentioned above, the carpenters normally used the timber in temporary works several times before it was discarded. If the masons were delayed, the sheet piling behind them could not be extracted and re-used ahead of them, delaying the foundation works. They, therefore, needed to have supplies of spare timber available and that, taken with a stock of prepared piles, cribwork timber, dressed masonry, mountains of sandstone rubble, mortar and gravel makes an impressive beginning for that state of complete chaos on the site which we have come to expect.

When the walls were complete, or near enough so for the main thrust of excavation to begin, further threats to orderly progress arose. Of these, by far the largest came from old works of one sort or another. First, there were the old works which fooled everybody because their existence was not previously known. These normally did not cause anything worse than delay while they were removed. The position, though, could be critical: demolishing a 10ft thick wall was not too difficult if it was in a position where explosives could be used, especially after the gradual introduction of high explosives which, for a given size of bang, had a more marked shattering effect on masonry. Dock Yard staff first witnessed a trial of dynamite in 1869, three years before it was patented, but at that stage of its development the nitro-glycerine was given to separating out, rendering its use extremely hazardous and they wisely decided to stay a while with their black powder and gun cotton. It is interesting to note that the Commonplace Book which mentions this also records exactly how dynamite was then prepared.[27]

If the offending piece of old work was too near to other structures for exposives to be an option, there could be weeks of grinding toil ahead, none of which had appeared in either the estimates or the work schedules. Taking down the North Wall at Wallasey Dock in 1876 was a planned part of the programme, but it happens to be recorded in Boult's notebook. Just one class of work – rock sawing – took 130.66 man-days. The effect on the rest of the site if such a task had to be taken on unexpectedly can easily be imagined. The Engineer's Report for 1881 includes the following: 'At the mouth of the [Canada] Basin it was unexpectedly found that the foundations of an Old Wall laid at a low level and extending across the opening had been left "in", this involved considerable extra work, but it has now for the most part been removed, though it will take some two or three months to complete.'

It is a characteristic of Lyster's reports that he passes over unpleasant occurrences as though they were of no account. With a total of nearly 3,000 men on site, the effects of a delay of such length must have been appalling. This particular task was rendered more difficult by the fact that the old wall was at a level where only limited tidal working was possible, though as mentioned above, the employment of arc lights on the job enabled work to continue on both low waters each day, which was particularly useful at spring tides. The last remains of it were eventually removed by the use of a large quantity of dynamite, the pieces being gathered up by a bucket ladder dredger.

It is not clear exactly what this old piece of foundation was, but the likelihood is that it had been put there during the working lives of some of the oldest men in the Dock Yard. Had anyone asked them? Its position (though not, of course, the fact it was still there) was almost certainly recorded in the considerable quantity of old drawings available. Finally, it should, in theory, have been detected in the process of test-boring at an early stage in the design process. In haste, one might assume that the failure to detect the old wall until it was physically uncovered was indicative of pretty poor planning. If it was, it was a degree of poor planning which was by no means peculiar to Lyster's establishment. The miraculous ability of a test-bore to 'just miss' a problem has been remarked upon before, and clearly there was a limit to the amount of boring which could be done, especially in a busy entrance which had to be kept in use during the design stages of the improvements. As late as 1926, when dock engineering was supposedly a fairly precise science, there was serious delay and overspending on the reconstruction of Alfred Entrance occasioned by the same quicksands with which John Bernard Hartley and G.F. Lyster had battled.[28] It was recently estimated that roughly half of all present-day major civil engineering works are delayed by nasty underground surprises of this kind.

Old sewers were another source of trouble. When Canada Dock was drained on 18 March 1862, the removal of the water pressure was sufficient to cause a sewer behind the East Wall to burst and the wall to settle. This was as nothing compared with the problems of Eckersley, Godfrey and Liddelow who got their plant rendered very wet and smelly when a blunder in temporarily re-routing a sewer caused three successive tides to enter the workings. Plans of sewers were normally available, so there was little excuse for failing to know that they were there, but predicting their behaviour was not always so easy.

There is a certain element of black humour in dock workings slowly filling up with a mixture of dirty water and sewage, but old structures could also cause major inundations to occur with such rapidity as to be fatal. Once in 1877 and twice in 1879, the New North Works were flooded through the failure of old walls which were serving as temporary dams. On each occasion it took weeks just to pump the workings dry again, and on the last the water rushed in so rapidly that two men were killed. If anything could happen to anybody, the reader will by now expect that it must have happened to the unfortunate Eckersley and his partners at Canada Branch: they were spared the sewage this time, and fatalities too, but they were flooded out from 15 February to 31 March 1893.[29]

The complexities of tidal working extended to far more than difficulties in tidal basins. Most of the docks constructed had sluicing systems of one form or another to try, often fruitlessly, to avoid dredging. If the dock bottom was below mean low water, then the work on the sluicing culverts would at best be so low that parts of it could only be undertaken at low water of the lowest spring tides and then only for a couple of frenzied hours at a time. The result was that much of the work had to be carried out in 'working cells' made up with miniature wooden dams in the deep trenches for the culverts. It seems somehow characteristic of the regime of the 1870s that although they adopted Jesse Hartley's well-proven shortcut of using huge cast iron pipes rather than building masonry culverts, they still ran into unforeseen difficulties which caused extra complication, delay and expense.[30]

## Working Conditions on Site: Accidents and Welfare Provision

It has long been clear that the work of navvies was incredibly hard, dangerous and unpleasant. Boult records that a man could raise 15 tons of spoil into wagons in a day, a performance which would be beyond most people today despite their generally better diet and health and the availability of celebrity work-out books. We are, on average, both bigger and heavier than Victorians were. What is superficially more surprising about Boult's figure is that it takes no account of the seasons. For, let us make no mistake, the works carried on all year round. On 4 February 1893, for example, Fielden Sutcliffe hired thirty labourers and eight bricklayers for the north works (presumably Canada Branch) and the following week another 18: to his description of the latter as labourers there is added in red ink in the hand of A.G. Lyster, by then effectively Chief, the word 'temporary'.[31] This clearly implies that the other nine labourers taken on that day, like the thirty the previous week, were not temporary. The hirings in the summer were no more numerous. We do not know what protection, if any, these men had against the weather, but it is safe to assume that most days in the winter they would remain in a constant condition of being miserably cold and wet all day. Small wonder they did their best to escape to canteens, pubs or beerhouses.

In Hartley's day, the in-house teams of skilled men with their attendant labourers had a markedly lower accident rate than did contractors' men engaged in the basic excavation work. That comparison, however, can be made because of the stroke of good fortune that Commissioner Dowling, Liverpool Police, happened to give evidence before the Select Committee on Railway Labourers (1846).[32] Only one such window of evidence exists for the later part of the century: from 1880 there are accident books, but they are not much help to us, for two reasons. The first is that they only apply to Board employees, and the second is that most of the time we do not know how many men were working on the sites, so it is impossible to find a percentage rate for accidents. In many cases the particulars in the books are so brief that we can form little idea of the cause or seriousness of an accident. It is not until after the turn of the century that statutory registers had to be kept, in a specified form giving fuller details of accidents. They

*Demolition work at Brunswick in 1908 gives a good idea of working conditions, and a first-class view of lightening arches.*

also state the average number of men employed during the course of the year. From the older (1880 pattern) books it seems that the accident rate was reasonably low by contemporary standards. The total number of men employed was always in the thousands, and the number of recorded accidents in the early 1880s ran at a few per month.[33]

The records of expenditure from the Charitable Fund, which are quite detailed for the 1820s and early '30s, also become less helpful as the century wears on. It seems quite likely that one of the reasons is that prior to the merging of the dock police with the town police in 1837, the Charitable

Fund benefited considerably from the improper practice of prosecuting thefts under bye-law.[34] This meant that in many cases it was possible to extract a fine from the person convicted, and under the 1811 Dock Act, two-thirds of the fines went to the Charitable Fund. This was altogether better news for those disabled in accidents than the knowledge that justice had been done and a petty criminal put behind bars. After the 'reform', the Charitable Fund was never quite the same again.

It was around this time that the real problem in quantifying accidents began. Dowling made passing reference in his evidence before the Select Committee to a welfare fund which Hartley organized for his men, from which they received benefits in case of illness or injury. He did not reveal its exact origin. The problem with what became known as the Dock Yard Work Men's Relief Fund is that it never produced any accounts of income or expenditure, and the working documents, which appear to have consisted only of a cash book, were not kept for any length of time either.

As is so often the case, it took a sniff of scandal to grub out the information for us, and as one might expect from the history of the Board in the 1870s and '80s, it was Harold Littledale who did the sniffing. On 20 December 1879, *The Porcupine* published an article entitled 'A Word to G.F. Lyster Esq.', suggesting that the Dock Yard Work Men's Relief Fund was at best immoral and at worst fraudulent. *The Porcupine*'s editorial policy had long involved systematic and well-informed attacks on the Dock Board and the possibility that their regular informant was at Board level – namely Littledale – cannot be discounted. Be that as it may, Littledale immediately gave notice that he would table a motion at the Board meeting on 24 December requiring a report on the origins and operation of the fund and the production of its balance sheets for the last five years.[35]

There was an immediate closing of the ranks among the Board 'in-crowd', and their chosen tactic was to dilute the issue with an amendment which also required a report on the Dock Gatemen's Mutual Benefit Society. The amendment was carried with only Littledale voting against. This was quite a clever ploy, as the Dock Gatemen's Society was an entirely legitimate organization. The Dock Yard Fund, it quickly emerged, was not. We have to remember that times had changed a great deal since its foundation. In the 1830s, memories of the terrifying times just after the Napoleonic Wars, when many quite sensible people lived in fear of a working-class revolution, were still strong. In particular, it was thought that friendly societies could be covert funding bodies for neo-Jacobin revolutionaries. It was, therefore, a perfectly acceptable piece of benevolent paternalism to deduct money from men's wages to pay into some form of 'sick fund' for the relief of workers incapacitated by illness or injury, and to place the administration of such a fund at the entire discretion of one senior officer, in this case Hartley. (Though presumably it was Gilbert Cummins who actually did the work.) By 1879, the establishment of mutual benefit societies of one form or another, governed and managed by the workers themselves, was the more normal way of doing things. Actuarial miscalculations had led to the collapse of fairly numerous relief funds of various kinds, with the result that there was specific legal protection for subscribers.[36]

There had been very marked changes in middle-class attitudes to the working classes in the interval. Writers like Samuel Smiles had successfully set out to demolish fears of Chartist (or other) revolution by the creation of a new stereotype: the Intelligent Artisan. He was the working man who wanted to improve himself by using public libraries and museums, who attended evening classes at Mechanics' Institutes and who was, above all, a wise and thrifty provider for his family. Men like these formed and governed large and successful organizations like the Odd-Fellows: they did not need to be coerced into being provident. The continuation of a system funded wholly by the deduction of two pence a week from the wages of those earning 15 shillings or more and a penny from those earning less was anomalous and offensive in the changed climate of 1880.

Frenzied indeed must have been the scene in the Solicitor's Office when the report was being drafted. As 'whitewashes' go, it was not a very good one, failing, for example, to find the exact origin of the fund.[37] It produced a scornful reaction in *The Porcupine* for 31 January 1880. It reveals, for instance, that the reasonable wage of 35 shillings was paid to the 'Sick Visitor': this person for whom the men were paying their pennies was not a nurse, but a former Regimental Sergeant Major, Royal Engineers, from which we may well judge his role in comforting the sick. It was admitted that no accounts for any year except 1879 could be produced, but the figures for that year at last give us a bit of useful information. The average number of contributors was 4,349, and they contributed £1,884 9s 3d, to which was added interest on the funds held amounting to £99 16s 10d. The surprising figure, in the light of the low accident rates recorded, is that no fewer than 1,708 men were recorded as having received relief that year. Assuming the books were not being cooked, that represents 39 per cent of the workforce. Furthermore, funeral allowances of £218 were allegedly paid out: even Littledale and the scurrilous *Porcupine* failed to notice that the report states that the funeral allowance was a flat rate of £2 10s – and £218 divided by £2 10s tells us that 87.2 men died!

What are we to make of figures which tell us on the one hand that the accident rate in the Engineer's Department was a few per cent of the workforce and on the other that 39 per cent received sick relief? Very few of the labourers employed were over 40, and indeed at times there was a definite policy of not employing men over 40 as extra labourers. Taken with the relief figure, this suggests exactly what one might expect, namely that the comprehensively vile conditions in which many, perhaps most, of the men had to work were seriously harmful to their health. Jesse Hartley's Report of 15 January 1829, which was the true origin of the fund, specifically mentions 'colds obtained from the works'.[38] It is true that either the relief figures or the accident figures may have been falsified, but when the statutory returns began, with a tighter definition of what must be recorded, there was no dramatic apparent increase in accidents. Unfortunately, after the Littledale allegations, the Relief Fund fades back into obscurity and provides us with no further information. The Charitable Fund was still in existence, and still paying money to accident victims, but by this date the beneficiaries were almost all men injured in warehouse accidents. Presumably this was because the men in the two most dangerous departments had their own benefit provisions.

Other records begin to become available from 1880 onwards which relate directly to changes in the law. Prior to 1880, workers had in theory a common law right to sue for damages where they could show that their injury resulted from negligence on the part of the employer. This was a long-standing right which went back at least to Noy's *Maxims* of 1641: *Qui facit per aliam facit per se* (He who does something through another, does it himself). Unfortunately, a string of leading cases from *Priestley v. Fowler* (1837) onwards had chiselled this right away until the worker had to show direct personal responsibility: if the injury could be shown to have been caused by a fellow-employee, then the employer had the defence of 'common

*The passage wall at South East Alexandra under construction, c. 1875. Because photographic emulsions were so slow, photographs like this were taken on sunny days: we tend to forget what it would be like to work there at 7.30 on a wet February morning.*

employment'. The Board was the employer, so any legal action relating to an accident caused by the acts or omissions of anyone from Lyster downwards would fail. The average casual labourer may not have thought of Lyster as a fellow-employee, but that is what the law said he was. During the enquiries of the Select Committee on Railway Labourers in 1846, the question had been raised of reinstating by statute the workmen's rights lost in the aftermath of *Priestley v. Fowler*, but the time was far from ripe for such 'intrusive' legislation.[39] The Employers' Liability Act did not arrive until 1880, and even then it was a pretty milk-and-water piece of legislation which proved to be largely unsuccessful. In particular, it meant that the victim needed the services of a solicitor, which most workmen probably could not have afforded even before becoming unable to work through injury. Whether or not any of the Engineer's men belonged to trade unions is unclear: certainly there is no recognition of any unions by the Board to be found in the accident records. Such cases as went to law appear in the records showing only the name of the victim and his dependants. It is possible that some actions may have been funded by a union, or by a benefit society which would otherwise have to pay out, but we have no way of telling.

Nevertheless, the Act's provision that the employer was liable for injuries resulting from any act, omission or instruction of a person in any supervisory capacity caused something near panic among employers. We may gain an impression of the Board's view on the safety of its workers from a memo sent by T.F. Squarey, the Board's solicitor, to the Chairman on 5 October 1880 in which he suggests that the Board might consider 'Whether it should be made one of the conditions of entering or remaining in the Service of the Board that Workmen within the meaning of the Act should enter into an Agreement, that the Act should not apply to their service.' We should notice especially the words 'or remaining in': Squarey was simply pointing out that men who would not renounce the protection of the new law could be summarily dismissed. He also suggested the possibility of setting up an insurance fund, paid for by deductions from men's wages 'with or without a contribution from the Board'.[40]

These suggestions sound to the modern reader like the proof of unmitigated villainy on the part of the Board. They are not, for late nineteenth-century ideas of industrial safety were very different from ours. Known accidental deaths in Britain in 1869, for example, totalled 13,521, a figure which is clearly below the true total since it omitted railway employees, a particularly high-risk group.[41] The 1870s saw major parliamentary enquiries into the working conditions of seamen, canal boatmen and railway servants as well as a number of specific safety problem areas such as boiler explosions. Prior to the passage of the Boiler Explosions Act of 1882, for example, it was an exceptional year in which fewer than 50 men died as a result of boiler explosions and collapses (on land) and the figure occasionally exceeded 100. By the early 1890s, the death toll had fallen well below 20.[42] In short, ideas were changing very rapidly and responsibilities were shifting as a result. We know from their other activities and from the decisions they took that the gentlemen of the Board at this time were not likely to be found at the leading edge of such changes.

Nevertheless, Squarey's second suggestion was also unreasonable: roughly speaking, the Engineer's Department accounted, as one would expect, for about three-quarters of accidents, and the men were already having deductions made from their pay for the Relief Fund. The next most dangerous department was the Harbourmaster's, where again the men paid into their own fund. These groups of employees were, in short, to be asked to carry what was now the Board's risk at their own expense, twice over. The Board did not adopt either of these suggestions, but the mere fact of their being suggested is itself informative. The system of 'contracting out' became a serious threat to the interests of those quayside workers who were not Board employees, which was the vast majority. It was to monitor the cost of damages, not through any interest in safety or welfare, that the new system of accident recording was introduced in 1880.

As a result, most of the entries have a record of the final settlement cost, which might seem at first to be a useful piece of information, providing some clue as to the nature and effects of the injuries. Unfortunately, we are concerned with civil, not criminal, law: the payments are not compensation but damages. They are, therefore related to the financial loss suffered by the dependants of the injured man, and vary not according to the severity of the injury but to the man's rate of pay, the number of his dependants, the degree of dependency and the length of time he was unable to work. If a man who was the sole breadwinner of a large family was killed, his widow would receive something of the order of £250, whereas the family of a young man with no dependants would receive only a few pounds for funeral expenses. A slightly bizarre illustration of this principle in action occurred in the case of John Peters, who died, after an accident, on 30 December 1904. His widow and 25-year-old daughter got only £30 on the grounds that he had left them and was living with another woman: they had managed without him before, they could manage without him again.[43] There was, of course, no question of any payment to the 'other woman'. In the case of non-fatal accidents which permanently disabled the victim from his existing job (through amputation or loss of sight, for example) an undertaking to find him suitable employment elsewhere within the Board often formed part of the settlement.[44]

Before the Select Committee whose reports had paved the way for the 1880 Act, there was no shortage of employers wanting to give evidence that industrial accidents were almost invariably the result of stupidity, carelessness or drunkenness on the part of the victims. Certainly we can find accidents which appear to arise from these causes. On 24 July 1901, Michael Letties, labourer, was killed by the explosion of 5lb of Tonite (high explosive). He had laid the charges for demolishing a piece of old masonry and either he or a companion then connected the battery to the detonator wire not of the charges laid but of another charge which was lying ready to be used – in his 'place of safety' from which the charge was to be fired. He, and the place of safety, were blown to bits.[45] Stupidity perhaps, but one might also query the wisdom of expecting an unsupervised labourer to be able safely to lay and fire charges of high explosive. It was, perhaps, the latter-day equivalent of the kind of accident that Dowling had explained was largely eliminated by the quality of supervision provided in the Hartley regime. Despite the considerable numbers of young inexperienced engineers, whether pupil or recently qualified, employed on the various working sites, not a single example has been found of any of them being injured in an accident. Clearly someone, perhaps a wise old Principal Foreman, must have been training them in self-preservation, and presumably supervising them as well, until they were known to be safe to let out on site alone.

On 3 December 1903, Frank Cowdrey, a millwright, and three others, were working on a steam crane at the Brunswick New Entrance works. It fell in the river, and all four were killed. Now had there been an engineer present (whether there was or not is not recorded), he would have been in the right place when the crane became unstable, namely somewhere else. That was not a question of 'leading from behind' but of knowing what would make a crane unstable: should not the men who were working on it have been either taught that or supervised by someone who knew?

The vast majority of accidents, however, lacked both spectacle and black humour: they related to the construction worker's oldest enemy; gravity. Men were killed or maimed by stone, timber, spoil or pieces of equipment falling on them, sometimes from lifting appliances, sometimes dropped by men working on a higher level, and surprisingly often by large baulks of timber left propped up which fell over. Elementary precautions, such as protective headgear or footwear were, of course, unheard of. In one sense many such 'simple' accidents clearly were the men's own fault, but again one must query the standard of supervision. Gravity also caused people to fall off or into things with a sad regularity. Stagings were erected with faulty timber or with the planks not properly lashed down. Men worked aloft on surfaces rendered slippery by the ubiquitous mud. Very occasionally we find miraculous escapes where a man fell 30 or 40 ft, landed in water or soft mud and escaped with only minor injuries: far more often, falls resulted in disability or death. The attribution of such accidents to drink was no doubt profoundly comforting to gentlemen who did not have to work to exhaustion in hypothermic conditions.

There are further improvements in the quality of accident recording after the 1897 Workmen's Compensation Act and the 1901 Factory and Workshops Act. It is perhaps revealing that when a new accident report form was introduced, M.K. Burton sent a memo about its use and an initial supply of forms to each principal officer. To most departments, the quantity was in single figures. The Chief Warehouse Manager got 14, the Harbourmaster 50,

*Construction of a new wall within what had been Brunswick Graving Docks in 1907 as part of the programme of enlarging passages under the 1898 Act. There is still plenty of scope for tripping, falling and having heavy things dropped on one's unsuspecting head.*

and Lyster got 300. The first volume of reports under the post-1901 system is 201 pages long, and 151 pages are occupied by the Engineer's Department.[46] Unlike previous improvements in record keeping, these books do appear to reveal a considerable rise in the number of accidents, but unfortunately the earlier volumes do not give the number of men employed. This was a period of major construction works, and the number of men employed in 'outdoor labour' (i.e. not including employees in the Dock Yard) was usually between 6,000 and 7,000. Given that it was now necessary to record accidents which caused only 'slight' injury (such as 'trod on half a brick when carrying a plank, turning his ankle over'), accidents occurring at roughly one per working day indicate a reasonable standard of safety.

Two threads emerge from these documents. The first, as mentioned above, is that the majority of accidents arose from simple, obvious and readily preventable causes. Failures of lifting slings, for example, were largely preventable by a simple inspection regime. When a diver was drowned in a lock because his 'air hose and safety line carried away' it is likely that better equipment inspection would have saved him. (It is interesting to note that he was attempting recover a carpenter's maul which had been dropped in the water – worth a few shillings.) The second is the high proportion of fatal accidents when compared with those causing 'severe' injury: in 1900, for example, there were only seven 'severe' injuries, four in the Engineer's Department and three in the Warehouses. There were 14 fatal accidents, all Engineer's men. In 1902, 10 Engineer's men were killed and in 1903, 15. The extraordinarily random nature of such happenings is shown by the fact that the Board's only fatal accident in 1901, when there was a good deal of major construction work proceeding, happened to an extra labourer in a warehouse.[47]

At the time of the Select Committee on Railway Labourers there was no such thing as an orthopaedic surgeon. Fractures were dealt with either by general surgeons, at that date still rather looked down upon by physicians, or by bonesetters. In the case of the surgeons the available anaesthetics were effective enough to make amputations a fairly simple matter. Because these operations took place in what were by later standards comprehensively filthy conditions, fatal infections were frequent, which is why so few 'serious injuries' were recorded: most of them lingered in agony a week or two before moving quietly across into the 'fatal' column of the table.

Bonesetters, regarded by the physicians as mere tradesmen, were at that stage the safer bet, relying as they did on skilfully designed splints and supporting devices to encourage injuries to heal naturally.[48]

It was the damaged limbs of, among others, dock construction workers which encouraged the fusion of traditions. Hugh Owen Thomas was the eighth generation of the famous 'Anglesey Bonesetters', whose father Evan Thomas practised in Great Crosshall Street, Liverpool. The son was an unconventional man who did not lack enemies, but at his surgery at his home in Nelson Street, real development came about. In the tradition of the bonesetters, he was a master of splint design, doing the woodwork himself and employing a blacksmith and a saddler on the premises for metal, leather and fabric parts. In a newer tradition, he had qualified at medical school and he recognized the benefits of antiseptic technique and applied it with the minute care which was necessary. He laid the groundwork for his nephew and sometime assistant, (Sir) Robert Jones, who may reasonably be termed the inventor of orthopaedics as a recognized specialism.[49] Both men had a happy knack of blending old and new methods: Thomas is said to have preferred the blacksmith's hammer (used for making bonesetting appliances) to the knife. Along with (Sir) Oliver Lodge, of Liverpool University, Jones pioneered the diagnostic use of X-rays, but deplored the idea that they might become the only diagnostic method.

Casualties from the docks used to attend the surgery in Nelson Street, but in 1889 Jones was appointed honorary surgeon to the Liverpool Southern Hospital, situated, like the Northern, close to the source of many of its customers, namely the docks. He had also been recently appointed Consulting Surgeon to a much larger source of strictly civil engineering casualties, namely the Manchester Ship Canal. Although the canal had a poor safety record, both the contractor and the company had at least taken a more responsible attitude to the victims of the inevitable accidents than was found on most such works, and had provided three 'field hospitals'. They needed to, for of their less than 20,000 men, some 3,000 called on the services of Robert Jones and his staff of 14 surgeons. It is said that Jones himself performed over 200 major operations. Later in life, Jones claimed that the methods used there reduced the mortality rate in those requiring major operations from 80 per cent to 20 per cent, a claim which, if true, is an appalling comment on the situation earlier in the century.

Jones' biographer suggests that it was only with the need to treat tens of thousands of Great War wounded that Jones' techniques became widely known and accepted. Sadly, it appears that their effects among the Dock Engineer's men were not as rapid or dramatic as one might hope: the figures for 1900, given above, show that 'serious injury' accidents still tended to become fatal ones. It is, however, worth remembering that the total accident figures, among a workforce of several thousand, were low by Ship Canal standards. Employer's Liability had been intended as a low-key way of improving industrial safety, by making accidents more expensive than safe working practices, thus doing away with cheap-skate methods like employing totally unskilled youths on site railways.[50] It was far short of being a complete answer, but it seems to have been beginning to have some effect. The unfortunate fact remains that there had been such backsliding in working practice and supervision that even after the first attempts at legislation it was still noticeably more dangerous for a man to work for the Engineer's Department at the turn of the century than it had been for his great grandfather in 1846.

# 7

# Fitting Out: Some Developments in the Equipment of the Docks

## Cranes and Cargo-handling Equipment

It is only natural that people nowadays assume that docks always had a plentiful supply of cranes. Extending beyond living memory and before most of the surviving photographs of ships in dock, quayside cranes were perhaps the most visually striking characteristic of general cargo docks, and present-day container cranes continue the tradition. For the same reason, the relatively few illustrations of late medieval quayside cranes which survive have attracted a degree of interest which is perhaps justified more by the intrinsic qualities of the machines than by the importance of the work they did.

In the days of the early dock engineers, there was not a great deal of cargo-handling equipment either provided or needed. Ships loaded and discharged their cargoes mostly in assorted bags, casks and other small packages by the use of their own tackle. It was not uncommon for sailing vessels to berth two or three deep and discharge across each other's decks. The quay margins were narrow, provided only really as walkways, and cargo was landed on gangways which normally sloped down from the ship's side into the shed, where it would be pounced on by several parties wanting to weigh it, count it, charge duty on it and, given half a chance, steal it or smuggle it. Very few items were carried which could not be manhandled. The cask was a particularly versatile form of packing, capable of being rolled easily on its bilge for some distance or of being rolled on its head to minimize the effort of stacking it two high. A glance through the Customs Bills of Entry will rapidly destroy any notion that casks were only for the transport of liquids, as we find them used for anything from nails to oysters. Most other packages could be moved from the foot of the gangway by the use of the two-wheeled porter's truck: a well made example of this apparently primitive vehicle could, if skilfully used, shift a quarter of a ton with relatively little effort. For some classes of goods, these techniques survived into the 1960s. At this stage in the development of cargo-handling, quayside cranes were comparatively little needed or used, and the cranes of which we do find records were not only few in number, but relatively large in capacity. They were, in short, intended for comparatively abnormal loads where the unit weight was measured in tons rather than a hundredweight or two.

The above remarks refer to the discharge of cargoes, where gravity was normally aiding movement down the gangways into the sheds. This was not always the case, however, for much of the dock system did not have entrance locks, but depended on half-tide entrances. This meant that as the high tides declined from spring to neap, water levels in the system gradually declined by approximately seven feet. At neap tides, a smallish vessel in a high-sided dock could easily find its side well below the copings until most or all of its

*Old style sheds at Clarence Dock, with narrow quayside and zero craneage. The sheds were built in the early 1830s, and this photograph was taken in 1928.*

cargo was discharged. This might seem to offer a handsome advantage in the use of cranes, but did not lead to their rapid spread in the days of sail. There are, of course, no photographs showing the techniques used in the first half of the century, but there was pressure on the Board during the 1860s to allow the use of steam winches on the quaysides.[1] These were normally used with a simple overhead purchase fastened to any reasonably strong bit of a building, though the technique sometimes known as 'Burtoning' was also practised. Burtoning involved lifting a parcel of goods on a hook on the ship's tackle, with a second hook attached to a rope which passed from the winch on the quayside over the overhead sheave. When the load was high enough, the ship's tackle was paid out and the quayside winch wound in, transferring weight until the load hung vertically from the overhead sheave, when the ship's hook could be unslung and the load lowered onto whatever truck was to move it out of the way. In general, ships were discharged fairly quickly – in the 1840s a moderate sized sailing ship, of say 500 tons register, could normally discharge in under a week.[2]

Export cargoes were a different matter: for preference, they should be trucked to the water's edge and then lifted vertically from the narrow quayside to clear the ship's side, which was normally above the copings, particularly in the early stages of loading and at spring tides. For this duty, quayside cranes were much more desirable than they were for discharging, though Burtoning could again be applied. Even so, it was not until 1833 that the Liverpool Shipowners' Association asked for the provision of quayside cargo cranes, and then it was 'to afford greater facilities in the *discharge* of vessels' cargoes'. Hartley was asked to prepare a plan, and on 8 May 1833 he was 'authorised to erect a Crane on one of the Dock Quays *by way of experiment* for the purpose of discharging vessels' [author's italics]. The following May, the Association was expressing 'great dissatisfaction' that only two cranes had been erected, that they were in the wrong places and that 'so heavy a charge has been made for the use of them that no-one is found willing to resort to so expensive a mode of discharge'. The Dock Committee was unmoved, and pointed out in reply that the cranes were admittedly experimental, that they had indeed remained unused, but no charge had been made for their use and none was, for the time being, proposed to be made.[3] Certainly there is no minute prior to that fixing the amount of any charge, as there should have been, so we may reasonably assume that the Association had been misinformed, and was simply indulging in the shipowners' favourite hobby of complaining about port facilities.

The crane authorized in 1833 was not, of course, the first crane on the dock estate. Jesse Hartley had reported on the state of the cranes on the docks in 1829, and John Foster had problems with people stealing the brass bearings from cranes.[4] The only conclusion to which one can come, given the 'experimental' nature of the 1833 crane, is that previous cranes were intended either solely or mainly for the use of the Engineer's Department in the construction or repair of docks and their equipment.

It will be noted that the practical considerations of loading and discharging cargo have been advanced as favouring cranes for loading rather than discharging, but that the experimental cranes were applied to discharging. The next reference to cranes in the minutes is for 5 November 1834, when Hartley was directed to prepare plans for sheds at East Princes and South Waterloo quays. Both of these were primarily export berths, (the division was not yet rigid) and there was clearly still an element of experiment, for the instruction was to provide 'cranes of two different [unspecified] kinds'. The earliest reference to general cargo cranes in Ritchie-Noakes' work on the South Docks is to those at Manchester Dock in 1789, but this was owned and directly administered by the Corporation, not by the Dock Trustees. The earliest she found on the South Dock Estate was the one fitted to a shed at Salthouse in 1853:[5] Salthouse, like Canning, served as the loading berths for vessels which had discharged at Albert.

The crane was a not-entirely-successful attempt to compromise between the needs of those wishing to load items their own tackle could not handle and the majority who wanted the maximum of shed space. In the case of discharging berths the pressure for shed space was proportionately greater and hence the provision of cranes even smaller.

The warehouse docks were as much a special case in handling equipment as they were in the general history of the port. Their *modus operandi* is often misunderstood: the idea was not that vessels discharged direct into the warehouses. The ground floors were open to the quaysides, and fulfilled the role of a transit shed, where goods were checked, counted and weighed. Some might be sent out directly via the 'wagon docks' provided on the outside of each block. Goods which were to be warehoused were then hoisted up (or down) the building for storage. That is why the only travelling wall-crane at Albert was an afterthought: the original working method had no need of a crane to move goods directly from a ship onto the storage levels of the building, nor to load goods from the warehouses aboard ship. It is also the reason why the first hydraulic lifting appliances in the port, and the first supplied by William Armstrong for port use outside of Newcastle, were internal goods lifts and 'low rise' quayside cranes at Albert. The arches which are such a prominent feature of the waterside elevations at Albert provided the working clearance for these quayside cranes: the great disadvantage of having warehouses rising sheer from the water was that they formed a considerable obstruction to the use of ships' tackle. Even at Albert, however, a comparatively small number of cranes was supplemented with the movable hydraulic winches known as 'elephants', which were used in conjunction with movable overhead purchases running on wire spans attached to the walls.[6]

The public quayside warehouses in Liverpool were notoriously controversial. Two powerful vested interests, namely the private warehouse owners and the carters, opposed them resolutely over many years. Merchants were generally in favour of them for the way they simplified procedures and reduced costs, especially before the rationalization and reductions in import duties of the late 1840s and early '50s. Shipowners' views seem to have varied according to their estimate of the saving or otherwise of time for their vessels. That saving might or might not be significant: in many cases, the finding and loading of an export cargo took so long that the saving of a day or two in discharging was of relatively little consequence. The reason why the warehouses had relatively sophisticated handling equipment, requiring the deployment of considerable resources from the dock yard in design, sometimes construction, and above all in maintenance may have become a matter of turn-round speed in later days: to begin with it was not.[7]

There was a crucial difference between discharging in a warehouse dock and discharging elsewhere: in the former the men were directly employed by the Dock Committee. They were not casual employees, but on the 'established list', they were comparatively well-paid and they qualified for such paternalist benefits as the Dock Charitable Fund. In short, if Mr Armstrong's hydraulic hoists saved, as he claimed, up to seven eighths of the cost of manual labour, it was at the warehouses that the investment would be made. To master stevedores and porters, who worked the berths in the open docks, the situation was altogether different. They employed casual labour at very low rates, so the payment of the charge for use of handling equipment provided by the Committee was not necessarily at all good value. As James Cropper had ironically pointed out in his anti-slavery campaigning, it was actually possible to exploit casual wage labourers in a more efficiently and systematically inhumane manner than it was slaves. That is why the wholesale provison of quayside cranes did not trouble our engineers until well into the age of steam: they might have done the work very nicely and properly, perhaps even safely, but with plenty of hungry Irish immigrants around, there were cheaper ways.

So late as 1884, this situation apparently still applied. For public use there was a total of 78 hand cranes, 15 hydraulic cranes, 3 steam cranes and 2 masting shears (one hand, one steam). At the warehouses, which represented only a few per cent of the total length of quayage at the port, there were 368 hydraulic hoists, cranes, jiggers, etc, as against only 39 hand cranes. The total income from all the public cranes, which included the special heavy lift cranes like the 87 ton steam crane at Gill Brook Basin, Birkenhead and the 100 ton hydraulic crane at Langton Graving Docks, was £3,929, which compared badly with £513 for the masting shears.[8]

The shortage, real or imagined, of quayside cranes, became a favourite complaint with customers.

> Q. Is there a sufficient amount of mechanical appliances for the quick unloading of cargoes?
> A. I think there is a great want of these for the quick unloading and sending away of cargo.[9]

The reader will notice that the witness has added the words 'and sending away' in his answer. The fact was that by 1873 ships' tackle was capable of discharging goods faster than they could be removed from the quayside. 'We can both load and discharge [with ships' tackle] more rapidly than cargoes can be manipulated down the quays.' In these circumstances it was scarcely likely that master lumpers would fall over themselves to hire cranes to increase the mayhem on the quayside. Charles MacIver considered that the donkey engines most steamers employed 'can discharge cargo faster than anyone can put up machinery to do'. If the lumpers did want extra lifting power they were far more likely to provide it themselves with portable or semi-portable steam winches. It was the porters who needed to be mechanized to speed the flow of goods, and that too could be much more than a mechanical issue. For every complaint the Board received from shipowners about delays in discharge, they received others from consignees that goods were discharged too fast. Back in the shipowner's camp, these complaints prompted further complaints that consignees deliberately dragged their feet in removing cargo and attempted to use the quaysides and transit sheds as free warehousing. In the case of cotton and some other absorbent materials, end users complained that the merchants deliberately left goods on the quayside to absorb water and increase their weight.[10] The Board was left in the position of referee, but the quayside disputes between shipowners and merchants were, of course, reflected within its own ranks, leading to more heated discussion than effective decision: 'every time the Traffic Committee met its time was occupied from three to four hours trying to settle disputes between shipowners and consignees.'[11] The warehouse docks added an extra twist to the congestion problem in that it was comparatively easy to widen a shed to accommodate an increased rate of discharge but virtually impossible to increase the throughput of the quasi-shed portion of a huge block of warehouses.

It may be thought that what was necessary to sort out the chaotic scenes on the quayside was a more forward-looking approach to the use of railways, employing quayside tracks to discharge directly into or load directly from, railway wagons. That would work with homogeneous cargoes, but in fact a high proportion of cargoes were mixed, so that completion of the quayside paperwork demanded the old-style working in sheds. (Or, in the warehouse docks, on the ground floor.) In the case of export cargoes matters were worse: Mr Lamport testified that his ships to Brazil could carry as many as 400 'different parcels' of goods, so that quayside railways were, to him, simply an obstruction in handling goods from the sheds to the ship's side.[12] So far from such views being contradicted by the railway companies we find them supported: Mr Underdown (of Cheshire Lines Committee) explained how they made extensive use of cartage and carried less than 1,000 tons per year on the Dock Line of Railway. Pressed in cross-examination, he retreated slightly, but summed up his position thus: 'I told you before I have nothing further to say about it beyond this fact, it is more costly and it takes more time, than to cart, and therefore the efficiency of it is not great and cannot be.' James Allport, of the Midland Railway, gave similar evidence.[13] Even so late as the Royal Commission on the Port of London, which reported in 1902, it was possible to find port users willing to testify that the flexibility of cartage made it preferable to railway carriage provided the distances were short and the consignments mixed.

The Cheshire Lines and the Midland Railway were trading on the river as well, using flats and barges from the tiny Egerton Dock, and in the course of questions about boats and boatage, it emerges that boats may well have been more important than has generally been recognized. According to Sir Edward Watkin (representing the Manchester, Sheffield & Lincolnshire Railway and also the Bridgewater Navigation Co.): 'You can get a ship loaded and unloaded more quickly by barges if you have two or three lighters, because you can load at every hatch. You often see a ship surrounded by lighters.'[14] His enthusiasm for overside loading from boats, which necessarily employed ships' tackle rather than cranes, was confirmed by Harbourmaster Thomas Hodgson's evidence to the effect that the east quay of Stanley Dock was reserved for ships to lie there to load coals from the [Leeds & Liverpool] canal.[15]

There were other points of view: it was usual to complain that when ships had to be lightened in the river because of lack of depth at the dock entrances, the cost of discharging was roughly doubled. Furthermore, there was a fairly constant hostility on the part of some shipowners, sometimes reflected in the attitude of the Harbourmaster and his staff, to having a lot of small craft around the docks getting in the way of the ships. It is clear, however, that the Engineer's Department took a different view and 'sold' it to the Board: in the works under the 1844 Act Hartley provided little separate boat locks at Salisbury Entrance and Passage and under the 1873 Act Lyster provided a little extra entrance at Harrington too small to be of any use except for boats. Even Lyster Jnr's new Sandon Entrance, which, used as a half-tide entrance, could pass vessels as large as *Lusitania*, could also be operated as a lock entrance for small craft.

While there was a great deal of politics involved, and it is true that craneage was only one part of a very complex ensemble of operations in loading or discharging a ship, the cranes provided in Liverpool up to the time of the 1873 Act had a simple technical disadvantage. Given that the docks were quite often completely full of ships, it was difficult to move a ship fore and aft on its berth to work the different hatches with a fixed crane. The device known, one presumes jokingly, as a 'portable' crane took several men and a winch some time to move it. Quayside equipment was therefore at a considerable disadvantage compared with the ship's tackle, which could work all the hatches without any need either to move the vessel or to move a 'portable' crane. By 1873, of course, steam deck winches were common, and they gave a considerable added advantage to the ship's tackle. A few small rail-mounted steam cranes were available and served well on minerals berths in Birkenhead, but they were viewed with profound suspicion for general cargo or timber berths on account of the fire risk which arose from their somewhat rudimentary boilers. Vertical cross-tube design was normal, and enthusiastic stoking combined with heavy work could produce not just sparks, but small glowing cinders and a substantial flame out of the chimney top. The author knows, because he has done it. Some steam cranes were under-boilered and ran out of puff when used continuously on the nastiest available coal, but this was not complained of with the few provided by MD&HB. Possibly the Liverpool practice was over-cautious, since large numbers of independent steam cranes were used without disaster in some continental ports, notably Hamburg.

The critical innovation was the travelling roof crane, devised by A.G. Lyster and applied by his father to the two-storey transit sheds built under the 1873 Act at Harrington and Toxteth docks. These machines ran on rails on the top of the shed wall and on the roof ridge, and were supplied with hydraulic power via a 'lazy-tongs' arrangement of elbowed pipes which allowed them to travel. They averaged out at one crane per 150 ft of shed, and were capable of working one lift of up to 30 cwt from the ship's hold to the first floor landing deck every minute. The intention, and the normal practice was that the cranes worked only the upper storey, leaving the lower to be worked by ship's tackle. It was technically possible for a ship to load at one hatch from the ground floor while discharging to the upper from another. This was not, however, the intended practice, since the west sides of both docks were provided with single storey sheds for export cargoes and the two storey sheds were for import cargoes.[16] Some advocates of double sheds thought the former the more effective practice: they may have been deceived

*The hydraulic roof cranes and landing platforms at Harrington two-storey sheds, completed in 1884. Notice that the ship's tackle is discharging to ground level and overside to a Mersey flat as well.*

by Lyster's statement in his 1889 Paper to the Institution that the cost per square yard of the double-storey sheds was little greater than that of single storey. This claim probably related to the repeated complaints made by some members of the Board that two-storey sheds were an extravagance. His own notebook[17] shows the East sheds at Harrington costing £59,000 for 11,916 sq yds, or £4.95 per sq yd, while the single storey sheds at West Harrington cost £33,500 for 16,580 sq yds, only £2.02 per sq yd. Given the notorious slowness with which export cargoes arrived, it would have been folly to do as Mr Hayter suggested in discussion on the paper and occupy expensive high-tech berths where the flow of export goods for loading would not fully occupy the plant. At Greenock, according to Mr Kinipple, two storey sheds were in service at the James Watt dock with cranes working on a similar principle but serving for both import and export cargoes. It may have been coincidence that 'unfortunately there was not sufficient trade at present to keep the cranes fully employed' or there again it may have been a

*The new sheds at Queens No. 1 Branch (1903) were a development of those at Harrington. Notice the flat in mid-frame which is fitted with a derrick lofty enough to deliver bunker coal, leaving the ship's tackle free to discharge cargo.*

misapplication of the system.[18] A.G. Lyster claimed that the Liverpool method of working could produce an annual return of 800 tons per yard of quayside, which was about double what a good old-style berth could manage.

As we have seen, the Port of Liverpool was quick to recognize the benefits of electric lighting. The same cannot be said for electric craneage. Electric travelling cranes were making their appearance in a number of factories by the early 1890s: Crewe Railway Works, for example, installed its first in 1890 and had ten in service by 1896,[19] and electric quayside cranes were a particular feature of the Port of Hamburg from 1890 onwards. Owing to concerns about hydraulics freezing up, Hamburg had also invested heavily in steam cranes – 280 of them – and by 1902 had added 101 electric cranes. (Though hydraulic lifting appliance were used in the warehouses.)[20] According to Ehrenfreund, the electric quayside cranes were a very mixed blessing, in that their transmission gearing, despite using compressed leather

*A recent view of Toxteth Dock, now part of the Brunswick Business Park. The single-storey sheds for export berths are in the foreground with the double-storey ones for imports facing them across the dock..*

pinions, was very rough and noisy, sufficing to 'set the whole crane in a tremor'. It was also, of course, a characteristic of steam cranes that a powerful braking effect could be obtained by using the reversing lever and of hydraulic ones that the load could be rapidly halted by closing the water valve. Electric cranes lacked these facilities and early examples 'ran on' rather than stopping immediately – which they could do in all movements, not just hoisting or lowering, with potentially unpleasant effects.

None the less, a number of other ports began to use electric cranes to a greater or lesser degree, including Mannheim, Rotterdam, Genoa and Middlesborough. In Liverpool, a report was commissioned from Sir William Preece in 1901, which has to be seen in company with the comments, sometimes acerbic, which A.G. Lyster made upon it.[21] The result was that the extension of electric lighting on the dock estate continued, but electric craneage was ruled out for the time being. Unadventurous as this might seem, it was probably the correct decision at the time: hydraulic cranes were a well-established and reliable technology, they were almost impossible to damage by rough handling and they were there, paid for. Electric cranes would, even at that comparatively late date, be something of a gamble, and the cost of electric power was only just beginning to come down from the 5*d* per horsepower/hour it had cost before municipalization: with other forms of power anything in excess of 1*d* would be considered expensive. The Board had a number of small generators for lighting systems, and it is fortunate indeed that when the Works Committee considered the subject on 11 November 1905 they did not succumb to the temptation to put in a system large enough for crane driving. They resolved instead to buy power from the Corporation. This was exactly the time when power station capacities had not merely to increase but to multiply in order to remain economic. The Board would have had insufficient use for a station producing several

*Liverpool Corporation's Pumpfields Power Station, built in 1902. Its output was a little over 11 megawatts: this was was what the Board would have had to compete with. No contest!*

megawatts, and anything less would have been uneconomic within a decade. The charge by then had fallen to about 3.6*d* per kilowatt/hour, or about 2.7*d* per horsepower/hour.

The reason the Works Committee had considered building a power station was that they had already gone to tender for the supply of the first electric cranes: on 24 November 1905 they accepted the tenders of the Glasgow Electric Crane & Hoist Co. for six 30 cwt transporter cranes at North No. 1 Kings Dock for £4,783 and of Royce Ltd for six 30 cwt movable luffing cranes at South No. 2 Kings for £5,181.[22] The reader who recalls the cranes 'of two different kinds' at Princes will already have guessed that the performance of the transporters and the luffers was to be compared. Unfortunately the joint report of the Engineer and the Chief Traffic Manager which was presented to the Docks & Quays Committee on 25 March 1908 seems not to have survived. From other incomplete evidence we may surmise that it showed the luffers to be the more successful design, and relatively few more transporters were built. More important, perhaps, was the fact that the electric cranes showed themselves more expensive in depreciation and maintenance but so much more effective and convenient in use that customers would pay extra for them as compared with the hydraulic roof cranes.

The transition would be comparatively slow. The finances of the Board at this time were in a singularly bad state, and huge expenditure for the Gladstone system was looming. Electric power was an altogether extra expense: it did not enable the closure of the hydraulic mains system, which would have to be retained because no-one had yet found a really satisfactory way of using an electric drive for gate engines, of which there were dozens in the more modern parts of the estate, or for sluices, or, indeed anything where a slow linear motion was required to exert a considerable force. It is also worth recalling that other ports, including Antwerp, came to the same conclusion, and that before the Royal Commission on the Port of London, Mr Owen gave evidence that the electric cranes at Hamburg were not as fast as ships' tackle.[23] What particularly irked him was the fact that an extra charge was made, not for the use of the cranes, but for the privilege of not using them. Unfortunately, whatever might or might not have irked Mr Owen, or whatever Lyster might think, the fact was that Hamburg's tonnage had overhauled Liverpool's as long ago as 1893 and we cannot ignore the possibility that better cargo-handling equipment was one of the reasons why shipowners went there.

Mountfield has remarked that the old sailing ship operators were relatively laid-back characters who did not worry about the passage of time in the same way that steamship owners had to. This sounds a dubious statement: could it perhaps be derived from the rose-tinted recollections of an old sailing ship man in around 1900? It is in fact eminently sustainable: in 1844, for example, the Chairman of the Liverpool Shipowners Association was pressed to tell the Select Committee which was considering the 1844 Dock Bill 'about what the average length of time' was that a ship remained in the docks. His answer was indeed fairly laid-back: 'It is impossible, because some times we take in for different parts of the world, and we lie there, perhaps two months to obtain cargo for a general ship.'

This, be it remembered, was not the skipper of a tramp, but the chairman of a trade association, who we have to believe was speaking for the experience of owners in general. If a ship was going to lie a couple of months at the export berth it was not worth paying charges which reflected state-of-the-art engineering in order to leave the import berth a day or two earlier. It is also interesting to note that once dock dues had been paid, a ship was allowed to remain in dock no less than six months before any further charge was made on it, though this figure was later reduced to sixty days.[24] Turn-round time was not necessarily a quay issue. This enraged steamship owners, despite the fact that the berths at which the sailing ships stayed were usually ones they would disdain to use. In some cases the sailing vessels were moored several deep or even, in some of the older squarer-shaped docks moored to buoys in the middle.

In retrospect, the warehouses built in Jesse Hartley's time may be viewed in two quite different ways. As warehouses, they were excellent and they continued to make money for at least a century. Their problem was that they rendered virtually impossible any extensive modernization of the docks alongside which they stood, so that changes in the shape or size of ships, or in the means of handling either them or their cargoes could be accommodated with extreme difficulty or not at all. This lesson did not take long to learn: Albert, Wapping and Stanley docks were past their best within twenty years.[25]

The result of this was a marked unwillingness on the part of the Dock

*When ocean-going ships became too deep or too high to use the coaling berths at Bramley-Moore, floating elevators were used for bunkering them in the newer docks, or even in the river. This photograph dates from c. 1910.*

Board to build any more general warehouses. They went further, and did their best to avoid providing special-purpose facilities at all. This frequently seems an over-conservative policy on their part, and it certainly enraged shipowners, but it was proven correct in a number of instances. The High-level Coal Railway, for example, never made any really worthwhile return for the Board and was a long-standing source of friction between the Board, the Lancashire & Yorkshire Railway and the customers. It was far from being the greatest-ever piece of engineering, in that its special wagon-tipping cranes never really got close to their theoretical performance, and the larger classes of ship soon got so deep that if laden down they could not get to the berths, while if light they could not get under the cranes. The same problem occurred in a less acute form with the more conventional wagon drop at Birkenhead. Similarly the Waterloo Corn Warehouses, which had a highly notable and innovative bulk grain handling system paid the penalty of the pioneer: their machinery did not perform to anything approaching specification and was soon rendered obsolete. The double-storey sheds at Harrington were able to discharge bagged grain substantially faster than Waterloo could discharge bulk. The dock itself soon proved insufficient in depth, but was virtually impossible to deepen: how did you underpin a wall which had a six-storey warehouse standing on it and vaults behind it? The answer was that it was so difficult it did not get done: it was easier to allow Waterloo to 'gravitate' and provide new facilities for the larger vessels in the grain trade elsewhere.[26]

In the latter part of the century, the grain trade was Liverpool's largest traffic in terms of tonnage. Life got slightly easier for the Board, in that as ever more areas of supply entered the market the trade became markedly less seasonal, improving the utilization of expensive special-purpose facilities. Unfortunately, the grain trade in North America grew so rapidly that there was a tremendous premium on improvements to handling equipment and this created an obsolescence problem for ports like Liverpool. As ever, the shipowners and the grain trade were able to manipulate port authorities into embarking on a course of expensive and unnecessary competition.

There were a few problem cargoes even at an early date. Long baulks of timber, for example, required a berth where they could be threaded out of the special bow ports provided in ships designed to carry them.[27] Such vessels had to be equipped for loading in places where the facilities were rudimentary or non-existent, and were capable of loading logs of greenheart up to about 70 ft long and 30 inches in diameter (weighing about 70 lb per cubic foot) from the water, using a temporary timber outrigger over their bow and a lot of rope and pulley blocks. (Since greenheart sinks in water, this required the services of native divers to place the slings: greenheart is mentioned here to illustrate the most difficult situation. Most timbers were much easier to load.) Their discharge berths might not need any very special equipment, but they did need an open quayside, with no shed near enough to get in the way of the emerging timber. Neither the Dock Committee nor their engineer had any choice in the matter: the timber trade had to be provided with those facilities or told to go and use some other port. Since one of the main uses for very long pieces of timber was the making of ships' masts, the larger ships got, the bigger these wide open spaces had to be: that at Brunswick, the first specialist timber dock, extended the full length of the dock for a depth of 300 ft. Alternatively, of course, timber could be

*Timber ships in Canada Dock discharging a mixture of deals (the larger class of sawn timber)*
*and baulk. Notice the man at the starboard bow of the nearest ship watching the progress of the*
*baulk which the men at the winch are extracting.*

discharged overside into the dock and then pulled to the quay and hauled
out. For both these purposes, a low sloping quay, such as that provided at
Brunswick Dock, was a considerable advantage. By 1885 there were also
timber quays at Hornby, Brocklebank, North Carriers and Canada docks and
at Gill Brook Basin in Birkenhead.[28] The use of timber ponds was not
normal in Liverpool, though there was a temporary one at Canada Dock in
the 1860s. In the early days of Birkenhead Docks, trade in general was so
slack that the Great Float itself was sometimes treated as a timber pond.
Because timber ships normally berthed bow-on to the quay, it was also
necessary to provide stern mooring buoys an average ship's length out from
the side. At Brunswick these consisted of large stone sinkers in the dock
bottom with about 36 ft of heavy chain (1.25–1.5 in iron) held up by the
buoy. When four or even six ships moored to each buoy the whole
arrangement was a little unstable and, of course, made movement within the
dock very inconvenient.[29]

Nice though it was for the timber importers to have these facilities, they serve as a good example of the reasons why the dock engineers and their masters always did their best to avoid providing special-purpose berths or equipment. The long timber nearly all arrived in the four months of July to October, which meant that for two-thirds of the year the timber berths were mostly not being used for timber. The cotton ships normally arrived between February and July, and the unlucky ones ended up in Brunswick, where their owners and the consignees of their cargoes complained noisily about the unsuitability of a dock which was quite admirable for handling timber, but less good for anything else. In particular, timber quays which were frequented for four months of the year by horses and timber bobs were unlikely to present an ideal surface for the storage of cotton, and the sheds whose absence was essential for timber were highly desirable for cotton. What port authorities and their engineers wanted was nice steady trades which could use the same basic 'highest common factor' facilities with complete interchangeability. But cotton and timber were the port's two biggest trades for most of the first half of the century, and between 1832 and 1852 Brunswick was its biggest dock. As time went on, two trades which one might imagine by their seasonal nature could have been complementary in their port needs, developed further apart as the cotton trade moved increasingly into steam while timber remained mainly in sail. In 1883, for example, 79 per cent of Liverpool's cotton arrived in steamships, but only 18.9 per cent of its timber.[30] The different requirements of sail and steam which crop up as causes of so many of the dock engineers' problems made the two trades more incompatible than before. A recurrent theme among the steamship owners was their resentment at a large and comparatively deep dock like Canada being given over to the timber trade when it was originally designed for steamships, and was obviously too good for anyone but steamship owners.

Cotton, timber and grain were Liverpool's three biggest trades, and those which made the most noise about dock facilities. It must not be forgotten that Liverpool was a general port *par excellence* and that there were few cargoes it did not handle to a greater or lesser degree. Some were old favourites like tobacco, which had been arriving in the late summer for over 200 years. It was not a specially demanding cargo except in respect of security, for then as now it was subject to very heavy import duties. Nor was the seasonal problem very acute: tobacco imports did peak in the late autumn, but *some* tobacco was coming in most of the time. It was, however, a low density cargo, and therefore came to be normally shipped as part of a mixed cargo. Until the end of the century, much the greater part of Liverpool's tobacco came from the United States in comparatively large ships which arrived at the north end. The tobacco warehouse was at the obsolescent Kings Dock about three miles away, a problem which was eventually partially solved by A.G. Lyster's vast new Stanley Tobacco Warehouse. Despite the fact that it was less than ideally sited, it was one of the Board's more profitable ventures, and was the biggest warehouse in the world at the time.

Fruit, mainly from the Mediterranean, had traditionally arrived in two main surges: fresh in the summer and dried (figs, dates, etc) in the autumn. The adoption of fairly fast screw steamships in the trade from the 1850s onwards posed a problem for the engineers in that they were relatively deep for their size, but helped solve another one in that their greater speed extended the area of supply and thus blurred the edges of seasonality. The process of rendering the fruit trade entirely non-seasonal is almost complete now, but the first major landmark was the arrival of ocean-going steamers which were fast enough and cheap enough to enable the importing of some of the more durable fruits from the southern hemisphere.

One of the abiding overall impressions which Hyde leaves on the reader is the enterprise and versatility of the Liverpool business community in the nineteenth century. The commercial skills they had developed were readily transferred to new fields such as the importing of Brazilian rubber, and some of those fields had very special requirements in the port. Perhaps the most obvious example is the very rapid growth in the importing of chilled and frozen goods, especially beef from Argentina and chickens (and eggs) from China, which had no special unloading requirements, but did need cold stores fairly near the discharging berths. The Board, having burned its fingers with the Waterloo Corn Warehouses, resolutely and successfully resisted pressure to provide such facilities, insisting instead that those that wanted them should provide them for themselves. The two main rivals in the trade, the Nelson brothers and the Vestey brothers did exactly that at Bramley-Moore and Alexandra respectively.

There were two fields in which the Board felt that the issues were too large and too serious to be pushed aside in that manner. The first was that of livestock importing. For centuries, livestock had arrived in Liverpool and been driven ashore at whatever seemed the most convenient place. It then mostly proceeded under its own power to the nearby abattoir, though some travelled further inland. The Contagious Diseases (Animals) Act of 1878 changed all that, requiring that foreign livestock be discharged at specially designed and designated foreign animals wharves where proper precautions could be taken to ensure to the identification of any infection and steps taken to prevent the possibility of its spreading. This involved the engineers in the design of secure cattle-runs and lairages from which infected animals could not escape, slaughterhouses, chill-rooms, and specially equipped rooms for all manner of unpleasant processes involving left-overs like blood, offal and manure. The facility for rapid distribution inland by rail enlarged the market, but also raised the stakes in the safety issue by threatening to spread imported diseases countrywide with fearful rapidity. It became the first steady large-volume high-value trade at Birkenhead, and it lasted over a century. Because the subject is well covered in Ken McCarron's *Meat at Woodside* it is passed over briefly here, but there was another new traffic which posed analogous problems to the engineers.

## The Problems of Specific Cargoes: Petroleum as a Case Study

The initial growth of the trade in petroleum was phenomenal. The first cargo which was landed in Liverpool arrived in 1862, and on December 17 that year there were 11 ships in dock discharging a total of 27,033 barrels.[31] Nationwide, imports of petroleum rose from 2,000,000 gallons in 1859 to 102,000,000 in 1889.[32] In the early stages, the moving force in Liverpool was a 'Petroleum Oil Broker' by the name of Alex S. Macrae. His occupation is placed in scare quotes because he also traded in quite a large way in what was then termed 'coal oil', and was quite happy to inform outsiders that either one or the other had the greater potential for growth.

It was normal for the Board's customers to accuse it of being slow to meet their needs, and there are undoubtedly cases where this was fair criticism. In the case of development of facilities for oil it probably was not fair. For oil in barrels, no special handling equipment was needed: all that was required was secure storage placed at a reasonable distance from domestic property, likely sources of ignition and other sensitive cargoes. As early as August 1862, Lyster reported to the Works Committee on his proposal for the storage of petroleum in barrels, which consisted of a fairly conventional transit shed with a very lightly constructed roof which would blow off easily in the event of disaster, in the manner usual in explosives factory buildings. What was far less conventional was the provision of underground cellular cast iron tanks for bulk oil. As late as 1889, the *Liverpool Journal of Commerce* castigated the Board for its failure to provide for bulk oil discharge and storage.[33]

The first bulk oil storage tanks in Britain appear to have been those at Mellish's Wharf, London, built 1868–9 for the reception of Scottish shale oil, but they were apparently intended more to avoid the problem of leaking barrels than to benefit from bulk transport. One stimulus to bulk carriage lay in the increasing importance of Russian oil, but only for the technologically mundane reason that it was hard to get suitable timber for coopering in the vicinity of the Russian oil fields. Early attempts to solve this problem lay mainly in fitting out sailing vessels with a number of built-in tanks: *Crusader*, which was one of the first to bring bulk oil from America (in 1876), used 45 tanks containing an average of 125 barrels each. Steam was treated with justifiable suspicion where such a potentially dangerous cargo was involved and larger tanks had been tried with a fairly predictable result. In the absence of adequate venting or provision for expansion and contraction of the cargo with changes in temperature, tanks could not be filled to the top, so in rough weather the oil slopped around with effects on the stability of the ship which were always distressing and sometimes fatal. The turning point, at which a recognizable forebear of the modern tanker became a practical proposition, was the production of steam tankers by Armstrong Mitchell in the late 1880s. These were the vessels which made it clear that bulk oil cargoes were not a far-off dream, but an imminent prospect. It is tempting, but dangerous, to suppose that the construction of the *Gluckauf* (completed 1886), which was the first steam tanker to use the hull as a tank rather than carrying tanks inside the hull, marked the obvious beginning of a complete change in the trade. Within ten years, Armstrong Mitchell built over fifty tankers.[34]

There was indeed still no bulk storage facility available in Liverpool in

1889, though there were two considerable developments in hand. What had happened to Lyster's initial far-sighted proposal? He had made the fatal mistake of proposing to place it on some otherwise empty land at the far end of the West Float where all the conditions mentioned above were met. The problem was that it was on the Birkenhead Docks, and the Birkenhead lobby, for whom the Board could do no right, was immediately up in arms, presenting a memorial signed by 374 Birkenhead residents.[35] These were, of course, substantial citizens, including some members of the Board, and such people did not live in the nearby dock cottages, but in rather grander places at some considerable distance from the docks. The Works Committee backed down, and allowed only limited imports of petroleum in barrels. Had they suggested a bulk facility in Liverpool at the time, they would have faced two problems. In 1863, Liverpool Corporation attempted a prosecution for nuisance for allowing the importing of oil in barrels at Carrier's Dock. After a great deal of out-of-court acrimony, they were forced to withdraw their charges, but the legal position remained unclear until the Petroleum Act of 1871 made port authorities themselves the licensing authority for storage and handling of petroleum on their property. The second problem would have been a memorial from Birkenhead accusing the Board of diverting a fast-growing and lucrative trade away from the under-used Birkenhead Docks and into the overcrowded Liverpool Docks.

The fact of the matter is that then as now, plenty of people wanted the products and profits of petroleum so long as the mess, smell and fire risk were in someone else's back yard. It is only fair to remark that the fire risk was greater than we might think. The Board had issued regulations for the handling and storage of petroleum as early as December 1862,[36] and these defined petroleum as 'including any product thereof which gives off inflammable vapour' at less than 100°F. It was only under the 1871 Petroleum Act that such niceties gained any wider application. Although most 'refined petroleum' at that date was lamp oil, the distillation process was comparatively crude, and hence the volatility of any particular consignment could be a doubtful quantity until a statutory procedure for its determination was developed and enacted.

The 1862 Regulations allowed the discharge of cargoes of petroleum only at a number of specified berths which were at the north and south extremities of the Liverpool Docks, and the westward extremity of Birkenhead, thus segregating petroleum, so far as was practical without a new purpose-built dock, from other cargoes. The Antwerp fire of 1889, when an explosion in a nearby cartridge factory started an oil fire which burned rather well for two days, provides retrospective justification for such caution.[37] What is surprising is that after that initial spate of activity, a profound silence pervades the records of the Board. Between then and 1881, the Engineer's Reports contain just two passing mentions of facilities for the petroleum trade, both relating to minor quayside and rail access improvements in Birkenhead. In 1881, we find the first reference to the 'Casemates' at Herculaneum Dock. As part of the continuing works under the 1873 Act, Herculaneum Half-Tide was being enlarged and deepened and provided with a long narrow branch inland of the graving docks. This required cutting back the low sandstone cliff there, and as this work was proceeding, it occurred to Lyster that it would be a good idea to excavate a series of small artificial caves and provide them with heavy iron doors as a storage place for dangerous goods, which would thus be both sub-divided and securely contained. While it is customary to describe the casemates as Liverpool's first purpose-built petroleum store, that is not strictly true: it was only after they were well under construction, and a few were actually in service that the emphasis shifted from dangerous cargoes in general to petroleum in particular.

It is clear that Lyster's idea seemed better at first hearing than it did on more mature reflection. First, there was the matter of obtaining an easement from Lord Sefton, without which he would only be able to tunnel back 23 ft. This was duly obtained, and the casemates built to a length of 51 ft. In the Engineer's Report for 1881 the cost of the casemates was said to be less than that of building sheds, but by 1882 we find that although 24 were complete, and 11 in use (having handled 7,676 barrels) 'The remainder are rapidly advancing towards completion, but as the excavation is all in rock, and the space for working cramped and confined, the progress is of necessity somewhat slow and tedious.'

The completion of excavation was not the end of the problems either: there was a good deal of controversy about the arrangements for dealing with any spillages, which was dealt with by the rather crude expedient of excavating the floors below quayside level and providing massive iron thresholds so that the casemate itself acted as the spillage container.[38] No

*The Herculaneum Casemates in course of construction: this view dates from July 1882, when Lyster was beginning to find their excavation tedious.*

explanation seems to have been offered for the complete change of philosophy, from having a 'blow-off roof' so that the energy of any explosion would be dissipated straight up in the air, to attempting to contain it in a rock chamber with massive doors.

Explosion remained a very real danger. In 1877, for example, there was an explosion on board the *Thomas*, which was discharging 'petroleum spirit' (in this case naptha) in barrels at Herculaneum. This followed the famous Regent's Park explosion of 1874, when four barrels of benzoline being carried on the canal boat *Tilbury* exploded, igniting some five tons of gunpowder which were also aboard, and appears in a litany of disaster recited by Boverton Redwood, who seems to have become the first acknowledged authority in matters of petroleum safety, in a paper read to the Institution in 1894.[39] What is interesting about that paper is the slowness of the process by which people became aware of the dangers of petroleum vapours and of the fact that crude oil could produce vapours more unpredictable, and hence more deadly, than the apparently more dangerous refined products with a nominally much lower flash point. Redwood describes long sequences of laboratory experiments to determine the proportions of vapour to air which were explosive, the nature of the vapours, flash points and flash ranges. From his account, this knowledge must have been gained at a terrible cost in facial hair, but it formed the basis of all subsequent safety measures for the handling of oil and oil products. The converse of that statement, that prior to then safety was often a matter of guesswork, was borne out by the continuing death and destruction. Nor should it be assumed that the arrival of the Armstrong Mitchell type of vessel necessarily solved all the problems: in October 1888 the steam tanker *Ville de Calais* suffered an explosion, shortly after discharging a cargo of crude oil, which killed several people, caused extensive damage ashore and wrecked the ship.[40]

This might suggest a rather ill-starred beginning to specialist petroleum facilities both locally and further afield, but in fact the casemates did good

*The effects of an explosion of residual vapour after discharging crude oil: this used to be the steam tanker* Ville de Calais.

business in the first few years of their existence, before bulk oil tankers became reasonably safe and reliable. In the year 1889–90, for example, they earned £2,234, nearly 2.5 times their earnings in their first full year of operation.[41] Again the criticism in the *Journal of Commerce* seems less than entirely fair: we must recall that when the Board had provided 'state-of-the-art' facilities for bulk grain at Waterloo they had found themselves ahead of the demand and had to put in additional equipment for handling the bagged grain which their customers kept insisting on shipping in there.

Petroleum was probably the most rapidly growing trade in the world at the time, but even the companies directly involved in it were not rushing to provide expensive single-purpose bulk facilities: the first on the Mersey appears to have been the installation in 1887 of a 6 in pipe on the north side of the West Float by the Liverpool Storage Company 'to enable them to discharge vessels carrying petroleum in bulk'. This was followed in 1889 by more extensive investment on the south side by the Anglo-American Oil Company and R. Stewart & Co, involving a total of seven tanks ranging from 1,500 to 2,700 tons capacity. The steam tanker *Phosphor* discharged the first cargo there, of 2,600 tons of oil, on 28 May 1889.[42]

These facilities were erected by the users, for their own exclusive use, on land leased from the board: they were not designed and constructed, like the Herculaneum casemates, for the casual use of all comers. This casts a slightly different light on the complaints in the *Journal of Commerce*: what was being advocated there was that the Board should put its money where someone else's mouth was. Clearly they would have to do that sooner or later, and it may be that they erred on the side of caution, one reason for which was probably that Lyster and his department had lagged behind on their research: when the time came to start laying out the first small tank farm, they had to seek specialist advice – the first time such a thing had been necessary since the days of Foster.[43] In the case of bulk grain, for example, both Lysters, father and son, went at various times and toured round what were then considered to be the best facilities in the world, and came back knowing enough to tackle the management of grain transit and storage projects, albeit not always entirely successfully. In this case the requirement preceded the knowledge, so that although the Board's first tanks were designed in-house, Boverton Redwood had been consulted first. The fear of explosion was probably the decisive factor. It also seems slightly strange that when the construction of the first Liverpool tanks was described before the Institution, it was described by S.H. Terry, of King, Masterman & Terry, who had rapidly become a specialist in the field.[44] At what was initially known as the Parkhill Depot (so called after the Parkhill Estate, purchased by the Board, on which it was built) Terry constructed two tanks of 2,500 and 2,000 tons respectively (about 1,260,000 gallons in total). Terry's account gives the impression that his firm was the moving force, though the Engineer's Report of 1890 makes clear that the largest tank ordered (of 3,000 tons) and one other of 2,000 tons were built by the Widnes Foundry. As appears from the examples of *Phosphor* above and *Beacon Light* below, the idea of having different tank sizes was to enable, so far as possible, the matching of one shipful to one tankful.

The tanks were placed on terraces cut on the rising ground immediately to the south of Herculaneum Dock, at a level about 15 ft above the quayside, and the pipes ran up from the Herculaneum Branch. On a lower terrace was the barrel-filling area. The obvious risk of leaking oil cascading into the dock or the river in the case of tank failure was met with what became standard practice, namely the construction of a concrete 'moat' around the base of the tank of sufficient volume to retain the entire contents of the tank. Sheds were provided for coopering, and for the external painting and internal gluing of barrels which were the best way known at the time of rendering oak oil-tight. There were barrel runways to ease handling. The general principle of bulk handling, of doing all the lifting at one early stage and then letting gravity do as much as possible of the work thereafter, was observed with the barrels as well as with the oil. The cooperage was on the same level as the tanks, so that empty barrels went down for filling and full barrels went down again for consignment by road or rail. The steam tanker *Beacon Light* discharged the first oil received at Parkhill on 19 June 1891.[45]

Once Parkhill was fully in traffic, the initiative for further development passed largely to the various tenants on the Birkenhead side, with minor improvements or extensions to their facilities being reported practically every year. Although these involved no direct expenditure by the Board, they did involve a certain amount of work for the Engineer's Department, for the permission of the Board was invariably required, and long-standing convention required that such permission was granted only on condition that the works were carried out 'to the satisfaction of the Engineer'. That clause

obviously did not weigh too heavily on the department when it related to any
of the innumerable trivia to which it was applied, but in the case of oil
installations, the Lysters were being asked to sign their names to a statement
that equipment capable of causing major disaster was not going to do so.
That demanded careful scrutiny of every plan and keeping up to date with
the technology. Parkhill itself remained adequate for the trade until the First
World War: after the war the oil industry grew even more rapidly in extent
and importance and the Manchester Ship Canal Company had begun its
momentous investment at Stanlow.[46] These events would force the Board's
hand into further development of tanker facilities, but they lie beyond our
present terms of reference.

## Dock Gates and their Associated Equipment

The gates of a dock are perhaps its most important feature after its retaining
walls: it is the control of water level which they provide which distinguishes
a dock from a mere basin or harbour. They are certainly its most important
'sub-assembly'. This being so, it is at first sight curious that works like
Ritchie-Noakes, or Skempton's papers on dock engineering in London,[47]
should have very little to say on the early development of dock gates. On
slightly closer inspection, the reason becomes clear: it is a marked lack of
contemporary source material. We know, for example, that normal practice
for canal works and small docks was to build straight mitre gates in a
manner which would have been familiar to Leonardo da Vinci. We also
know that as entrances began to get wider, engineers adopted curved mitre
gates, but gates were very rarely described in any detail, and prior to the
rapid extension of the use of technical drawing in the 1820s and '30s, very
few were accurately drawn either. Jackson's re-drawing from Rennie's plan
for the Grimsby entrance lock clearly shows curved gates in 1797,[48] but
whether that was another of the numerous innovations by a man who was
among the most distinguished and innovative dock engineers of all time is
not clear.

The purpose of making gates curved was quite simple: it was readily
apparent that when a pair of gates was resisting the pressure resulting from
the water level being higher on the inside than the outside it had to be

resolving those forces and feeding them back into the masonry. It was, in fact, behaving as an arch laid on its side, and it therefore made sense to construct it in the time-honoured shape for an arch, namely curved, and the amount of curvature was normally known as the 'rise', making the conceptual origin pretty clear. It was also fairly obvious that if the gates were considered as an arch, then a line of thrust could be drawn through them: if straight gates were used as a rough approximation to an arch, then some parts of the line of thrust would lie outside the thickness of the gate – a classic condition for causing failure. Straight gates could and did work perfectly well, but only by being superfluously strong, heavy and expensive as compared with the preferable form.

Attempts to build a proper theoretical basis for gate design began with Peter Barlow's paper of 1836, and continued through the century, with worthwhile contributions from two men from the Liverpool Dock yard, A.F. Blandy and William Brodie.[49] It is from Blandy's paper that we gain an inkling of why it was that gate construction seemed to remain something of a Cinderella among dock engineering specialisms. In a forest of mathematics, we are able to discover the dire effects of 'nip'. Nip was the phenomenon which occurred when a gate met its partner not quite full-face at the mitre, so that the load, instead of being uniformly distributed across the thickness of the gate, was concentrated at the inner or outer edge. The effect was that the strains on particular parts of the gate could accidentally get multiplied by up to seven. The avoidance of nip was therefore essential if gates were to be designed and constructed on any sort of scientific basis: there was no point in trimming weight and strength to save money by getting down to a factor of safety of, say, three, when nip could turn that into a factor of 0.5 or less.

The secret of success in getting gates to close exactly as designed did not lie directly in the hands of the engineer. Two large timber structures had to be constructed to an accuracy of perhaps a quarter of an inch in forty feet. Their heelposts had to stand vertical in their hollow quoins (the rounded recesses in the masonry in which they were housed) to within a similar tolerance in both planes, which required not only high skills on the part of the gatebuilders, the stonemasons and the smiths, but a high degree of collaboration. The final fitting of the mitre posts was by chalking – a tolerance of perhaps a thousandth of an inch![50] They did not have to get it wrong by much to ruin the best efforts of the man in the drawing office. It seems plain that Blandy knew this, though he hesitated to spell it out too clearly among his peers in the Civils, when his brief was to treat the subject scientifically. The reason why some engineers preferred to stick with straight gates where they could get away with it also becomes apparent: Blandy was working in the dock yard, with its tradition of excellent craftsmanship; he was not presiding over a scratch team of carpenters from one firm, masons from a second and smiths from a third. His men were used to making the bottom rail of the gate meet the sill snugly and to not having the heelpost bind in the hollow quoins through a minor discrepancy between the masons who chased out the grooves for the heelstrap anchorplate and the smiths who made the strap.

One aspect of Blandy's paper which aroused a little controversy was his advocacy of 'trucks', or bearing rollers, which ran on a curved metal (or occasionally granite) track set into the sill to relieve the heelpost of some of the weight of the gate. These were said to be difficult and unreliable: in discussion of the paper, Mr Phipps spoke in favour of an ingenious system of 'suspended truck' using a deadweight loading so that the weight carried by the truck remained constant. Mr Browne gave the game away with an

*Looking down on a passage gate at Albert: it has been dismounted and then secured as a display piece, giving a good view of the hollow quoin, heelpost and heelpost anchor. The passage was first in service in 1845.*

*A particularly large and elaborate heelpost strap anchor leaded into the masonry.*

anecdote about how a pair of gates at Bristol had been removed, and it had become clear that the rollers had never in fact run on the track, being about a quarter of an inch clear of it. This reveals Bristol as a port where a gate designed to work with a roller was built so far over the actual strength required as to work happily without one, and, more particularly, as a port where the craftsmen could not be relied upon to get it right. Almost certainly what went wrong in that instance was not that the engineer or the craftsmen at Bristol were incompetent, but that they were not, as at Liverpool, a permanent and specialized team used to working together.

The basics of gate design were sufficiently worked out under Jesse Hartley that the rapid growth in width necessitated by the arrival of paddle steamers did not require any radical re-think. It became increasingly difficult to get large enough baulks of oak for gates, which was possibly one reason for adopting the millwright's sound but very labour-intensive practice of quartering and reversing the timber used for mitre and heel posts, giving a little extra strength and stability for any given size of timber used. The obvious answers lay in other forms of timber or in the adoption of iron. The water in Liverpool Docks in the 1840s, when the oak problem was getting serious, contained a fairly high concentration of sewage, which did little for the health and appetite of woodboring worms, but there were enough of them around to do fairly rapid and serious damage to any delicious softwoods, such as Memel Pine, which the engineer might be unwise enough to use for gate construction. The consequence could be the abrupt de-watering of a dock: if it were full of ships at the time, the cost in compensation would be enormous, so the risk was worth avoiding. Iron gates had their enthusiastic advocates, but they had their disadvantages too. If castings were used for the structural members they were dangerously fragile if struck by a ship or battered by a heavy sea at high tide when the water level inside and out was roughly the same. Wrought iron corroded fairly rapidly in Liverpool's polluted waters, and iron gates were less flexible than wooden ones, which enhanced the risk of minor accidents like a bit of wood getting trapped in the mitre causing serious damage.

The answer lay, therefore, in finding a new kind of wood which was available in very large pieces, did not readily rot in dirty water and was unappetizing to worms. Greenheart was just such a timber and had appeared in Liverpool in the 1830s.[51] From a brief paper by John Bernard Hartley, it seems clear that systematic trials in the use of greenheart were carried out in the dock yard over a period of some years, and the results were satisfactory enough that it was adopted throughout the port. Jesse Hartley, in evidence before the Royal Commisson on Harbours of Refuge, sings the praises of greenheart, and mentions the failure of experiments where other woods were 'pickled with arsenic and all sorts of things' but still got eaten.[51] A limited capability for re-constructing old greenheart gates survived into the 1970s. In the interval, such important works as the new Brunswick Entrance (1903) had been equipped with traditionally constructed greenheart gates, which it retained until closure in 1975.[52] Brysson Cunningham, writing in 1906, described Liverpool as the centre *par excellence* of the construction and use of greenheart gates, with just one set of steel gates in use.[53]

The accusation might well be levelled at both Lysters, and indeed some of their successors, that they showed little innovation in gate design, and were content to accept the methods inherited from the Hartleys with only minor updating. It is broadly speaking true that they did so, but the old methods had their advantages.

There seems little doubt that, strength for strength and size for size, iron or steel gates were cheaper to build by, at the latest, 1890. Cunningham gives us the example of two pairs of gates built for the Manchester Ship Canal, both of the same size, one of greenheart and one of steel. The former cost £8,489, the latter £5,760, corresponding to 49s 9d/sq ft and 33s 9d/sq ft respectively – a conclusive difference.[54] But in fact matters were not that simple: there were clearly other variables to take into account, since the greenheart gates built for the New North Works in Liverpool averaged 46s 6d/sq ft, while apparently similar ones for the South Works shortly afterwards were only 32s 10d. The yardstick price for roughly estimating the cost of gates in Liverpool was 50s/sq ft: that was supposed to err heavily on the side of generosity, but the 82 ft steel gates at Dunkirk North Lock actually cost 49s, despite their relatively modest height of 39 ft.[55]

Cunningham also confidently asserts that steel gates were generally only about half the weight of equivalent greenheart gates, but then goes on to give figures which appear completely to disprove the suggestion. He gives the weight of one greenheart leaf on the 90 ft passage at Huskisson, 44 ft 3 in high as 165 tons, while the steel gates at Greenland Lock (London) closed only an 80 ft passage and were only 38 ft 2 in high, yet weighed 185 tons each. Metal gates could, and normally did, include flotation compartments, which greatly reduced the effective weight in use, but were held by some engineers to be more trouble than they were worth to keep watertight. The evidence that greenheart had had its day is, in short, inconclusive.

Greenheart was possessed of three important advantages. The first was that a wooden gate was more elastic than a steel one. There were many ways of damaging a gate by carelessness, stupidity or haste, of which crashing ships into them was just the most obvious. It was at one stage the practice to run some sluicing water through Canada Basin on the ebb: if the outer gates were allowed to seat and sluicing water was then run so as to cause the level inside the gate to fall faster than that outside then, unless very firmly prevented, the gate would drift open. When the sluices were closed, the level outside would fall rapidly in relation to that inside, causing the gates to crash together. William Brodie tells the tale of the gates of the 85 ft entrance at Birkenhead being let 'out of control' when water was flowing out between them at some speed. One gate hit the sill before the other and 'its lowest part being thus stopped the top part was flung out of the plumb to an extent which witnesses said must have been 12 ft, the gate recoiled, and luckily the two leaves "mitred", that is, came fairly together. No apparent damage was done to that gate by that extraordinary test.'[56]

A steel gate would be permanently distorted by such abuse, requiring a complete rebuild. Such accidents normally required, of course, serious incompetence or neglect of duty by the Gatemen, but such things happened. Damage aside, greenheart gates were generally accepted as lasting longer than iron: when Canada Entrance was deepened in 1895, the new gates incorporated all the old horizontal rails recovered from the old ones, which were said to be as good as the day they were made – which was nearly 40 years ago. It was considered unusual for iron or steel gates to last more than 20–30 years, or at least it was by some engineers: Mr Newell (of Hull) claimed, in a letter commenting on Brodie's paper that he had recently removed for overhaul some iron gates which were 28 years old in which the material was 'in all respects equal to the day in which the gates were constructed'. Newell held other views on the subject of gates, however, with which the majority of his colleagues did not agree. Finally, metal gates required scaling and painting, preferably every year and certainly not less than every three years, which greenheart ones did not.

All these advantages of greenheart bear heavily on the question of operation. Scaling and painting a gate sounds easy when you say it quickly, but at a half-tide entrance, as provided at many of the Liverpool Docks, it required either the draining of the dock or the construction of a coffer-dam. (Though a ship caisson came to be used later.) Either way, at least the entrance, and sometimes several berths as well, were put out of commission for a minimum of a few days. That was much more than just bad customer relations – it was serious loss of revenue. The deepest of the newer entrances did not dry out even at low water of equinoctial springs, so that any painting or repair work required a caisson or a coffer-dam on the outside as well. Even where there were full entrance locks with gates at either end, these difficulties continued to apply until the arrival of floating cranes capable of lifting a gate and putting it down on the side for attention.

It is also only fair to remember that some later experiments by the Board involving rolling caisson gates and radial sector gates have not proved to be any very great advance in practical terms. The Manchester Ship Canal, despite the apparently conclusive evidence in favour of steel being cheaper, did not do away with greenheart gates, indeed it has not done so to this day.

The steel gate to which Cunningham referred appears to have been a one-off experiment, since another writer tells us that all the MSC gates were of greenheart.[57] For so long as greenheart and the men to work it were readily obtainable, it probably made good sense to stick with what they were good at. What is rather more open to question is the methods by which gates continued to be opened and closed.

The delightfully simple arrangement used on most English canal lock gates, of extending the top rail of the gate as a balance beam, which both balances the gate on its pivot and serves as a lever for opening or closing it was not applicable to gates of the size needed for docks. No details have survived of the earliest gate engines in Liverpool, but there is no reason to suppose that they would have been different in principle from the oldest ones which still survive, at the Canning Graving Docks.[58] These were made by the famous Phoenix Foundry, Liverpool, at the time when it was a branch of the Coalbrookdale Company, whose name is cast into the capstans. They were installed when the docks were deepened and modernized, a project completed in 1813. The south capstan hauls a single chain, one end of which opens the south gate while the other end closes the north. The north capstan

*An early gate engine, in service from 1813, at Canning Graving Docks: the positions of the chain tunnels are clearly visible.*

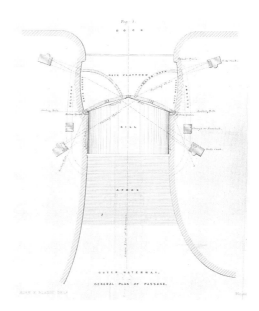

*Diagram showing a pair of gates*
*opened and closed on the four-engine*
*system.*

works in a similar manner to close the south and open the north. This economical arrangement was improved upon at later entrances by having four drum winches, one to open and one to close each gate, allowing the chains to be run at more favourable angles.

These worked well enough on passages of 45 or 50 ft width, though even there, and with everything in perfect order, a force of about 2 tons per leaf was needed for opening and more than 1 ton for closing. This meant that, regardless of all the other tasks which had to be performed to open a gate, such as removing the detachable post-and-chain handrail from its top, at least four men were required simply to work the winches. Nor was it a simple matter of exerting a constant force on the winch. The Mersey is an unfriendly river, and is rarely still. In particular, it develops a miniature version of an ocean swell which will reach four feet on an only moderately rough day: the discomfort this caused to the men winding the handles is easy to imagine as the partly-open gates were alternately pushed and pulled by the water. In 1859, the Canada Entrance was opened to traffic, 100 ft wide, each gate weighing some 129 tons,[59] and this had forced Hartley to investigate the application of mechanical power to gates. Probably with some trepidation,

Canada was equipped with the first hydraulic gate engines in the port.[60] They were clearly successful, for the entrances at Herculaneum, Huskisson, Sandon and Wellington were converted to hydraulic operation during the years 1863 to 1866, and the Alfred Entrance, Birkenhead, completed in 1866, was designed for hydraulic operation from the start.

The application of hydraulic machinery to gates brought about an enormous saving in labour, revealed by a series of experiments carried out by Lyster's staff at Sandon and Huskisson in April and May 1866, when they compared the performance of the new machinery with that of the old hand-operated engines. (Which had, of course, been left in for standby use.)[61] At Sandon Entrance, they found that opening the outer gates required 6 men to make 462 turns of the 'crab handles', and 4 men made 540 turns to open the inner gates. These operations took respectively 31.5 and 21 minutes. Closing the outer gates took 8 men 33 minutes and closing the inner took 4 men 22 minutes. By hydraulic power, the outer was opened in 3 minutes 20 seconds and closed in 4 minutes 20 seconds, while the inner was opened in 3 minutes 5 seconds and closed in 4 minutes 8 seconds. Certainly this saved a good many man/hours, but converting an entrance to hydraulic operation cost several thousand pounds, while the men doing the winding would be earning about 6d per hour. The real saving lay elsewhere: from the point where the entrance was watertight to the point where it was fully open for vessels, and back to watertight again, took roughly an hour and five minutes by handpower and roughly eight minutes by hydraulic power. That meant that the entrance was available to shipping some 55 minutes longer when operated hydraulically. On a feeble high-water neap that would amount to an increase in the ship-passing capacity of the entrance of nearly 50 per cent and even on a good tide of fully 25 per cent. The cost of the hydraulic machinery was not, therefore, to be weighed against the cost of manual labour but against perhaps one-third of the cost of building an extra entrance. By that standard of comparison, hydraulic machinery represented extremely good value.

Initially, the favoured form of hydraulic machine was very recognizably a mechanized version of the manual winches, with a two or three cylinder rotative hydraulic motor providing the power to turn the drum. These appear to have given good service and were still being installed in the 1890s, but they did lack one of the great qualities of most other forms of hydraulic

*The remains of an early type of hydraulic gate engine – basically a manual engine with an hydraulic motor added on. This one was installed second-hand in about 1906.*

machinery, namely a minimum of moving parts, which gave relatively idiot-proof operation and cheapness of maintenance. They were, therefore, gradually supplanted by the single ram gate-engine, which had become more or less universal by the time of the works under the 1898 Act. This device was simply an overgrown version of the well-known 'jigger' (as used for cranes and hoists) laid in a long pit in the passage side. The only application for which it was not suitable was at double entrances, such as the new Sandon Entrance, where there was insufficient space on the island to accommodate its considerable length. The so-called 'overgate' system of operation[62] allowed the jigger-type gate engine to lie parallel with the passage wall and only just below surface, making maintenance easier, because it led the chains through sheaves along the top of the gate, down its face and back to an anchor in the wall. Its main disadvantage was that where

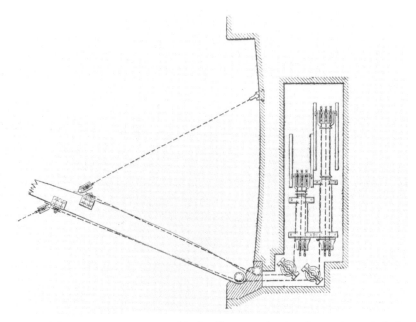

*Diagram of the overgate arrangement of hydraulic motor, showing the opening and closing rams in their pit.*

the low-level jigger pulled directly on the gate at something close to an optimum angle, the 'overgate' arrangement took the chain through three superfluous right angles.

Well before the end of the century, both these devices had been recognized as retaining one of the disadvantages of hand operation, namely the continued use of cross-over chains which had to lie in the bottom of the passage when the gates were open. At the very least, these created a 6 inch 'lump' where they crossed over each other, with the distressing possibility that a ship might foul them. This could be overcome by providing a little extra depth at the point where they lay, but there was no way of preventing the possibility that they might 'bunch' or 'festoon' as they were paid out and sank to the bottom. Furthermore, because a gate was designed to withstand a load which centred at about one-third of the height of the gate, that was the best point at which to attach the chains, which meant that the amount of slack which had to be paid out and then wound back in again was considerable. The obvious answer to this was to apply a direct-acting

*A 'trucked' greenheart gate designed in 1828 in the open position at Clarence Graving Docks. Note in the extreme foreground the crossover of the operating chains.*

reversible ram directly to the gates, but in order to obtain a short enough travel and to keep the angular deflection of the cylinder within reasonable limits as the gate opened or closed, it was necessary to attach the ram fairly close to the heel-post. That meant the exertion of a localized force of many tons on the gate, and the general view was that this was not a good thing to do to a greenheart gate. Iron or steel gates, whose inflexibility was in other respects a disadvantage, would withstand this treatment, as they did at Barry Dock, completed 1889, which seems to have been the first application of direct-acting rams in this country.[63]

The extent of the works which needed to be undertaken as a result of the recognition of the Board's problems by the 1890 Special Committee, combined with the effective transfer of power from G.F. to A.G. Lyster, indicated the need for construction of large numbers of new gates for new or deepened entrances at just the time when it might be thought that steel gates were becoming a valid option. Lyster Jnr was faced with a decision which could have quite long term effects: he needed expanded gate-construction facilities in the dock yard, but were they to be for wood or for metal? A number of piecemeal improvements were made in the Dock Yard from about

*Trying the fit of a top rib in its heelpost in the gateshed. The short ladder in the left middle ground gives an idea of the size of the pieces.*

1890, but the *Engineer's Report* for 1894 mentions that machinery for preparing greenheart timber for gates had been ordered from Henry Robinson of Rochdale (a famous manufacturer of woodworking machinery) and that alterations to the gateshed preparatory to its installation were in hand. Payments for the machinery appear in the *Annual Accounts* of 1894–5–6, totalling over £2,000. It seems to have been an impressive set-up, and must be taken as representing a decision that Liverpool would continue to rely on greenheart gates for quite some years to come.

It is very difficult to determine what it was like to work on the making of gates. We know that until the acquisition of the 200-ton capacity floating crane *Mammoth* (under First World War reparations) it was normal practice to make gates at the dock yard but then to dismantle them again for transport and erection on site. This obviously required – and enforced – workmanship of a very high order. Brodie, speaking of the dismantling and partial re-use of the old Canada gates, remarks on the fact that all the joints were a beautiful fit, and, specifically, that joints had not been cut slack inside to enable a quick fix and a neat appearance on the outside (a practice common among house carpenters and the nastier class of furniture maker). That, of course, was in part because the workmen could not make up a poor joint, secure in the knowledge that once they had put it together no-one would see the inside of it again for 50 years or so.

Prior to the installation of the Robinson machinery, gate construction required an enormous amount of handwork, mainly using very simple traditional tools. Flat surfaces, such as the mating faces of the mitre post, were roughed out with the adze and then finished with a drawknife, followed by a smoothing plane, while curved surfaces like the turn of the heelpost were roughed out with a shipwright's spar axe. Much of the fitting of parts one to another was done by comparison rather than measurement, using calipers and chalklines.[64] The subtlety of forms involved was considerable: heelposts, for example, were commonly made eccentric so that as they opened the clearance between them and the hollow quoins increased: this both diminished wear and helped prevent small bits of flotsam lodging in the gap when the gate was open. The size and weight of virtually every part was enormous (greenheart weighs about 70 lb/cu ft) and, as mentioned above, the need for constant collaboration with the smiths and the masons was crucial. This is probably why gates took so long to make: in the incomplete sequence of *Work and Cost* books, we find, for example, that the middle pair of gates for Langton No. 1 graving dock was under construction for some two years, and that at times the cost mounted remarkably slowly. The eventual cost of the pair was £2,302 1s 9d, but between 12 October 1878 and 4 January 1879, only £28 11s 2d was spent, a sum corresponding to not much more than one skilled man's wages.[65] Are we to take it that one man chipped away on his own for months, cutting vast interminable mortices and tenons, with occasional help from a labourer or two when he needed to try the fit? It certainly seems possible, for the quarterly expenditure then rose rapidly, corresponding perhaps with the payment for the planking, transport and erection on site (which required a large team) and then dwindled again, probably reflecting the last minor adjustment of fits and the assembly of accessories like the walkway on top. There were certainly enough operations in building a gate which could be carried out by one man: there were, for

*A selection of traditional shipwright's tools as used by gatebuilders, still used daily by technicians at Merseyside Maritime Museum.*

example, dozens of bolts holding a gate together. The practice was not to use, as one would now, countersunk coach bolts with a square under the head and tighten the nut from the other side. The Dock Yard practice was to cut a small mortice into which a rectangular 'captive nut' was set and then drive a square-headed bolt into it, the head disappearing into a counterbore: the mortice and the counterbore were then plugged with tight-fitting greenheart plugs set in marine glue. Correctly performed, this operation completely protected the bolt and nut from the corrosive ravages of Mersey water: presumably it did so effectively enough to enable the bolt to be removed at a much later date, or it would not have been possible to take the Canada gates to pieces, as described by Brodie, without seriously damaging the tenons of the pieces we are told were re-used.

The men who built the gates were traditionally shipwrights rather than carpenters, over whom they enjoyed a small pay differential. While there is no doubt that their job was a hard one, made more unpleasant by the fact that greenheart splinters caused an apparently trifling injury which nearly always went septic, it was an elite job which provided a man with a great deal of self-respect. By the standards of the day it was well paid: rates varied a certain amount, but in the early '90s a board shipwright was normally paid 6*s* 6*d* per day, as compared with 6*s* 4*d* for a mason or about 6*s* for a carpenter. His labourer would be lucky to top 3*s*.[66] A wage of 39*s* per week, when a working class luxury like good quality steak (none of your cheap frozen imported rubbish) cost about 8*d* per pound, enabled reasonably comfortable living and exceeds Hobsbawm's threshold for membership of 'the aristocracy of labour'. It exceeded the wages of the lower-paid draughtsmen and bridged the blue-collar–white-collar divide by running well into the salary range of the lower clerks. For those who 'got their blocker', like Moses Boustead, promoted Foreman Shipwright on 24 February 1894, the rate of pay was not less than 50*s* per week. As Brodie was generous enough to admit, as late as 1897, the forces acting on dock gates were still inadequately understood: the conclusion must be that the talents of Moses Boustead and his like still made a significant contribution to the strength, durability and reliability of Liverpool dock gates.

The question remains whether in the field of gate construction the Liverpool engineers made any contribution to more general dock engineering practice comparable with Hartley's walls or Lyster's electric lights. It is a difficult question to answer, for although engineers commonly differed noisily on professional matters, it is usually possible (if only by cheating with the use of hindsight) to see which ones were right. In the case of gates this does not seem to be so: the Liverpool style of gate, with its characteristically flat-arched form (known as a low 'rise') and its ponderous yet elastic greenheart structure served Liverpool docks well, but so too did Hull's apparently eccentric 'truckless' metal gates in the very different circumstances of the Humber, with its smaller tidal range, calmer and less polluted waters and even worse silting problems. Certainly Blandy's paper made a contribution on the theoretical side which long continued to be read and referred to, and it seems that either Jesse or John Hartley was the first fully to realize the potential of greenheart. Beyond that it might be dangerous to go, for not only was it a field notably lacking in black and white answers,[67] but also one which, as we have seen, was rich in conflicting evidence – and some of that originated with a Liverpool engineer, namely Brysson Cunningham, as well.

## Movable Bridges

In the early days of the Dock Estate, the docks were not a coherent system, as they later became: several of the early docks had no direct communication with each other. One result of the use of little separate river entrances, coupled with very free and easy pedestrian and vehicular access to the quays, was that the need for movable bridges was comparatively small – or so it seemed to the engineers. Traffic management virtually always involves the resolution of conflict, and dock bridges were no exception. To those who wished to get to and from the west quays of the old Wet Dock, the need seemed rather larger: the provision, opening and closing of bridges was a long-term bone of contention between the conflicting interests of those who had to provide, operate and maintain them, those who wanted to cross them and those who wanted freedom of movement for vessels.

As in the case of dock gates, the eighteenth century evidence is extremely sparse. A little is known about the timber 'drawbridge' used at the mouth of the Old Dock, largely because it succeeded in being controversial from time to time.[68] It appears to have worked on the principle of the lift bridges used on the Ellesmere Canal, of which a few examples still survive, with a horizontally pivoted deck whose raising was aided by a substantial overhead counterbalance mounted between pivoted top beams. A painting by Robert Salmon, depicting the opening of Princes Dock (1821)[69] gives a fair impression of the general appearance of such a bridge. This apparently cumbersome arrangement is actually quite clever: a simple beam bridge of forty or so feet span was too heavy to lift conveniently without a counterweight. The provision of a ground-level counterweight would require the digging of a large, expensive and inconvenient pit behind the passage retaining wall. Falling deadweight counterbalancing would fail to take account of the fact that as the deck approaches the vertical, its effective weight falls almost to zero, so that the centre of gravity of the counterbalance needs to move closer to the pivot point at the same rate as that of the deck. The overhead beams were the answer, and they served

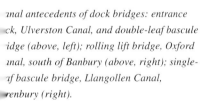

Canal antecedents of dock bridges: entrance lock, Ulverston Canal, and double-leaf bascule bridge (above, left); rolling lift bridge, Oxford Canal, south of Banbury (above, right); single-leaf bascule bridge, Llangollen Canal, Wrenbury (right).

tolerably well. An alternative arrangement at Queens Dock Entrance is shown in Ritchie-Noakes with a double-leaf drawbridge employing massive overhead balance-beams with bar or cable staying.[70] This arrangement had the advantage that the beams had only to balance the weight of half the total span, which they could be made long and heavy enough to do without the complication of a balance box.

Both arrangements shared two main disadvantages: in common with any wooden structure, they were prone to the ravages of rot, and they were remarkably easy to crash into, whether with a ship or a road vehicle. It should be remembered that while the vast majority of road vehicles were small, a gross weight of over two tons was fairly common, while the timber tugs, the juggernauts of their day, might gross ten tons or more, excluding the weight of the horses which would amount to at least another two tons. Such a vehicle colliding with a movable timber structure which held a large counterweight thirty or so feet up in the air could cause severe damage, possibly even collapse. All that weight aloft was inherently dangerous. The original drawbridge at the Old Dock was notorious for its narrowness, and may not have accommodated such vehicles – it was, after all, possible to go round, but the west quay of Georges Dock was an artificial island, so one or both of the bridges spanning its entrances had to be capable of carrying heavy vehicular traffic.

During the latter stages of the construction of Princes Dock, there was a great deal of difficulty in obtaining two cast iron 'swivel bridges' from Messrs Aydon & Elwell of Bradford. Ritchie-Noakes suggests that the design which was sought was that which they had executed for Rennie at the Wapping Entrance, London Dock in 1805.[71] Certainly the Dock Committee Minutes reveal Foster engaged in fairly frequent reference to Rennie on minor questions during the construction of Princes Dock, though the bridges are not specially mentioned until his advice was sought in finding an alternative contractor after Aydon & Elwell had failed to deliver.[72] This supports the Ritchie-Noakes thesis, for if it were Rennie's design, it would be to Rennie that Foster had to turn when the firm which possessed the foundry patterns defaulted: he had no choice. Whose property those patterns were is not clear, but there are cases where Foster had pattern work invoiced separately from production of castings, presumably to prevent difficulties of that kind.

*The double swing bridge at Albert Entrance before restoration. The bolts in the foreground are a repair to a damaged rib casting.*

Hartley adopted this type of bridge as a more or less standard design, and we are fortunate that one of them was retained and restored by the Merseyside Development Corporation at the entrance passage to Albert Dock. It is a fine example of the way that practice and operational experience evolved designs which were simple and effective both in detail and in principle. In detail, it is provided with a cart way in the middle with runner baulks for low rolling resistance at the sides and wood block paving to provide grip for horseshoes in the middle. Sturdy cast iron flanges protect twin footways to either side. The handrails fold down to prevent their fouling the warps or rigging of ships using the passage when the bridge is off. The bridge is moved by twin manually operated engines, one per leaf,

*Another view of Albert Bridge showing how the leaf nests in the passage side.*

*Detail of the above, showing the running gear, the end of the rack and the 'abutment' which takes the thrust when the bridge is behaving as an arch.*

*Surfaces for the job: the restored Hartley bridge at Albert Entrance.*

which have cruciform handles on a horizontal axis driving a vertical shaft by bevel gears. At the bottom of that shaft is a pinion which engages with a curved cast iron rack which moves the leaf on its roller track. The rollers are slightly coned to obtain an almost pure rolling motion at both the inside and outside edges of the track. The ends of the leaves are straight for about half the width and curved for the other half, to prevent them jamming when the bridge is being swung.

Structurally, these bridges are rather odd. From a distance, they look like an arch, but they have no abutment in the conventional sense and, because of the need for a working clearance and allowance for thermal expansion at the centre, they have nothing performing the role of a keystone. In an unladen or lightly-laden condition, they are twin cantilevers, balancing the load on the span against the weight of the balance boxes in the tail ends of the leaves. If the load on the span exceeds that which the balance boxes will support, there

*215*

is sufficient play on the leaf pivots to allow the clearance at the centre to be taken up, so that the bridge then behaves effectively as a three-pin arch, feeding a horizontal load into the base of the pivot. This does not sound at all like what engineers call 'an elegant solution', but it is actually a fine example of the old practice of turning inaccuracy to the engineer's advantage. In the recognition that it was both difficult and expensive to make the pivot precise, the bridge pivots took the form of a short stumpy post with a large hemispherical head. These pivots were said to be almost immune from collision damage, and it is interesting to speculate on whether they were deliberately intended to absorb collision energy by raising the weight of the leaf partially off the pivot. Their shape suggests that as a possible intention.

Speculation aside, the main purpose of that form of pivot was that they allowed the bridge to tilt slightly. In the case of the Hartley bridges constraint on excessive tilting was provided by a bearing surface on the outside of the roller track casting which enabled the whole groundworks of the bridge to act as an abutment when it was behaving as an arch, and the substantial nose castings on each leaf butted together to act as the pin. In those parts of the Dock Estate which were allowed to 'gravitate' to the general coasting trade, where consignments remained relatively small and numerous, these bridges continued to serve well into this century. Although they were slow in operation compared with hydraulically driven ones, the advantage of hydraulics was much smaller than that found in gate operation. A thoroughly awkward hand-operated bridge could take up to fifteen minutes and require perhaps a dozen men, while hydraulic bridges typically took between one and two minutes.[72] The reason Hartley persisted in their construction for so long was that they were a proven design which sufficed until the need arose for substantially longer spans and heavier loads. Then, and not before, was the time to innovate.

One of the marks of a good engineer is that he recognizes when it makes more sense to duck problems than to solve them. The commonest large indivisible loads in mid-century were pieces of machinery, such as railway locomotives, for export and heavy components such as boilers or propellor shafts being delivered to ships using the graving docks. The former could be, and were, largely kept off bridges by the simple expedient of providing heavy lift cranes only on the east quays. (At, for example, Coburg, Sandon and Langton.)[73] Placing a bye-law weight restriction on the bridges was then only minimally inconvenient to the customers. The latter loads form a largely unnoticed criterion in the siting of graving docks. Canning and Queens graving docks were on artificial islands requiring the crossing of a bridge, but the last of these was completed in 1796, when heavy repairs to steamships were not a problem. Clarence, Sandon, Herculaneum, Princes, Brunswick and Langton graving docks (a total of 18 docks) were all accessible without crossing a bridge. Given that the easiest place to build a graving dock is where it can drain straight into the river on the ebb tide (with or without the use of pumps) with the minimum length of culvert, there has to be *some* reason for consistently constructing them in such apparently perverse places for almost a century.

When entrances and passages began substantially to exceed the 50 ft or so which had been more or less standard for the first half of the century, the traditional two-leaf bridge was nearing its limits. In 1896, the Docks & Quays Committee decided that the bridge on the 60 ft South Passage at Nelson should have hydraulic motors added: it was said to be so difficult to operate as to require 10 men. That was no doubt partly because it was nearly

*One of the heavy lift cranes, completed in 1883, provided landward of any bridges. (This machine lifted direct from the hydraulic cylinder suspended from the jib: it was a silly idea and necessitated the early purchase of the 100 ton crane barge* Atlas.*)*

*The 100 ton barge crane* Atlas *carrying one leaf of an old swing bridge in Coburg Dock.*

50 years old, but the engineer did *not* report that mechanizing it was useless and that what it actually needed was a full and careful overhaul to make it work properly again by hand, like it was meant to.[74] At Waterloo, however, the new hydraulic bridges installed during the reconstruction programme completed in 1868 were still double leaf, though with wrought iron main girders. When the bridge was 'on' substantial hydraulically operated bolts slid from one leaf into the other, 'adding to the strength and steadiness under passing loads'.[75]

But 60 ft really was about the limit, and by mid-century the quest was already on for a new type of bridge which could become a design norm for longer spans and heavier loads. This seems to a be a field in which the dock engineers did not make any very decisive contribution to technology, mainly because the railway engineers had faced the problem earlier – and in a different manner. The dock engineers were providing infrastructure for the activities of others, while the railway engineers were providing directly for the traffic of the companies which employed them. In the circumstances, the problem bore much more immediately on the latter group. Furthermore, railway bridges often needed much longer spans than dock bridges and almost invariably involved heavier loadings, forcing the railway engineers to work beyond the limits of previous technology.

A number of forms of movable bridge could be largely discounted for dock use. Bascule bridges, which later became widespread in the Scherzer rolling-pivot form, were held to offer obstruction to the yards and rigging of sailing vessels and the considerable proportion of steamers which carried some auxiliary sail. There was also great concern about the amount of windage of large bascules when raised in windswept places like Liverpool. This not only increased the force needed to raise them by some tons, but did so in a non-uniform manner as the wind swirled and gusted. At the passage to the barge dock at Birkenhead Granaries these objections did not apply, and an ingenious little double-leaf hydraulic bascule was employed, but it was a rare example. The only hydraulic bascule in the Liverpool South Docks was designed and built by Armstrong's in 1878, and failed after only seven years.[76]

Vertical lift bridges were obviously out of the question because of the enormous headroom required, and Mr Kinipple's Patent Sinking Bridge – a lift bridge which opened downwards – seems to have sunk into the obscurity that its neglect of the problems of silting deserved. Centre-pivot swing bridges had the great advantage of wasting no quayspace for 'nesting' when swung off, but few docks had, or would have benefited from, double passages with a central island to carry the bridge. Since vessels in Liverpool docks contrived to collide fairly frequently with anything that stood still long enough, massive protective dolphins would have been needed for the ends of the spans when swung 'off'. A reading, therefore, of the standard engineering works of the day initially convinced the author that such bridges would not find a place in Liverpool Docks. We should know the Hartleys well enough by now to refrain from jumping to such conclusions. The new double entrance at Huskisson (completed 1852) was provided with a long central island which included a centre-pivot swing bridge. The two passages being of unequal width, the passage sides were built up with 'gangways' and the bridge 'rollers' were in fact wheels of over 5 ft diameter. A crab, or

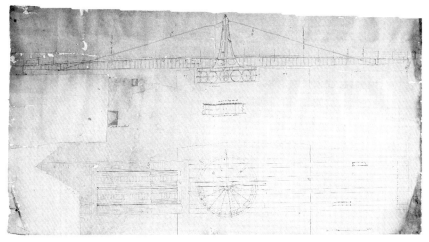

*The sole surviving general arrangement drawing of the centre-pivot swing bridge at Huskisson Entrance, opened in 1852.*

bridge engine for swinging the bridge was provided at the centre, and two others, one at each side, operated an ingenious screw-actuated system of locking wedges to render the bridge immovable when swung on. The crabs were of similar design to those still in service on the bridge at Albert. The span was a massive wrought iron beam structure almost 200 ft long, with a fancy cast iron portal at the centre which served to support a large ornamental lamp – and the bar-staying for the span.

But Huskissson was an exceptional circumstance: in practical terms, the objections to other forms of movable bridge left one clear favourite, the single-leaf swing bridge. These were not free of disadvantages: they required long passages, which represented expensive wasted space, to nest in and their foundation loadings were high, both of which considerations made their substitution as an upgrade of an old double-leaf bridge a difficult and expensive matter. On the whole, however, they became the best option and they remained so for the rest of the century.

Like the double-leaf bridge, single-leaf swing bridges turned out to be structural hybrids, acting as cantilevers when swinging and as simple beams, trussed beams or bowstring arches when on their bearers. Unlike the double-leaf bridges, they were invariably equipped with some means of changing

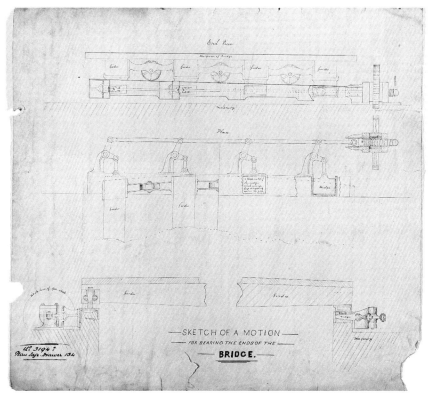

*Detail drawing of the arrangement for taking the weight of the span when the bridge was 'on'.*

them positively from one mode to the other, by lifting or tilting the bridge or by lowering its bearers, in order to swing it. Many and various were the possible ways of achieving this, of which what were known as toggles were the most generally adopted in Liverpool. These consisted of an arrangement of links, operated by hydraulic cylinders, under the ends of the span which took its weight off the roller track and, in conjunction with horizontal sliding bolts, locked the span firmly in place, allowing it to behave for the time being as if it were a fixed bridge.

The main alternative, adopted for example at Morpeth and Canada, was to place the central pivot on the head of an hydraulic ram of sufficient size to lift the bridge bodily off its bearers and then revolve bridge and ram together. This was found to cause fairly rapid wear on the ram, and some

CROSS SECTION THROUGH CENTRE OF BRIDGE

*Cross section of the*
*running gear of the*
*Huskisson Bridge. Note*
*the pronounced 'coning' of*
*the bearing wheels.*

designs tried placing an hemispherical bearing between the socket on the
underside of the main yoke of the bridge and the head of the ram. Short of
making the ram square (which does not seem to have been considered) there
was no way of preventing the operation of Sod's Law, which in this case
stated that however low the friction in the bearing, that in the ram would
remain lower so that the ram continued to turn. A further disadvantage was
that it was possible for a fault in the hydraulic interlocking to cause the
water supply to the lifting ram to remain on. According to Brysson
Cunningham, in the rare instances of this happening the ram was driven right
out of the cylinder, capsizing the bridge.[77] There were several well-known
methods of preventing such an occurrence in other types of hydraulic
appliance, so why they were not employed in this case remains a mystery
which is rendered the more puzzling by the extreme seriousness of the
consequences. It is interesting to note in passing that although the first swing
bridges with full hydraulic operation were put in at Birkenhead, there
survives a copy of a drawing showing an hydraulic pivot for a hand-swung
bridge dating from 1846.[78] There were, of course, no hydraulic pumping
stations on the estate at that date, so the ram must have been raised either by

*A typical single-leaf swing bridge dating from the works under the 1898 Act.*

a hand-pump or by water from the town mains. The drawing is a copy from one of Rendel's and the design pre-dates Hartley's first meeting with Armstrong. This suggests that Hartley was looking into hydraulics earlier than we knew, and may disprove Armstrong's unkind accusation that Hartley was in general over-conservative and in particular only convinced with difficulty of the merits of hydraulics.[79] He had built a 70 ft entrance at Coburg and was probably already thinking of yet larger ones, so investigation of improvements to bridges would certainly have occurred to him as desirable.

The great dilemma with a single-leaf bridge was how to balance it while it was swinging. General opinion was that to get and keep it exactly in balance over the pivot point was impossible, and not necessarily even desirable. The nearer the bridge was to an exact balance, the more fragile its equilibrium as it it swung and the greater the risk of injury or severe damage from one recurrent non-engineering cause, namely men riding on the bridge while it

*223*

swung. In May 1884, the Board published and posted notices forbidding this practice, but workmen in a hurry consistently ignored them. On 4 June 1884, Thomas Parry was fined 2*s* 6*d* and costs for riding on the Langton/ Brocklebank bridge when it was moving, and dozens of others over the years both preceded and followed him into the courts. To an uneducated man heading for his lunchbreak or risking getting his pay docked by returning late, the idea that his weight could harm a structure weighing over a hundred tons would seem laughable, but the very real nature of the risk was demonstrated on 31 March 1897, when a number of Cunard workmen rode the bridge at Canada/Huskisson passage. Standing on the nose end, their weight was sufficient to topple the bridge, and only the fact that it fell on to the passage gates, which were already closed, averted disaster.[80]

In general, the Liverpool engineers' practice was to make the nose end heavy. The Duke Street bridge (Birkenhead) was the first large one in action. It had wheels under the nose end which ran on to a track on the abutment, an unsatisfactory arrangement which was often put out of action by breakage of the wheels or their spindles. The response to this was not to change to a tail-heavy arrangement, but to place an inverted track at the tail end with wheels

*Construction of the new (Scherzer-type) Duke Street Bridge, showing the 1860 hydraulic swing bridge in the foreground.*

running underneath it, which seems to have been much more satisfactory.[81] The fact remains, however, that during the 1880s and '90s, authority was granted to the Engineer to close bridges for repair at the rate of about one every month, and many of these repair jobs took over a week to effect, so that on any given day there was at least an even chance of finding men out somewhere mending a bridge – and a lot of people getting very bad-tempered because they could not use it. Few of the engineer's activities seem to have caused more irritation at every level from labourers who were fined for abusive conduct towards bridgemen to gentlemen who wrote incandescent letters of complaint.[82]

One result of the ill-feeling thus engendered was an attempt to carry out bridgeworks overnight and at the weekends, and most minor jobs such as replacing a wheel or roller or two were performed during brief closures at those times. Despite the generally autocratic management style of the Board and the relatively downtrodden (by modern standards) condition of its workers, this was an expensive business, because enhanced overtime rates were payable, including double time on Sundays. A foreman millwright who spent a Sunday supervising a bridge repair cost as much in the day as a semi-skilled man like a blacksmith's striker earned in a normal week. We should expect, therefore, that Lyster and his team would apply themselves to the problem of developing a thoroughly reliable form of swing bridge.

At the only paper given to the Institution specifically on movable bridges there was no contribution from Liverpool, and conversely, none of the papers given by Liverpool engineers has anything to say about movable bridges. The Engineer's Commonplace Books, a treasury of information on some subjects from the late 1860s onwards, contain no accounts of testing or development in the Dock Yard and very few references to improvements effected elsewhere. It is quite obvious, for example, that making the wheels by machining them from solid mild steel blanks would have prevented them breaking, yet they were not so made. Surprisingly, when we enquire whether this was because the engineers thought an unbreakable wheel would simply cause something more expensive, like the track, to break instead, we cannot find any answer. Part of the reason for this may be that some of the bridges were produced as complete 'design and build' projects by Armstrong's and other builders, but that does not account for the majority, which were not. In so far as one can generalize, the commonest procedure was for the Dock Yard to build the bridge and a specialist contractor to provide and install the hydraulic machinery. It really seems that one of the most operationally important pieces of dock equipment continued to be produced in an unsatisfactory manner with no systematic attempt made to improve it. One of the priority tasks in the 1920s, when the Gladstone system was nearing completion, was the wholesale replacement of hydraulic swing bridges, mainly with Scherzer-type rolling bascules. Of nine swing bridges in Birkenhead, only two survived until the redevelopments of the 1980s, both of them still remembered by local residents as likely to misbehave, causing long delays to road traffic. It has to be admitted that in the specific field of movable bridge design and construction, the Dock Yard did not become a centre for the dissemination of expertise. There were some interesting ideas between about 1845 and 1870, but none of them turned out to be of great merit.

## A Matter of Detail

In 1964, Quentin Hughes produced a delightful picture-book called *Seaport*. It is difficult now to appreciate the impact it had at the time, for it treated obsolescent or obsolete dockland buildings and structures not as so much junk to be cleared away, but as aesthetic assets. Despite the fact that the book was probably instrumental in the complete turn-round in attitudes which has caused old docks to be conserved and converted, and in several cases to become significant tourist attractions, there is one respect in which it has been unhelpful, perhaps even harmful, to our understanding of the work of the dock engineers.

It was only logical that a Professor of Architecture should write about old warehouses in the language of his profession, and scarcely surprising that he would enthuse about the form, proportion and variety of mooring bollards. The problem is that he did it so well that people still tend to see them as public sculpture. The Hartleys and the Lysters may have had occasional flights of architectural fancy, and many of the designs which came out of their offices are dignified by a fine intuitive grasp of line and proportion. This does not alter the fact that these men were engineers, and the things they built were built like they were to discharge mundane everyday jobs.

Bollards were no more designed for admiring and photographing than five-barred gates were put there for romantic poets to lean on. As a result of this gap in understanding, a whole mini-industry of dockland groundscaping has grown up which picks and mixes features and details in a way which is often completely meaningless and can amount to actual falsification. Even in the best examples, it becomes difficult to understand what all the various minor features were for and why the engineers laid them out the way they did. For, let us make no mistake, the aspects of dock construction and equipment mentioned thus far would provide a dock which was beautifully designed and built, stable and reliable – and almost totally impossible to use.

We can pick out a few themes in the detailing of old docks. One is traction. Granite setts made a good durable surface, but they were expensive and they did not provide a particularly low rolling resistance for the wheels of hand trucks. Their specific purpose was to provide grip for the back edges of horseshoes, for that is the point at which the tractive effort of a horse is concentrated. Hand trucks, on the other hand, ran very nicely on smooth truckways of stone or asphalt, but these surfaces made a horse incapable of keeping its footing when pulling hard. Where neither of these requirements

*A bit of original groundscape: the avenue, where horses needed to gain traction is paved with granite setts. The quayside, where they did not, is paved with beach cobbles.*

applied, including a lot of quay margins, and all that was needed was a firm surface to put things on, beach cobbles were the cheapest and were therefore employed. The choice of the correct surface was a matter of some importance, and one which has sometimes been obscured by the modern practice of blanketing conservation areas with setts laid in fancy patterns.

We may also observe that the copings on quaysides were flat, but that the copings round older river entrances rose towards their edge by about two inches, in a smooth curve. This too was a matter of traction: when a vessel was about to enter, it needed to get a rope ashore, and the man ashore had to catch the heaving line and then pull ashore a considerable length of manila rope. In anything less than optimum conditions, the ship would be heaving around a fair amount and the rope would be soaking wet and therefore heavy. Furthermore, this might well be all happening in the dark. The upstand is not a virtuoso mason's self-indulgence: it is a foothold and a locating-point which was a matter of life and death for gatemen.

In sailing ship days, bollards were not invariably provided for mooring vessels. In some docks recessed canal-style mooring rings were provided for smaller vessels, but even Mersey flats used ropes of 4 in circumference, which were not too easy to double through a ring when wet. (The only quick way to pass a long mooring line through a ring is to pass both the free end *and a bight* through the ring and take both back aboard for belaying.) Albert Dock has few bollards, and when Princes Dock was modernized in 1904–5 one of the improvements was the addition of the bollards it had lacked since 1821. The sprouting of large mooring bollards along every quay is a development which belongs to the age of the large steamship. Before then, vessels simply tied themselves to anything that looked reasonably immovable, like the columns of a warehouse or transit shed. The large numbers of old bollards we see seem to be concentrated around half-tide docks and passages, and if we are suprised by this it is only because we have not stopped to think what bollards were actually for, which was the movement rather than the mooring of vessels. They were necessary in half-tide docks because these could get quite turbulent when the river gates were open, and they were necessary for vessels warping themselves through entrances or passages. A particularly copious supply of bollards was needed at graving docks, where ships had to be pulled to an exact position over the graving blocks and held there while the dock was drained.

Another theme which it is helpful to consider is rope. Rope was, as mentioned above, the principal way of manoeuvring sailing vessels in, around and out of dock, which had certain implications for the arrangement of other quayside equipment. It was, for example, desirable to have some form of barrier to reduce the risk of people wandering over the edge of docks in the dark, but from the days of the Old Dock onwards, these had normally to be readily detachable posts and chains to allow their being removed to prevent them fouling ropes. Lamp posts on the quayside were a nice idea for some purposes, but needed to be set back several feet at least. Fixtures like gate engines became a recognized obstruction and forms were adopted for them which facilitated ropes riding over them. Bollards were useful, but too many of them got in the way of the ropes, so a smaller number of bollards was made to suffice by supplementing them with 'mushrooms' – little idler rollers which stood only a few inches high which could be used to modify the direction of pull exerted on a bollard. Bridges and gates needed to have folding or readily detachable handrails.

There was also the question of getting the ends of ropes to the right places. The reason most old docks have either flights of steps cunningly

*In working days, chains and stanchions like these were all readily demountable to prevent their fouling ropes.*

*Canning Dock: notice the beautifully designed and constructed recessed steps in the corner.*

*An inset ladder for boatmen, at Canning Half-Tide.*

*The remains of the track of a small sliding bridge for pedestrians at Albert Entrance.*

recessed into corners or iron ladders set into the walls is to provide access for the boatmen who carried ropes across docks. Similarly, because strong winds may make it difficult or even impossible to heave a line across a 50 ft passage, movable pedestrian bridges were often provided. The so-called 'Rennie Bridge' (it was in fact designed by Hartley) at the Canning-Canning H-T passage is the only survivor, and is a more substantial structure than was strictly necessary: the later practice employed lightweight rolling drawbridges, and part of the track for one of these may still be seen at the Albert Entrance passage: its position right alongside the double-leaf swing bridge makes clear that its purpose was enabling men to get across quickly and conveniently during ship-moving activities – it could be rolled on and off very rapidly.

Very few of these things were written down at the time, because they were simply accumulated common knowledge of the way to make a dock easy to operate: not many cookery books tell you how to cook chips. This does not alter the fact that there is some skill in cooking a good chip, and we should not forget the detailing skills the dock engineers had to amass and practise in order to keep their customers, and the men from the Harbourmaster's Department, alive and happy. In order to appreciate them, we have to piece together bits of documentary information with the material evidence on the ground. The trouble is that the latter has probably been prettified. The key to the whole business is simple: it is to remember that what dock engineers did, they usually did for a simple commonsensical operational reason. When we recognize the need to find that reason, we are already most of the way to finding the answer.

# Postscript

# Changing Times:
# the Dock Yard in Distress

The organization of the Mersey Docks & Harbour Board had grown up in a fairly haphazard manner with the result that a lot of unnecessary work was done and far too many people were paid to do it. The Special Committee of 1890 which investigated the work of the Board hacked out some of the waste, but a good deal of it sprouted again. The Lynch case illustrated the gross inefficiency which still existed in the Engineer's Department, and the reader will recall that Mr Hughes was the member who spoke scathingly of A.G. Lyster and his administrative system. A.G. Lyster appears to have been more successful in his engineering than his father was, particularly in his 'strategic vision' of long-term needs. This did not prevent Hughes from giving him a hard time on several occasions, and in 1911 Hughes proposed the appointment of another Special Committee which was to seek improved economy and efficiency in every part of the business of the Board. Because the Engineer's Department was the biggest spender, it was bound to come under very close scrutiny. It was criticized for keeping up too many plant depots and for keeping stocks of materials which turned over too slowly. Severe personnel problems were identified within the dredging department, and men from the Engineer's Department were found in all sorts of crannies of the estate performing jobs which were promptly re-allocated to other departments. The question was raised whether it was necessary to retain the Birkenhead Dock Yard, and the Coburg Dock Yard was criticized as ill-planned, old-fashioned and inefficient.

That it should be so is hardly surprising, for although it had been enlarged and improved a great deal since Hartley built it, it had never really been re-planned as an entity. Metal-working and woodworking trades were reasonably logically gathered in groups, but there were serious defects. The two shops, boilermakers and gateshed, which used the most cumbersome materials to produce the largest workpieces were tucked in awkward corners.

Among the shops which enjoyed the best access – on the main avenue – were those of the blacksmiths and fitters who mainly worked on comparatively small items. It would have been hard to place the foundry further from the pattern store.

There were many recommendations which must have been irksome. The 'electric motor car' provided for the use of the Engineer-in-Chief was to be sold, as were the horse and trap used by the Principal Assistant (Birkenhead). This latter realized the sum of £12, which suggests that the reason for its sale may have been more ideological than strictly financial. That was probably a very minor annoyance compared with the decision that a member of the General Manager's Department should conduct an annual inspection of stores to ascertain that stocking levels were not too high. This was a major breach of the professional ramparts of the engineers. The architectural draughtsman, when he retired, was not to be replaced. During the deliberations of the Committee, Lyster announced his resignation. Reading between the lines of the minutes, the Committee was far from unhappy about this, not only because it would put an end to recent conflict but because it offered the opportunity to alter the management of the department before the new man had his feet properly under the desk. It may be significant that Lyster's successor was not an internal promotion as was the norm in other departments at the time. Thomas Newell had worked in the Dock Yard as a pupil of Lyster Snr, but had been working for the Hull Docks Company since 1889: a clean break might be easier than if, say, William Brodie had been promoted. That a clean break was at least contemplated is indicated by the most radical proposal of all, albeit unimplemented, that there should be a Chief Engineer (Civil) and a Superintendent (Mechanical and floating plant) standing side by side in a diagram which had the General Manager at the top. That the President-elect of the Institution should no longer be a principal officer of the Board was reason enough, one suspects, for him to be on his way.

In 1925, a special sub-committee set up by the Works Committee investigated the serious overspending which occurred on the modernization programme at Alfred Entrance. Members suspected that the project had got completely out of control, and they seem to have been right. They also discovered that the Engineer had doctored estimates of the further amount required to complete the work, presumably with the intention of 'hiding' the extra expenditure somewhere else. The key revelation, however, was the provenance of the original, hopelessly low, estimate. For a complex operation involving demolition of a lot of Hartley granite and the sinking of new foundations in extremely treacherous ground, the estimates were prepared, not by an engineer, but by an assistant draughtsman who had never visited the site. It is scarcely surprising that they were inaccurate. One might suggest that an historian, who would at least have known about the quicksands, could have done better. The reporting lines within the department had failed completely.

It is always tempting to think that organizations or institutions can adapt to constant change over long periods of time by a process analogous to natural evolution. Some can, but others develop a corporate culture which itself evolves, and in so doing, conditions the evolution of the whole organization. Under Jesse and John Hartley and in the earlier years of G.F. Lyster, the Engineer's Department had a corporate culture which believed in itself as the best of its kind and mostly lived up to that boast. By about 1880, strategic errors both by Lyster and the Works Committee were clearly nibbling away at that self-belief, while at the same time, other departments were attempting to undermine the primacy of the Engineer. The process is a familiar one to museum curators and archivists, who often encounter the results of a collapse of corporate morale when acquiring material from liquidators. Like dry rot, it creeps through the structure to the point where nobody believes that a job will go right, because someone else is bound to foul it up. That means there is no point trying, and that is how disasters like the Alfred Entrance estimates occur. It was also the underlying cause of the Lynch disaster, where the check office staff were, according to Lynch, stupid, idle and frequently drunk.

Before about 1880, having worked on the Liverpool Docks was a jewel in the CV, which meant that very talented young men made for the Dock Yard. That impetus was lost, and the Board became more known as a reliable employer offering reasonable pay, conditions and security. As the rot spread down the managerial and clerical ranks, it eventually crippled the tradesmen too. The culture became one where over-manning, pilferage and doing 'foreigners' were, if not the norm, at least far from uncommon. The systematic misrecording of work, whether to conceal other misdeeds or to try to make an inoperable system work, was widespread. Criticisms of the system as being over-complex were also made in 1867 and 1887, and on both occasions the response to the perceived inadequacies was the addition of more book-keeping and further levels of bureaucracy. To liken the growth to that of a cancer is undoubtedly a cliché, but no more appropriate metaphor springs to mind.

Some (few) members of the board, inevitably including Harold Littledale, thought they saw this happening at least as early as 1883, when there was pressure for the new two-storey transit sheds to be put out to tender because they thought the estimates were too high. The attempts at reform in 1890 and 1912 definitely did some good, and it might be thought that a combination of those reforms with more work being sent out to tender might bring the Dock Yard back to life when it had to compete with the real world outside. Unfortunately, the recent history of the specification and supervision of contracts with, for example, Armstrong's suggests contract work would provide no instant cure either: contractors were able to get away with inadequate, overdue and over-priced work as well.

Of course the Dock Yard would remain an important place for decades: the sickness identified above was in its very early stages, and around 1905 the department really seemed to be on the way back to health, with some highly successful major projects. The deepening and modernization of the South Docks under the 1898 Act, while slow and expensive, was exceptionally effective. But, as appears from the findings of the 1912 Committee, it was only an upwards blip on a generally declining graph. Despite many expressions of pious intent, the Coburg Dock Yard never received the thorough-going modernization it had needed from about 1880 onwards, and died a lingering death. By the time that all of it except the new (1960) gateshed and sawmill closed in 1976, it would have been worthy of consideration for preservation as an industrial museum, were it not for the fact that a good deal of piecemeal demolition had gone on. The boiler shop, for example, still had a hand-operated gantry crane built of timber with composite cast and wrought iron trussing. Strewn about almost everywhere was the detritus of days gone by, like a large stack of brand new hydraulic mains which would never see water, a foundry pattern for the impeller of a long-gone impounding pump. It looked as though the place had died of shame. The little building which once housed Mr Hartley's coach was still there, but Hartley's successors were long gone: the management and the drawing office had moved into the new offices at Pierhead in 1907, effectively destroying the integration of the Dock Yard.

That brings us back to where we began. The period in which Liverpool was the centre of the specialism of dock engineering was also the period when the Dock Yard was the centre of the action in Liverpool and the Engineer was the key figure among the officers. Although many other factors were involved, the decline of those two positions can be roughly correlated with the decline in Liverpool's competitive position within the port services industry. The dramatic revival of the port over the last few years has been very differently driven, partly through changing times, but partly also because the old system had so conspicuously failed to evolve from its days of greatness. It took a 'near-death experience' to bring it back to life.

# Notes

## Sources and Abbreviations Used in the Notes

Almost all the unpublished material cited in the notes is in the Mersey Docks & Harbour Board Archive in the Maritime Archives and Library, Merseyside Maritime Museum, Liverpool L3 4AQ (MAL). Locations are given for documents elsewhere, for example at the Archives of the Institution of Civil Engineers (ICE). The absence of a location means that the document is in MAL.

A few words of explanation are needed for some of the more frequently cited MD&HB documents. From 1836, the Dock Surveyor, later Chief Engineer, later still Engineer-in-Chief, produced a published annual report each July (in theory: it was a frequent cause of complaint that these reports and the *Annual Accounts* came out months late). To reduce confusion a little, these documents have always been cited as *Eng Rep* and *Ann Acc* respectively, regardless of the exact title for the year in question. Nor, in contexts like this where the difference is of no account, has any distinction been made between the Dock Trustees and the MD&HB. As any student of the MD&HB knows, that is far too simple to be the whole story: there are also short sequences of *Surveyor's Reports* and *Reports of the Engineer*. These are actually internal unpublished reports, often of great interest, by Hartley and Lyster respectively, and they have been cited by the exact title. Similarly, there are *Engineer's Commonplace Books*, which contain a wide variety of notes, jottings, calculations and drafts of reports in a variety of hands. There is also Lyster's personal equivalent, rather grandly bound and fitted with a lock, which is cited as *Lyster's Commonplace Book*. To make matters worse, some of this material arrived quite recently, in the latest tranche of MD&HB material, and has so far only got as far as provisional listing.

*Worked-up Papers (WUP)* are subject-based files compiled for the Board or its standing committees. They mainly contain transcripts of minutes relating to their chosen subject, but may also include press cuttings, reports, published pamphlets and the like. They are bound in foolscap folio volumes. Exactly the same except for the binding are *Unbound Worked-up Papers (UWUP)*. The reason for their being unbound may be brevity or an opinion (within MD&HB) that they were of secondary importance. Both classes are extremely useful and accessible.

The various sequences of minute books have been comparatively little used, because they are brief, formalized and frequently refer, without transcribing them, to reports which have not survived. Where possible, *WUP*s and the *Newscuttings* volumes have been cited instead as being both more accessible and more informative. These objections apply less in the early years, when the minutes were fuller and there are fewer surviving alternatives. The *Minutes of the Dock Committee* are cited as *DCM* even when the material in question is transcribed from another source, because if it is in that book, it is part of the proceedings of that committee. The sequence of minutes known as *Discussions at the Board* is fragmentary but at times extremely useful: it is made up of verbatim accounts of speeches made at board which were normally chosen for this treatment on grounds of either importance or contentiousness.

## Printed Sources

By far the most valuable printed source is the *Minutes of the Proceedings of the Institution of Civil Engineers (Min Proc ICE)*. Everybody who was anybody in dock engineering after 1818 was a member of this, the world's senior engineering institution. (Referred to in the text as either the 'Institution' or the 'Civils' as seems appropriate in the context.) Other engineering institutions or societies are named in full. The scope of its papers is wide in disciplinary terms and global in its geography. The only other journal which even approaches *Min Proc ICE* for either quantity or quality of material on dock engineering is the *Transactions of the Liverpool Engineering Society (TLES)*. *The Engineer* and *Engineering* have been comparatively little used and their titles are cited in full. The bibliography contains a few textbooks used by (or at least intended to be used by) dock engineers: the works of Brysson Cunningham have been principally used in the preparation of the text because of his intimate knowledge of dock engineering in Liverpool.

There is comparatively little recent material which has proved helpful. The most recent works are N. Ritchie-Noakes, *Liverpool's Historic Waterfront*, London, 1984, and A. Jarvis, *Liverpool Central Docks 1799–1905*, Stroud, 1991. Both S. Mountfield, *Western Gateway*, Liverpool, 1964, and F.E. Hyde, *Liverpool and the Mersey*, Newton Abbot, 1972, are getting slightly dated but have yet to be superseded. The Historic Society of Lancashire and Cheshire mainly occupies its *Transactions* (*THSLC*) with what one might term traditional-style history, but occasionally includes papers on port-related subjects.

## Introduction

1. The different editions are considered in A. Jarvis, 'An Attempt at a Bibliography of Samuel Smiles' *Industrial Archaeology Review* XIII No. 2 (Spring 1991), pp. 162–71. This paper also indicates the extraordinary breadth and extent of Smiles' writings.

2. See, for example, J. Rickman (ed.) *Life of Thomas Telford by Himself*, London, 1838; M. Arago, *Historical Eloge of James Watt*, London, 1839; J. Muirhead, *Origin of the Mechanical Inventions of James Watt*, London, 1854.

3. The original, and possibly still the best, historical appraisal of George Hudson and his activities is in R.S. Lambert, *The Railway King*, London, 1934.

4. N. McKendrick, 'Literary Luddism and the Businessman' in P.N. Davies, *Sir Alfred Jones*, London, 1978; Simon Dentith, 'The Fraud in Literature', in A. Jarvis and P. Rees (eds) *Nineteenth Century Business Ethics*, Liverpool, 1992.

5. S. Smiles, *Self-Help*, was not published until 1859, but had several forebears. His pamphlet *The Education of the Working Classes*, Leeds, 1845, is the best-known example.

6. H. Spencer, 'Railway Morals and Railway Policy', *The Edinburgh Review* 100 (1854), pp. 420–61; C. Dickens, *Little Dorrit*, London, 1857; T. Carlyle, 'Hudson's Statue' in *Latter-day Pamphlets*, London, 1850. See also Dentith, op. cit.

7. This issue is considered in A. Jarvis, 'The Censoring of Samuel Smiles', *Journal of the Railway and Canal Historical Society* 31 Pt 4 (November 1993), pp. 176–85.

8. S. Smiles, *Lives of the Engineers*, London, 1862 (3 vols), vol. 1, pp. 22–5. Guthlac is excised from the 1874 edition. Some might say that the real importance of land reclamation was that it made money for landowners, but Smiles, a veteran of the Anti-Corn Law League, would scarcely mention that. The specific choice of Guthlac was also significant: he was regarded as being perhaps the 'most English' of the Anglo-Saxon saints.

9. Charles Hadfield, *Thomas Telford's Temptation*, Cleobury Mortimer, 1993, suggests that the paucity of work on Jessop results from foul play by Telford and by Rickman, his first biographer. James Walker (1781–1862) was one of the most prolific engeeers of his

generation, working on docks, harbours, canals, sewerage schemes, lighthouses, bridges and even a couple of railways. He was President of 'The Civils' for no less than eleven years and the index entries for his contributions to their *Minutes of Proceedings* occupy two pages. The discrepancy between his fame during his lifetime and his historical obscurity now is astonishing. His 'Memoir' (i.e. obituary) is in *Min. Proc ICE* XXII (1862–3), pp. 630–3.

10. Robert Stephenson and I.K. Brunel died in 1859, Joseph Locke – and Jesse Hartley – in 1860. This was perhaps the most concentrated battering a profession took until the world of music lost Holst, Delius and Elgar in 1934.

11. J.M. Dobson, 'Buenos Aires Harbour Works', *Min Proc ICE* CXXXVIII (1898–9), pp. 170–243, at p. 176.

12. The historiography of these issues is enormous, but is summarized in the papers in A. Jarvis and P. Rees (eds), *An Empire in Decline?*, Liverpool, 1994, which also presents evidence for the shipping industries being an exception.

## 1 Dock Engineers: the Professional Origins

1. N. Ritchie-Noakes, *Liverpool's Historic Waterfront,* London, 1984, p. 19. By the time of the 1714 Act, £11,000 had been spent as against an estimate of £8,000.

2. A. Jarvis, *Liverpool Central Docks, 1799–1905*, Stroud, 1991, pp. 85 *et seq.* See also I. Weir, 'Port of Liverpool Quay Walls', unpublished MSc dissertation, University of Liverpool, 1993, p. 28. A published version is forthcoming.

3. Weir, loc cit.

4. This and the following paragraph are largely derived from M. Clarke, 'Thomas Steers', in A. Jarvis and P. Rees (eds) *Dock Engineers and Dock Engineering*, Liverpool, 1993.

5. Adam Blandy and William Brodie published papers on the subject: for the men, see chapter 5, for the gates, chapter 7, below.

6. D. Swann, 'The Engineers of English Port Improvements 1660–1830' 2 parts, part 1, *Transport History* 1 (1968), pp. 153–68. For a naval comparison see R.C. Riley, 'The Evolution of the Docks and Industrial Buildings in Portsmouth Royal Dockyard 1698–1914', *The Portsmouth Papers* 44 (1985).

7. H. Peet, 'Thomas Steers', *THSLC* 82 (1930), pp. 163–206.

8. See N. Ritchie-Noakes and M. Clarke, 'The Dock Engineer and the Development of the Port of Liverpool' in V. Burton (ed.), *Liverpool Shipping, Trade and Industry*, Liverpool, 1989, and Clarke, 'Thomas Steers'.

9. H. Malet, *Bridgewater, the Canal Duke*, Manchester, 1977, first drew attention to the contribution of the Duke himself, and P. Lead, *Agents of Revolution*, Keele, 1989, has put the case for a substantial input by the Gilberts.

10. Clarke, 'Thomas Steers', p. 8.

11. Ritchie-Noakes, *Waterfront,* p. 19.

12. G. Jackson, *History and Archaeology of Ports*, Tadworth, 1983, p. 90.

13. A. Jarvis, 'Liverpool Dock Engineers, Railways and Engineering Ethics', in Jarvis and Rees, *Nineteenth Century Business Ethics*, pp. 25–40.

14. In the 'Old Dock' file, Merseyside Dockland Survey records, MAL.

15. Weir, 'Port of Liverpool', p. 30.

16. The supply of stone for Princes Dock was the source of much controversy: see A. Jarvis, *Princes Dock*, Liverpool, 1991.

17. L.L. Mayfield, 'Limestone Additions to Portland Cement: An Old Controversy Revisited', *Cement, Concrete & Aggregates* 10 No. 1 (Summer 1988), pp. 3–8, at p. 4. It should be remarked in passing that what I have here rendered as 'Pozzualana' was spelled many different ways in nineteenth-century engineering documents: if the word looks vaguely like that, it is the same stuff they are talking about.

18. M. Taylor (ed.), *Reports of the Late John Smeaton*, London, 1837, 2 vols, vol. 2, pp. 421–3.

19. Ritchie-Noakes, *Waterfront*, p. 21; R.A. Stephenson, 'The Development of the Liverpool Docks System', *Transactions of the Liverpool Nautical Research Society*, vols 7–9, pp. 61–76. (These volumes were bound as one.)

20. Contribution of Robert Rawlinson to the discussion of J. Grant, 'Experiments on the Strength of Cement', *Min Proc ICE* XXV (1865–6), pp. 66–159, at pp. 115–16. It should be mentioned that around 1830, Hartley was importing some hundreds of tons of 'Pozzualana' per year at considerable expense: presumably he later discovered it unnecessary, as the 'recipe' given by Rawlinson does not employ it.

21. E.g. S.H. Ellis, 'Notes on some Hydraulic Limes', *TLES* XXVI (1904), pp. 37–66.

22. Clarke, 'Thomas Steers', p. 6.

23. The last-mentioned was the fatal inundation at Victoria Dock, Birkenhead, in 1909: for details see Weir, 'Port of Liverpool', p. 47.

24. The first proposal to start the 'Dock yard Work Men's Relief Fund' appeared in 1829 and it specifically mentioned the 'relief of various workmen and their families in cases of misfortune: or indisposition brought on by Colds [Hartley's capital] obtained in the Works' *Surveyor's Report*, 15 January 1829. For further details of the Fund, see Chapter 6.

25. K. Macleod, 'The Old Dock', unpublished paper, in MDS files, p. 18.

26. Ritchie-Noakes, *Waterfront*, p. 21.

27. The first effective dredger in Liverpool seems to have been built as late as 1823, by which time silting problems at Kings, Queens and Princes entrances were acute. The specific problem of the Old Dock appears in *DCM* 29 April 1806.

28. Though the primary cause was held to be the failure of a drain behind the wall: Weir, op. cit., p. 40. The wall fell through a loss of equilibrium from both sides.

29. Almost any of the older histories will suffice: probably the best for this purpose is T. Baines, *History of the Commerce and Town of Liverpool*, London, 1852.

30. Ritchie-Noakes, *Waterfront*, gives details of the sizes, and changes, in all the southern docks.

31. Ian Weir is working on a paper on Morris, but finding him an elusive subject.

32. We had to wait for F.C. Mather, *After the Canal Duke*, London, 1970, to learn about them.

33. J. Longmore, 'The Development of the Liverpool Corporation Estate', unpublished PhD thesis, University of Reading, 1982, gives the definitive account.

34. The Gregson Papers, in Liverpool Record Office, contain a number of documents which were clearly collected and retained by Mathew Gregson, brother-in-law of John Foster, with a view to discrediting or even incriminating him.

35. The report is transcribed in *DCM* for 1 May 1800.

36. Ibid., 14 August 1809.

37. Ritchie-Noakes, *Waterfront*, p. 97.

38. The *Mercury*'s suggestion is cited in Ritchie-Noakes and Clarke, 'Dock Engineer', p. 93. The ineffective safeguards are spelled out in the *Audit Commissioners Minutes*, ref. 19/4. Their preliminary report on the alleged improprieties at Princes is dated 28 December 1822.

39. Transcribed as Appendices ix and x in G. Jackson, *Grimsby and the New Haven Company*, Grimsby, 1971.

40. Or so it would appear, from the multitude of payments entered in *DCM* and the fact that the Audit Commissioners never succeeded in producing an exact final account for the works at Princes.

41. As he did in the case of James Pinkerton's errors on the Barnsley Canal: see W.N. Slatcher, 'The Barnsley Canal: Its First Twenty Years', *Transport History* 1 (1968), pp. 48–66.

42. *Ann Acc* for the years mentioned.

43. See the descriptions in Baines, *Liverpool*, of the docks in question. Any such figures should be treated with some caution, but serve to give a general indication of cost. The true cost of Princes, when we add in the late payments, was probably about £650,000.

44. *Ann Acc.*

45. Ritchie-Noakes and Clarke, 'Dock Engineer', pp. 93–4.

46. N. Ritchie-Noakes, *Jesse Hartley*, Liverpool, 1980, p. 7, gives her cost at £2,186 6s 8d, as against an estimate of £1,800. According to her entry in the *Liverpool Shipping Registers*, vol. 52 No. 244, 7 September 1836 she was ketch-rigged, 105.54 tons. For a short history of the quarries see J.R. Cutland, *The Story of Ferrytown of Cree and Kirkmabreck Parish*, Kirkmabreck, UD (1985).

47. His evidence before the Admiralty Enquiry into Proposed New Docks, *MD&HB Legal*, A1/1 is a good example, as is that before the *Royal Commission to Enquire into Harbours of Refuge*, BPP 1847 (411) LXI.1.

48. J.B. Hartley, 'On the Effects of the Worm on Kyanised Timber', *Min Proc ICE* I (1840), pp. 84–5; 'Formation of Embankments and Filling in Behind Retaining-walls', *Min Proc ICE* I (1841), p. 143; 'Piles and Pile-driving', *Min Proc ICE* III (1844), p. 200.

49. *Ann Acc.*

50. In a letter dated 22 May 1882; ICE Archives, *Tracts*, vol. 451.

51. The narrative which follows is mainly based on House of Lords Sessional Papers, Reports, Committees XXI (1850), pp. 131–49. There is also a good account in *The Times*, 8 March 1850, p. 6. The Sheriff's Court Proceedings (which only took about 10 minutes) are in *The Times* for 2 April 1849. Special thanks to Carol Arrowsmith (ICE Archives) for her trouble in tracking down several James Thom(p)sons for me.

52. The MS version is in *Surveyors' Reports* Vol. 3, the published version forms the first of the *Eng Rep* sequence.

53. Some account of the activities of the years 1844–8 is given in Jarvis, *Central Docks*, chapter 4 for works north of Pierhead and in Ritchie-Noakes, *Waterfront*, for those to the south.

## 2  Planning and Decision Making

1. The management of the estate is covered in great detail in J. Longmore, 'The Development of the Liverpool Corporation Estate 1760–1835', unpublished PhD thesis, Reading University, 1981.

2. D. Fraser, *Power and Authority in the Victorian City*, Oxford, 1979. Chapter 1 gives a good account in a small compass.

3. For example, Foster was authorized to 'apply to Mr Rennie for a model of an improved caisson for the purpose of building the foundations of the sea wall on the west side of

Georges Dock', *DCM*, 2 July 1811. For the problems at Grimsby, see G. Jackson, *Grimsby and the New Haven Company*, Grimsby, 1971, chapter 2.

4.  The original documents are in the ICE Archives at T/LM 13, and the key points are summarized in R.H.G. Thomas, *The Liverpool and Manchester Railway*, Newton Abbot, 1980, pp. 50–3.

5.  So pleased was Liverpool Corporation with its showing that it pre-empted the official publication of the Enquiry (BPP 1835 (116) XXVI.1) by publishing its own volume of minutes of evidence in 1833 as *A Report of the Proceedings of a Court of Enquiry into the Existing State of the Corporation of Liverpool*. It did not, of course, save them from being reformed, as the commission was a clear case of 'sentence first, evidence later'.

6.  T. Webster, *The Port and Docks of Birkenhead 1844–52*, London, 1873, is one of a string of volumes published by the leading Counsel for Birkenhead's various parliamentary sorties. For the land issue, see pp. xxiv, xxx–xxii.

7.  Recited in reasonable detail at the beginning of the proceedings of the Select Committee on Local Charges on Shipping, BPP 1856 (332) XII.1. The papers of the case itself (which was extremely long and complex) are in MD&HB Legal H18–H24.

8.  P. Sulley, *Ancient and Modern Birkenhead*, Liverpool, 1907, has some purple passages on these themes. Webster took a more sympathetic view: *Birkenhead*, pp. xlv–xlvi

9.  By this date, the Old Dock had become obsolete and been filled in, so there was no excuse for thinking that docks lasted for ever. Every pre-Princes (1821) dock had been heavily modernized.

10. Webster recounts the 1855 Act with ill-concealed glee: *Birkenhead*, pp. xlvii–xlviii. The costs are easily found from 'skimming' *Ann Acc*.

11. See Note 7.

12. The Mersey Docks & Harbour Board Act, 20 & 21 Vict. c.162, 1857.

13. Most unusually, the two Hartleys 'share' a *Memoir* in *Min Proc ICE* XXIII (1871–2), pp. 216–22.

14. Ibid., p. 217.

15. BPP 1846 (530) XIII.425, beginning at Question 3042. For some commentary on his evidence see Jarvis, *Liverpool Central Docks, 1799–1905*, Stroud, 1991, pp. 79–85.

16. For Rendel, see M. Lane, *The Rendel Connection*, London, 1989, and for Meikle S. Smiles, *Lives of the Engineers*, London, 1862, 3 vols, vol. 2, pp. 106–16.

17. Implicitly admitted by his obituarist: *Min Proc ICE* CXXXIX (1899–1900), p. 57.

18. This theme is explored in A. Jarvis, 'Liverpool Dock Engineers, Railways and and Engineering Ethics', in A Jarvis and P. Rees (eds), *Nineteenth Century Business Ethics*, Liverpool, 1992, which also provides further references.

19. See A. Jarvis, 'Harold Littledale: The Man with a Mission', in H.M. Hignett (ed.), *A Second Merseyside Maritime History*, Liverpool, 1991.

20. This and similar problems in the decision-making process are considered in greater detail in A. Jarvis, 'The Members of the Mersey Docks & Harbour Board and their Way of Doing Business, 1858–1905', *International Journal of Maritime History* VI, No. 1 (June 1994), pp. 122–39.

21. Just two volumes of the volumes *Damages to Dock Works* survive. Vol. 1 folio 2 shows seven entries in late 1877 involving a total of £3 4*s* 6*d*. Each was referred to the gentlemen of either the Docks & Quays or the Marine Committee.

22. Details of these and similar absurdities may be found in Jarvis, 'Members'.

23. He was, for example, a proprietor at the Wellington Rooms, then Liverpool's most exclusive club. At the Board meeting of 3 November 1881, Alfred Holt referred to his Overhead Railway proposal as having 'received the support of another gentleman whose position was only second in influence to that of Mr Brocklebank's [the Chairman] – he meant Mr. Lyster the Dock Engineer', *Liverpool Daily Post*, 4 November 1881.

   For the ticket incident, see Jarvis, *Central Docks*, pp. 140–1, for the joinery, UWUP 116[a].

25. G. Woodward, 'Staite and Petrie: Pioneers of Electric Lighting', *Proceedings of the Institution of Electrical Engineers*, 136 Pt A (1989), pp. 290–6.

26. See Jarvis, *Central Docks*, pp. 153–67.

27. The drawings survive: MD&HB/Princes/3/10.

28. At Salisbury, for example, he had to sacrifice the ornamental upperworks of the clock tower, but the dock was otherwise built as planned.

29. G. Jackson, 'Do Docks Make Trade?' in L.R. Fischer (ed.), *From Wheel House to Counting House: Essays in Maritime Business History in Honour of Professor Peter Neville Davies*, St John's, 1992, argues the importance of the commercial infrastructure.

30. The fruits were published locally, later the same year, under the title *Proposed Dock Extension 1872*.

31. A. Jarvis, 'G.F. Lyster and the Role of the Dock Engineer', *The Mariner's Mirror*, 78 No. 2 (May 1992), pp. 179–99.

32. One issue which embraced all of these was the supply of hydraulic equipment, see Jarvis, 'Harold Littledale', p. 7.

33. Prior to 1848, only Brunswick had an entrance of over 50 ft, and most were less. Then came Salisbury, 1848, 60 ft; Sandon, 1851, 70 ft; Huskisson, 1852, 80 ft; Canada, 1859, 100 ft.

34. In *Report of the Engineer to the Special Committee on Dock Extension, 27 September 1872*.

35. *Ann Acc*, 1873.

36. Again the hydraulic equipment forms a good example (see n. 32).

37. For the suggestion that Webb continued to hold his job after significant deterioration of his faculties, see W.H. Chaloner, 'Francis William Webb (1836–1906) of the London & North Western Railway', *Transport History* 1 (1968), pp. 169–78.

38. The Great Low Water Basin attracted a great deal of interest – and controversy – nationwide. When its failure was recognized as total and permanent, Lyster published a little pamphlet (*The History of the Birkenhead Great Low Water Basin*, Liverpool, 1864) seeking to exonerate himself. His professional peers were deeply divided on the subject.

39. The Board published tide graphs to help estimate depths on sills: the one the author uses is in his 1920 Member's Pocketbook.

40. J.C. Hawkshaw, 'The Construction of the Albert Dock at Kingston-upon-Hull', *Min Proc ICE* XLI (1874–5), pp. 92–113.

41. See Chapter 7.


## 3  How Good an Investment was Dockbuilding?

1. G. Jackson, *History and Archaeology of Ports*, Tadworth, 1983, Preface.

2. F.E. Hyde, *Liverpool and the Mersey*, Newton Abbot, 1972, pp. 115–20.

3. From the retrospective tables in the back of *Ann Acc*.

4. At the beginning of this century Cunard alone was paying roughly twice as much in dues

as the entire coasting trade. *Discussions at the Board* 16 November 1905, gives the figure for coasting, that for Cunard is from an internal return of 12 May 1900, to be found in *WUP* 177.

5. Just the part of George's Dock which the Corporation bought for road improvements yielded over £300,000, virtually the price of the palatial new Dock Offices built on a bit more of the site. But the only other lucrative sale of that kind was at Clarence in 1928.

6. On 2 December 1816, for example, it was reported to the Dock Committee that the subscription stood above £21,000, five years' interest on which would suffice to employ 500–600 men through the present winter.

7. This subject has a huge bibliography: for a brief account and further references see A. Jarvis, 'The Golden Age of Municipal Engineering: A Liverpool Overview', *Municipal Engineer*, 109 (1995), pp. 264–70.

8. The most obvious examples are the gateman's and landing waiters' 'huts' – beautiful little granite houses – built at entrances like Salisbury and Canning which were effectively for coasters only by about 1900, and closed around forty years ago.

9. For the effects of the Blitz in Liverpool, see J. Hughes, *Port in a Storm*, Liverpool 1993. J.A. Tallis, R.D. Taylor and T.J. Dishman, 'Restoration of Albert Dock', *The Structural Engineer*, Vol. 64A No. 10 (November 1986), pp. 291–8, gives an account of what was wrong and what still sound at Albert when restoration began.

10. I. Weir, 'Port of Liverpool Quay Walls', unpublished MSc dissertation, p. 42.

11. In *Min Proc ICE* XXV (1865–6), at pp. 114–16.

12. W.S. Boult, 'Walls in Portland Cement Concrete, Low Water Basin Conversion, Birkenhead', *TLES* I, pp. 1–10.

13. William Doherty, who had a couple of tilts at Lyster, alleged in a discussion at the Institution that one of the Birkenhead graving docks had been so plagued with 'springs' that its use as a graving dock had to be abandoned. In fact, Lyster had had serious trouble with it but had solved the problem by 1867. *Min Proc ICE* LV (1878–9) at p. 98 and p. 120.

14. *Min Proc ICE* II (1841), pp. 143–6.

15. W.G. Armstrong, 'The History of the Modern Development of Water-pressure Machinery', *Min Proc ICE* L (1876–7), pp. 64–102, at pp. 68–9.

16. For further details of Berrington's career, see Chapter 5.

17. The New River Approaches were controversial, and thus generated a good deal of paperwork over many years, adequately summarized in *Eng Rep* 1872–4.

18. This is obviously a gross simplification of a highly complex topic. A. Holt, 'A Review of the Progress of Steam Shipping during the last Quarter of a Century', *Min Proc ICE* LI (1877–8), pp. 2–11 comes from the horse's mouth, since Holt was an engineer as well as a leading shipowner. Everybody who was anybody in naval architecture was present at the meeting, and the discussion extends to p. 135!

19. This issue is considered in greater detail in A. Jarvis, 'The Port of Liverpool and the Shipowners in the Late Nineteenth Century', *The Great Circle* 16 No. 1 (1994), pp. 1–22.

20. *Surveyor's Reports*: 19 July 1836 and 2 August 1836.

21. Given in evidence to the 1872 Special Committee on Dock Improvement by Mr Cunliffe.

22. Boult's *Notebook* and the *Engineer's Commonplace Book* for 1876 both give details of systematic evaluation of ladder pumps.

23. Hartley's earliest sorties into hydraulics relied on the head of the town water supply. The

installation at Stanley Dock (1854–5) seems to have been the first substantial steam-pumped one

24. W.J. Doherty, 'Description of Cofferdams Used at Dublin, Birkenhead and Hull', *Min Proc ICE* LI (1877–8), pp. 146–9.
25. Notably at the abortive Great Low Water Basin, Birkenhead, where an engine of 112 HP was installed to provide power to control the enormous greenheart paddles, first operated in January 1864.
26. These drawings survive. MDHB/Princes/3/10.
27. Holt was a leading player in persuading the Board of Trade to accept higher pressures and stronger, lighter boilers. Holt, 'Progress of Steam Shipping'.
28. See D.M. Williams, 'The Quality, Skill and Supply of Maritime Labour: Causes of Concern in Britain, 1850–1914' in L.R. Fischer *et al.* (eds), *The North Sea: Twelve Essays on Social History of Maritime Labour*, Stavanger 1992, pp. 41–58.
29. Alfred Jones was one of the few: interview in the *Liverpool Mercury*, 5 November 1904.
30. Jarvis, *Liverpool Central Docks, 1799–1905*, Stroud, 1991, chapter 6. In the introduction of the report of the 1890 Special Committee, Mr Coke specifically admitted that routine and trivia occupied so much time that members never got to discuss 'some general question' – or policy as he might have called it.
31. For a short account of this conflict, see K.G. Smith and A. Jarvis, 'Princes Jetty, Liverpool: A Case Study of a 19th Century Concrete Maritime Structure', in A. Jarvis and P. Rees (eds), *Dock Engineers and Dock Engineering*, Liverpool, 1993.
32. See for example the evidence of Daniel Adamson and Marshall Stevens before the Select Committee of the House of Commons on the 1883 Manchester Ship Canal Bill.
33. In his response to the discussion of his paper to the Institution, *Min Proc ICE* C (1889–90), pp. 79–81.
34. William Becket Hill (Allan Line), for example, testified to the Royal Commission on the Port of London that quayside railways could be slow, costly and ineffective. BPP 1902 (1151) XLIII.222, Questions 2258–9.
35. The tale of the endless alterations needed at Waterloo is detailed in WUP 13/1 and summarized in Jarvis, *Central Docks*, chapter 7.

## 4 The Problem of Competition

1. The famous case is that of the *J.C. Boynton*, stranded in Princes Half-Tide Entrance on 28 February 1871 and not refloated until 4 March, *UWUP* J7.
2. This will one day make a nice paper: the starting point is *WUP* 171.
3. In Hartley's time individual salaries were published in *Annual Accounts*. By Lyster's time they were aggregated, requiring recourse to *Staff & Wages* File SW/1/19. Burton was employed on £2,000, while the full salary of the Engineer was £4,500. (Lyster was actually job-sharing with his son at the time, but had been paid that amount from 1874 to 1890, and when he retired in 1897 his son received the full amount.)
4. The Regulation of Railways Act 1844 contained powers to nationalize railways, and works like W. Galt, *Railway Reform*, London, 1865, make the case at the later date.
5. *Ann Acc*, 1880.
6. It was successfully completed by G.F. Lyster and opened in 1866 (*Engineer's Report*, 1866.)
7. B.T. Leech, *History of the Manchester Ship Canal*, Manchester, 1907. For a revisionist

view of the Ship Canal project see A. Jarvis, 'The Opposition to the Manchester Ship Canal: A Re-appraisal', in P. Rees (ed.) *The Manchester Ship Canal Centenary*, Liverpool, 1994. A couple of small examples: Leech describes the use of concrete mixers by the contractor as innovative, when they had been in use in Liverpool (and Birkenhead) since Lyster's early venture in concrete, mentioned in Chapter 3. He expresses awe at the removal of 54,000,000 cubic yards of spoil in seven years: *Leviathan* alone could lift enough sand in that length of time to fill the Ship Canal in again.

8. D.A. Farnie, *The Manchester Ship Canal and the Rise of the Port of Manchester*, Manchester, 1980, chapter 1.

9. Though, of course, the ratepayers gained in other ways in the long term: with hindsight the Ship Canal can be seen as highly important, successful and beneficial.

10. For a graphic account of child labour, see J.L. and B. Hammond, *The Town Labourer 1760–1832*, London, 1917 (repr. Stroud, 1995).

11. In particular through the stimulation of mercantile activities which were potentially more extensive and profitable than shipowning.

12. A. Jarvis, 'Beyond the River Wall: The Attack on the Mersey Bar, 1890–1923', in G. Milne (ed.), *Maritime Engineering around the Irish Sea*, Liverpool, 1995, summarizes the main theories about river bars.

13. *WUP* 48/1 contains a wide selection of letters, including one to the *Liverpool Daily Post* of 21 November 1884 in which Russell Aitken refers to the Ship Canal evidence. According to Farnie, *Manchester Ship Canal*, p. 31, Liverpool was galvanized into action and 'dredged away the Mersey Bar between 1890 and 1894'. Would that it had been so easy.

14. W.H. Wheeler, 'Bars at the Mouths of Tidal Estuaries', *Min Proc ICE* C (1889–90), pp. 116–216, at p. 140.

15. In a report dated 6 August 1889, included in *WUP* 48/1.

16. The progress of the operation may be traced from the *Eng Rep* and also from the (published) *Reports of the Acting Conservator*.

17. See the illustrated article in *Engineering*, 23 April 1909, pp. 570–4.

18. *Report of the Acting Conservator*, 1899.

19. *Eng Rep, 1906–9*.

20. For a good general account of these and later works, see J.A. Cashin, 'Engineering Works for the Improvement of the Estuary of the Mersey', *Journal ICE*, vol. 32 no. 7 (1948–9), pp. 296–367.

21. In *UWUP* C169.

22. According to C.E. Lee, *The Blue Riband*, London, ND (*c.* 1931), p. 189 the increase in *Mauretania*'s speed from 25 to 26 knots took an extra 16,000 horsepower, some 23 per cent of the total.

23. *Liverpool Daily Courier*, 11 April 1911.

24. *Journal of Commerce*, 29 February 1912 and 22 February 1913.

25. Reported in *Journal of Commerce*, 25 March 1911.

## 5   The Staff in the Dock Yard and their Work

1. A drawing which allowed calculation of how much stone had actually been used at Princes Dock would have embarrassed Foster and a drawing of the retaining wall foundations at Kings Dock would probably not have enhanced Morris' reputation either.

2. At this early stage, individuals are named in *Ann Acc*. For Lyttleton Harbour see G. Thornton, 'Method of Blasting Rock for the Lyttleton Harbour Works, Canterbury, New Zealand', *Min Proc ICE* LVI (1878–9), pp. 275–6. We should recall that some engineers worked well beyond 'retirement age', like Jesse Hartley (80) and G.F. Lyster (75).

3. In 1836 there were only 238 members, by 1908 there were 8,555. J.C. Inglis, 'Presidential Address', *Min Proc ICE*, CLXXV (1908–9), at p. 19.

4. These are preserved in the ICE Archives.

5. T. Fletcher, *Autobiographical Memoirs of Thomas Fletcher of Liverpool*, Liverpool, 1843, pp. 171–2; 'Memoir of Mr Jesse Hartley', *Min Proc ICE* XXXIII (1871–2), pp. 219–22. James Walker LL.D, FRS, (1781–1862) is possibly the most distinguished civil engineer of whom no biography has been written. A man of wide-ranging talents, he was President of the Institution for eleven years. His 'Memoir' is in *Min Proc ICE* XXII (1862–3), pp. 630–3.

6. J.M. Dobson, 'Buenos Aires Harbour Works', *Min Proc ICE* CXXXVIII (1898–9), pp. 170–243, at pp. 198–9.

7. 'Memoir', *Min Proc ICE* CVI (1890–1), pp. 321–35.

8. 'Memoir', *Min Proc ICE* CXXXIV (1897–8), pp. 386–91.

9. Hartley's *Notebook* is a miscellaneous accession, ref DX/86.

10. 'Memoir', *Min Proc ICE* CXVI (1893–4), pp. 353–4.

11. No 'Memoir' exists, but his candidate circular does.

12. His service record is in SW/1/20.

13. K. McCarron, *Meat at Woodside*, Liverpool, 1991, pp. 23–9; le Mesurier's letter is in *Min Proc ICE* CXXIX (1896–7), pp. 43–5.

14. SW/1/8, and 'Memoir', *Min Proc ICE* CVI (1890–1), pp. 319–21.

15. SW/1/8.

16. From his candidate circular and SW/1/20.

17. SW/1/19 and SW/1/23.

18. SW/1/20.

19. N. de la Puerta Rueda, *El Puerto de Bilboa como Reflejo de Desarrollo de Viscaya, 1857–1913*, Bilbao, 1994.

20. 'Obituary', *Min Proc ICE* 240 (1934–5), pp. 787–9.

21. The issue of municipal trading at that date is covered by MD&HB Newscuttings file 113.

22. Candidate circular and SW/1/20. See also Bibliography, below.

23. 'Memoir', *Min Proc ICE*, LXXVIII (1883–4), pp. 445–6.

24. The account of the establishment of the society is based on that given in the 'Preface', *TLES*, vol. I, (1877–81); lists of members were published in each volume.

25. 'Obituary' in *TLES* XXXIII (1912), p. 382.

26. *TLES* XL (1919), p. 450.

27. Candidate cirular, ICE.

28. SW/1/20 and SW/1/23.

29. *Hiring Book*.

30. *Notebook* of W.S. Boult, Liverpool Record Office, ref 680.BOU.

31. The papers relating to this incident are gathered in *UWUP* E25[b]

32. One of the earlier entries in Boult's *Notebook* is a 'recipe' for waterproofing boots!

33. William Brodie (see above) was one such.

34. *Dock Extensions Estimate Book*, p. 172

35. For an account of coal at Bramley-Moore, see Jarvis, *Liverpool Central Docks 1799–1905*, Stroud, 1991, chapter 4.
36. Rolled Plans Collection ref H16.
37. E.g. the improvements at Brunswick (completed 1905); N. Ritchie-Noakes, *Liverpool's Historic Waterfront,* London, 1984, p. 44.
38. *WUP* 75/1 covers telegraph developments.
39. C.S. Pain, 'The Means of Communication Between Liverpool and the Cheshire Side of the Mersey – Past, Present and Proposed', *TLES* I (1877–81), pp. 169–76.
40. Select Committee of the House of Commons, Question 1007.
41. *WUP* 116 contains the details, and some drawing exist at ref. Y141.
42. This plan was published by the board as a companion volume to the *Report of the Special Committee on Dock Extension.*
43. These plans were published in exactly the same way in a report of 1854.
44. *Ann Acc*, 1872.
45. *UWUP* P125. P88 contains information on the illegal practice of paying workmen's wages on licenced premises. (For which an expectant landlord would pay a commission to a crooked pay-clerk.)

## 6 *After the Silver Spade: Sitework and Site Management in the Late Nineteenth Century*

1. B.T. Leech, *The History of the Manchester Ship Canal*, Manchester, 1907, is superbly illustrated and L.T.C. Rolt (ed.), *The Making of a Railway*, London, 1971, contains a fine selection of Great Central photographs.
2. BPP 1878–9 (224) XI.375, Question 1319 *et seq.*
3. *WUP* 17/1 contains the documentation of the important claim against the Board by Messrs Eckersley, Godfrey and Liddelow, which gives an idea of the extent of plant on site.
4. *UWUP* D116ᵃ.
5. Jarvis, *Liverpool Central Docks 1799–1905*, Stroud, 1991, pp. 54–8. The original documents are in *Legal* E6 and E7.
6. *Discussions at the Board*, 19 March 1903.
7. They persisted until 1907.
8. The essence of their claim was that the Engineer's Department was an absolute shambles, which had resulted in losses to them of over £40,000.
9. *WUP* 55/1 contains a selection of press cuttings relating to these.
10. Claim 30 relates to their being flooded out from 15 February to 31 March, owing to the 'water breaking through from Canada Dock'.
11. In Eckersley *et al.* (n. 3 above) Claim 20 charges each machine at 46*s* per day.
12. G. Anderson, 'Inequalities in the Workplace: The Gap Between Manual and White-collar Workers in the Port of Liverpool from the 1850s to the 1930s', *Labour History Review* 56 no. 1 (Spring 1991), pp. 36–47 gives the impression that there was a great gulf fixed: perhaps in general there was, but the Superintendents and Principal Foremen of the Engineer's Department form a significant exception. So did John Templeton, started as a granite piece mason in 1842 on 28*s* per week, appointed Assistant to the [Dock yard] Chief Clerk in 1872 at £300 p.a.
13. SW/1/8.

14. In 1873 the North Entrances were to be 9 ft below ODS; in 1876, 12 ft. In 1890, plans for deepening were approved and then changed three more times before completion.

15. On Brysson Cunningham's candidate circular for transfer to full membership of the Institution, A.G. Lyster is described – presumably with his approval – as Engineer-in-Chief from 1890, supporting the present author's suspicion that Lyster Snr may have been losing his faculties.

16. Described in Jarvis, *Central Docks*, chapter 3. See also the evidence of Commissioner Dowling to the Select Committee on Railway Labourers.

17. The total consumption of coal at the Canada-Huskisson improvement works begun in 1890 ran at about 3000 tons per year! *WUP* 100.

18. Given in his evidence on lighting by electricity (n. 2 above).

19. J.D. Derry, Lt. J.F. Miller, Major R. Home RE and Colonel J. Crofton RE, 'Earthwork Experiments on the Sirhind Canal', *Min Proc ICE* XLI (1874–5), pp. 234–6.

20. *Min Proc ICE* LII (1877–8) contains a sequence of short contributions on excavating machines at pp. 250–69.

21. Eckersley *et al.* (n. 3 above) Claim 20. The number of labourers is not given, but from the sum claimed was approximately 65. This, of course, was a relatively small and highly mechanized job.

22. *Eng Rep*, 1908.

23. J.B. Hartley, 'On the Formation of Embankments and the Filling-in Behind Retaining Walls', *Min Proc ICE* II (1841), pp. 143–6; G.F. Lyster, 'Recent Dock Extensions at Liverpool', *Min Proc ICE* C (1889–90), pp. 2–114.

24. Boult's *Notebook*. It appears that these experiments were specifically geared to determining for what (if any) purposes the relatively new high-speed centrifugal pumps were more suitable than the old types.

25. This is, of course, why the Board employed so many extra labourers even on sites where the excavation work was by contract: the amount of fetching, carrying and stacking up was large.

26. *Engineer's Commonplace Book* no. 1.

27. The problems at Alfred Entrance appear in *UWUP* A47, entries for 4 September 1926 *et seq.*

28. Eckersley *et al.* (n. 3 above) Claim 30.

29. This author used to believe that Lyster introduced iron culverts. Hartley refers to them in a Report of 5 May 1835 (*Reports of the Surveyor*), but they were clearly nowhere near the size of those used by Lyster.

30. 'Hiring Book'.

31. BPP 1846 (530) XIII.425

32. The accident books 1880–97 are in SW/2.

33. *Legal* H25 contains evidence given before a parliamentary committee by Dowling (then a Superintendent) on this subject. The Dock Committee was seriously displeased with him for letting the cat out of the bag.

34. This incident forms the subject of *UWUP* E32.

35. For a history of benefit societies see P.H.J.H. Gosden, *Self-Help: Voluntary Associations in the Nineteenth Century*, London, 1973.

36. Whence Ritchie-Noakes' suggestion that the fund began in the early 1830s, *Liverpool's Historic Waterfront*, London, 1984, p. 94. The report is in *UWUP* E32.

37. In *Reports of the Surveyor*. (This important record has been found since Ritchie-Noakes wrote *Waterfront*.)
38. The *Report of the Select Committee on Employers' Liability*, BPP 1876 (372) IX.669 provides a good potted history of the subject in the recital at the beginning.
39. In *UWUP* E35. Contracts of employment such as Squarey was suggesting were outlawed by the Workmen's Compensation Act of 1897, indicating that plenty of others had thought of it too.
40. *Return of the Number of Lives Lost through Accident During the Last Two Years*, BPP 1871 (488) LVI.591. The Board of Trade's Accident Returns for 1875 show 765 railway employees killed and 3,619 injured.
41. W.H. Fowler, 'Boiler Explosions', *Min Proc ICE* CXX (1894–5), pp. 152–209, at pp. 176–7.
42. SW/3/1.
43. SW/3/1 gives many examples. Office cleaning was the usual standby for those seriously incapacitated, though at an earlier date disabled men were paid to pick oakum in the dock yard.
44. Again, one of many from SW/3/1.
45. Burton's Memo is in *UWUP* E35
46. *Register of Accidents* SW/4/1.
47. SW/3/1.
48. For the Anglesey Bonesetters, see T.H. Bickerton, *A Medical History of Liverpool from the Earliest Days to the Year 1920*, London, 1936, pp. 143–5.
49. See F. Watson, *The Life of Sir Robert Jones*, London, 1934.
50. This pernicious practice led to a particularly hideous accident on the Ship Canal when a train of spoil wagons fell on a gang of navvies working below.

## 7  Fitting Out: Some Developments in the Equipment of the Docks

1. *WUP* 90 contains a wide variety of applications from shipowners, merchants, master lumpers and others for authority to use portable or semi-portable steam winches on the quaysides. By 1871 power to allow these was delegated to the harbourmaster, and a standard application form was in use.
2. *Select Committee of the House of Lords on the 1844 Dock Bill*, Evidence of George Kendal, p. 139, P/1/10.
3. *DCM*: the request minuted on 5 March, the complaint and response on 7 May 1834.
4. *DCM*, 3 August 1819.
5. N. Ritchie-Noakes, *Liverpool's Historic Waterfront*, London, 1984, p. 136.
6. Ibid., p. 125.
7. Evidence of George Kendal (n. 2 above).
8. *G.F. Lyster's Commonplace Book*, p. 80, gives the list of appliances; the income is from *Ann Acc*.
9. *Select Committee of the House of Lords on the 1873 Dock Bill*, evidence of David Duncan, Questions 2751–52.
10. *Select Committee of the House of Commons on the Manchester Ship Canal Bill*, 1883, Evidence of Daniel Adamson, Questions 2675–82.
11. Reported in the *Liverpool Mercury*, 9 February 1888.

12. *1873 Bill*, Question 470.
13. For Underdown, ibid., Questions 2542–9, for Allport, 2637–9.
14. Ibid., Questions 2704–7
15. Ibid., Question 1146.
16. Described in G.F. Lyster, 'Recent Dock Extensions at Liverpool', *Min Proc ICE* C (1889–90), pp. 29–30.
17. *Lyster's Commonplace Book*, p. 62.
18. In the discussion of Lyster's paper, at p. 49.
19. H.W. Ravenshaw, 'Electric Lifts and Cranes', *Min Proc ICE* CXXX (1896–7), pp. 11–47, at p. 46.
20. E. Ehrenfreund, 'Equipment of Large Mercantile Ports', *Min Proc ICE* CLIII (1902–3), pp. 365–72.
21. Both are in *WUP* 25.
22. *WUP* 11/2.
23. Though he thought they were hydraulic! *Royal Commission on Port of London*, Question 5155.
24. *Select Committee 1844*, p. 202, Evidence of Eyre Evans.
25. By 1872 Albert ranked fifth by value of trade and seventh by tonnage. Stanley, not yet 20 years old, was not far behind, Wapping was. *Ann Acc.*
26. Namely at Alexandra, *Eng Rep*, 1895.
27. For a description of their use, see *Select Committee 1844,* pp. 117–18. The section which follows is based on the account given in R.W. Stevens, *On the Stowage of Ships and their Cargoes*, London, 1869, p. 603 *et seq.*
28. *Lyster's Commonplace Book*, p. 56.
29. *Reports of the Engineer*, Report of 2 April 1862, p. 57.
30. *Lyster's Commonplace Book*, p. 56.
31. In a letter from A.S. Macrae: *Works Committee File: Petroleum Storage No. 1*.
32. R. Pickwell, 'Petroleum Storage Installations at Avonmouth and Cardiff', *Min Proc ICE* CIV (1890–1), pp. 249–58.
33. Lyster's proposal is in *Reports of the Engineer*, dated 28 August 1862. Complaint in a letter in *Petroleum Storage No. 1*.
34. D. Dougan, *The Great Gunmaker*, Morpeth, 1991, pp. 144–8.
35. *Petroleum Storage No. 1*.
36. Ibid.
37. W.T.H. Carrington, 'The Reception and Storage of Refined Petroleum in Bulk', *Min Proc ICE* CV (1890–1), pp. 108–46, at p. 123.
38. The comings and goings over the safety of the casemates are in *WUP* 37/1 between August 1881 and June 1882.
39. According to *The Times*, 18 September 1877, p. 10, the smack *Thomas* was actually laden with 214 barrels of naptha. The captain was seriously injured and died three days later, two crew members were less seriously injured, though one was 'blown into the air and he fell into the dock'. The vessel was 'burned to the water's edge'. The MD&HB archive is, amazingly, silent on the subject. B. Redwood, 'The Transport of Petroleum in Bulk', *Min Proc ICE* CXVI (1893–4), pp. 177–257.
40. Ibid., p. 184.
41. *Petroleum Storage No. 1*.

42. *Eng Rep*, 1889.

43. Excluding one or two consultations for political reasons, e.g. Cubitt on the Floating Stage.

44. For Redwood's advice see *Petroleum Storage No. 1*; for S.H. Terry, see his contribution to the discussion of Carrington, 'Petroleum', p. 125 *et seq.*

45. *Eng Rep.* 1891.

46. This is not to imply that there was no oil traffic on the Ship Canal before then: the first bulk oil cargo arrived in 1897. D.A. Farnie, *The Manchester Ship Canal and the Rise of the Port of Manchester*, Manchester, 1980, pp. 144–8.

47. A.W. Skempton, 'Engineering in the Port of London 1789–1808' and 'Engineering in the Port of London 1808–34', *Transactions of the Newcomen Society* 50 (1978–9), pp. 87–108 and 53 (1981–2), pp. 73–96.

48. G. Jackson, *Grimsby and the New Haven Company*, Grimsby, 1971, unpaginated fold-out at rear cover.

49. Barlow's paper, *Trans ICE* I (1836), p. 67 is fairly enthusiastically rubbished by W.R. Browne, 'On the Strength of Lock Gates', *Min Proc ICE* XXXI (1870–1), pp. 317–57. A.F. Blandy, 'Dock Gates', *Min Proc ICE* LVIII (1878–9), pp. 154–221. [The discussion and correspondence on this paper appear in vol. LIX]. William Brodie, 'Dock Gates', *TLES* XVIII (1897), pp. 142–71.

50. One post was chalked and offered up to its mate: when a uniform chalkmark transferred from one to the other, the fit was deemed acceptable. This does not, of course, mean that the gates were accurate to a 'thou', only that they fitted to each other within one.

51. J.B. Hartley, 'On the Effects of the Worm on Kyanised Timber Exposed to the Action of Sea Water, and on the Use of Greenheart Timber from Demerara, in the Same Situations', *Min Proc ICE* II (1840), pp. 84–5. *Royal Commission on Harbours of Refuge*, BPP 1845 (611) XVI.1, at p. 178. T. Baines, *History of the Commerce and Town of Liverpool*, Liverpool, 1852, p. 800, erroneously states that greenheart was first imported from Trinidad in 1849. Possibly that was when it was first on open sale in Liverpool.

52. Ritchie-Noakes, *Waterfront,* pp. 114–15.

53. B. Cunningham, *Dock Engineering*, London, 1906, p. 303.

54. Ibid., pp. 305–6.

55. *Lyster's Commonplace Book*, pp. 88–9; Dunkirk price from Cunningham, *Dock Engineering*, p. 349.

56. Brodie, 'Dock Gates', p. 157.

57. W.G. Wales, 'Caissons and Gates for Closing Lock- and Dock-Entrances', *Min Proc ICE* CXXII (1894–5), pp. 343–54.

58. The name used varied – sometimes they were 'engines', sometimes 'capstans', perhaps most often 'crabs'.

59. For opening, *Eng Rep* 1859: for dimensions, *Engineer's Commonplace Book* 1, p. 107.

60. Ritchie-Noakes' statement (*Waterfront*, p. 114) that 'The application of hydraulic power to the dock gates in Liverpool was not introduced until the 1860s' is in need of slight modification: *Eng Rep* 1858 states that 'The Lock of 100 ft in width, prepared so to be applicable as a graving dock, with its Gates and Hydraulic Machinery, is in a state of satisfactory progress towards completion'.

61. *Engineer's Commonplace Book* No. 1, p. 49.

62. Wales, 'Caissons and Gates', p. 345.

63. J. Robinson, 'The Barry Dock Works, Including the Hydraulic Machinery and the Mode of

Tipping Coal', *Min Proc ICE* CI (1889–90), pp. 128–84, at pp. 139–40. Mr A.C. Andros, in correspondence of Blandy, 'Dock Gates' (at LIX p. 20), described the machinery 'almost invariably adopted' as 'antiquated, barbarous, costly and unmechanical', illustrating this attack with a diagram of the overgate system as described, but not illustrated, in Wales, 'Caissons and Gates'.

64. Verbal information to the author from James Lightfoot, retired shipwright from the Gateshed, in 1971.

65. These volumes were produced for major projects, in this case *New Works, North*, and arranged by task and date.

66. *Hiring Book.*

67. Engineers often claim that there are *never* black and white answers, but their textbooks seem to suggest otherwise.

68. Ritchie-Noakes, *Waterfront*, p. 163.

69. In the Portland Museum of Art, Portland, Maine. Reproduced in A. Jarvis, *Princes Dock, Liverpool*, 1991.

70. Ritchie-Noakes, *Waterfront*, p. 1. At p. 163, she tells of the misfortunes of this bridge.

71. Ibid.

72. On 26 May 1820, Foster was instructed to 'apply to the two firms recommended to him by Mr Rennie . . .' (*DCM*). The price was high, so on 29 June the solicitors were 'instructed to take legal measures for enforcing the Contracts for the erection of the bridges by Messrs Aydon and Elwell'.

73. *Lyster's Commonplace Book*, p. 80.

74. On 18 November: *WUP* 146.

75. J. Price, 'Movable Bridges', *Min Proc ICE* LVII (1878–9), pp. 1–76 at p. 32.

76. Ritchie-Noakes, *Waterfront*, p. 164.

77. Cunningham, *Dock Engineering*, pp. 432–3. On 16 August 1877 an unspecified 85 ft bridge met with a serious accident. Armstrong's offered to repair the girder work at their own expense 'if the Board will place the detached portion of the structure on the site of the bridge'. We may surmise that the detached portion was reposing on the bottom of the dock following the occurrence Cunningham describes.

78. Ibid., p. 436.

79. These and similar incidents are in *WUP 146*.

80. Price, 'Movable Bridges', p. 10, 32n and 35n.

81. Preserved for our delight in *WUP* 146.

# Bibliography

The main part of this bibliography contains only works mentioned in the text or cited in the notes. Anonymous publications, such as obituaries, are given separately in date order at the end. A small supplementary bibliography is appended which includes works used as background information.

G. Anderson, 'Inequalities in the Workplace: the gap between manual and white-collar workers in the Port of Liverpool from the 1850s to the 1930s', *Labour History Review* 56 (1991), pp. 36–47.

M. Arago, *Historical Eloge of James Watt*, London, 1839.

W.G. Armstrong, 'The History of the Modern Development of Water-pressure Machinery', *Min Proc ICE* L (1876–7), pp. 64–102.

T. Baines, *History of the Commerce and Town of Liverpool*, London, 1852.

P. Barlow, 'On Lock Gates', *Transactions ICE* I (1836), pp. 67–77.

T.H. Bickerton, *A Medical History of Liverpool from the Earliest Days to the Year 1920*, London, 1936.

A.F. Blandy, 'Dock Gates', *Min Proc ICE* LVIII (1878–79), pp. 154–221.

W.S. Boult, 'Walls in Portland Cement Concrete, Low Water Basin Conversion, Birkenhead', *TLES* 1 (1877–81), pp. 1–10.

W. Brodie, 'Dock Gates, *TLES* XVIII (1897), pp. 142–71.

R. Browne, 'On the Strength of Lock Gates', *Min Proc ICE* XXXI (1870–1), pp. 317–57.

T. Carlyle, *Latter-day Pamphlets*, London, 1850.

W.T.H. Carrington, 'The Reception and Storage of Refined Petroleum in Bulk', *Min Proc ICE* CV (1890–1), pp. 108–46.

J.A. Cashin, 'Engineering Works for the Improvement of the Estuary of the Mersey', *Journal ICE* 32 No. 7 (1948–9), pp. 296–367.

W.H. Chaloner, 'Francis William Webb (1836–1906) of the London & North Western Railway', *Transport History* 1 (1968), pp. 169–78.

M. Clarke, 'Thomas Steers' in Jarvis and Rees, *Dock Engineers*.

B. Cunningham, *Dock Engineering*, London, 1906.

B. Cunningham, *Cargo Handling at Ports*, London, 1926.

J.R. Cutland, *The Story of Ferrytown of Cree and Kirkmabreck Parish*, Kirkmabreck, 1985.

S. Dentith, 'The Fraud in Literature', in Jarvis and Rees, *Nineteenth Century Business Ethics*.

J.D. Derry *et al.*, 'Earthwork Experiments on the Sirhind Canal', *Min Proc ICE* XLI (1874–5), pp. 234–6.

C. Dickens, *Little Dorrit*, London, 1857.

J.M. Dobson, 'Buenos Aires Harbour Works', *Min Proc ICE* CXXXVIII (1898–99) pp. 170–243.

W.J. Doherty, 'Description of Cofferdams used at Dublin, Birkenhead and Hull', *Min Proc ICE* LI (1877–8), pp. 146–9.

D. Dougan, *The Great Gunmaker*, Morpeth, 1991.

E. Ehrenfreund, 'Equipment of Large Mercantile Ports', *Min Proc ICE* CLIII (1902–3), pp. 365–72.

S.H. Ellis, 'Some Notes on Hydraulic Limes', *TLES* XXVI (1904), pp. 37–66.

D.A. Farnie, *The Manchester Ship Canal and the Rise of the Port of Manchester*, Manchester, 1980.

T. Fletcher, *Autobiographical Memoirs of Thomas Fletcher of Liverpool*, Liverpool, 1843.

W.H. Fowler, 'Boiler Explosions', *Min Proc ICE* CXX (1894–5), pp. 152–209.

C.D. Fox *et al.*, five short contributions on excavating machines, *Min Proc ICE* LII (1877–8), pp. 250–69.

D. Fraser, *Power and Authority in the Victorian City*, Oxford, 1979.

W. Galt, *Railway Reform*, London, 1865.

P.H.J.H. Gosden, *Self-Help: Voluntary Associations in the Nineteenth Century*, London, 1973.

J. Grant, 'Experiments on the Strength of Cement', *Min Proc ICE* XXV (1865–66), pp. 66–159.

C. Hadfield, *Thomas Telford's Temptation*, Cleobury Mortimer, 1993.

J.L. and B. Hammond, *The Town Labourer 1760–1832*, London, 1917 (repr. Stroud, 1995).

J.B. Hartley, 'On the Effects of the Worm on Kyanised Timber', *Min Proc ICE* I (1840), pp. 84–5.

J.B. Hartley, 'Formation of Embankments and Filling in Behind Retaining Walls', *Min Proc ICE* I (1841), pp. 143–6.

J.B. Hartley, 'Piles and Pile-driving', *Min Proc ICE* III (1844), p. 200.

J.C. Hawkshaw, 'The Construction of the Albert Dock at Kingston-upon-Hull', *Min Proc ICE* XLI (1874–5), pp. 92–113.

A. Holt, 'A Review of the Progress of Steam Shipping During the Last Quarter of a Century', *Min Proc ICE* LI (1877–8), pp. 2–135.

J. Hughes, *Port in a Storm*, Liverpool, 1993.

Q. Hughes, *Seaport: Architecture and Townscape in Liverpool*, London, 1964.

F.E. Hyde, *Liverpool and the Mersey*, Newton Abbot, 1972.

J.C. Inglis, 'Presidential Address', *Min Proc ICE* CLXXV (1908–9), pp. 3–29.

G. Jackson, *Grimsby and the New Haven Company*, Grimsby, 1971.

G. Jackson, *History and Archaeology of Ports*, Tadworth, 1983.

G. Jackson, 'Do Docks Make Trade?', in L.R. Fischer (ed.), *From Wheel House to Counting House: Essays in Maritime Business History in Honour of Professor Peter Neville Davies*, St John's, 1992.

A. Jarvis, 'An Attempt at a Bibliography of Samuel Smiles', *Industrial Archaeology Review* XIII (1991), pp. 162–71.

A. Jarvis, 'Harold Littledale, the Man with a Mission', in H.M. Hignett (ed.), *A Second Merseyside Maritime History*, Liverpool, 1991.

A. Jarvis, *Liverpool Central Docks 1799–1905*, Stroud, 1991.

A. Jarvis, *Princes Dock*, Liverpool, 1991.

A. Jarvis, 'G.F. Lyster and the Role of the Dock Engineer', *The Mariner's Mirror* 78 (1992), pp. 179–99.

A. Jarvis, 'The Censoring of Samuel Smiles', *Journal of the Railway & Canal Historical Society* 31 (1993), pp. 176–85.

A. Jarvis, 'The Members of the Mersey Docks & Harbour Board and their Way of Doing Business', *International Journal of Maritime History* VI (1994), pp. 122–39.

A. Jarvis, 'The Port of Liverpool and the Shipowners in the Late Nineteenth Century', *The Great Circle* 16 (1994), pp. 1–22.

A. Jarvis, 'Beyond the River Wall: The Attack on the Mersey Bar, 1890–1923', in G. Milne (ed.), *Maritime Engineering around the Irish Sea*, Liverpool, 1995.

A. Jarvis, 'The Golden Age of Municipal Engineering: A Liverpool Overview', *Proceedings of the Institution of Civil Engineers, Municipal Engineer* 109 (1995), pp. 264–70.

A. Jarvis and P. Rees (eds), *Nineteenth Century Business Ethics*, Liverpool, 1992.

A. Jarvis and P. Rees (eds), *Dock Engineers and Dock Engineering*, Liverpool, 1993.

A. Jarvis and P. Rees (eds), *An Empire in Decline?*, Liverpool, 1994.

J. Lambert, *The Railway King*, London, 1934.

M. Lane, *The Rendel Connection*, London, 1989.

P. Lead, *Agents of Revolution*, Keele, 1989.

C.E. Lee, *The Blue Riband*, London, ND [*c.* 1931].

B.T. Leech, *History of the Manchester Ship Canal*, Manchester, 1907.

J. Longmore, 'The Development of the Liverpool Corporation Estate', unpublished PhD thesis, University of Reading, 1982.

G.F. Lyster, *The History of the Birkenhead Great Low Water Basin*, Liverpool, 1864.

G.F. Lyster, *Report of the Engineer to the Special Committee on Dock Extension*, Liverpool, 1872.

G.F. Lyster, 'Recent Dock Extensions at Liverpool', *Min Proc ICE* C (1889–90), pp. 2–114.

K. McCarron, *Meat at Woodside*, Liverpool, 1991.

N. McKendrick, 'Literary Luddism and the Businessman', in P.N. Davies, *Sir Alfred Jones*, London, 1978.

H. Malet, *Bridgewater: The Canal Duke*, Manchester, 1977.

F.C. Mather, *After the Canal Duke*, London, 1970.

L.L. Mayfield, 'Limestone Additions to Portland Cement – an Old Controversy Re-visited', *Cement, Concrete & Aggregates* 10 No. 1 (Summer 1988), pp. 3–8.

J. Muirhead, *Origins of the Mechanical Inventions of James Watt*, London, 1854.

C.S. Pain, 'The Means of Communication Between Liverpool and the Cheshire Side of the Mersey – Past, Present and Proposed', *TLES* I (1877–81), pp. 169–76.

H. Peet, 'Thomas Steers', *THSLC* 82 (1930), pp. 163–206.

R. Pickell, 'Petroleum Storage Installations at Avonmouth and Cardiff', *Min Proc ICE* CIV (1890–1), pp. 249–58.

J. Price, 'Movable Bridges', *Min Proc ICE* LVII (1878–9), pp. 1–76.

W.J.M. Rankine, *The Steam Engine and other Prime Movers*, London, 1859 (numerous reprints).

H.W. Ravenshaw, 'Electric Lifts and Cranes', *Min Proc ICE* CXXX (1896–7), pp. 11–47.

B. Redwood, 'The Transport of Petroleum in Bulk', *Min Proc ICE* CXVI (1893–4), pp. 177–257.

J. Rickman (ed.), *Life of Thomas Telford by Himself*, London, 1838.

N. Ritchie-Noakes, *Jesse Hartley*, Liverpool, 1980.

N. Ritchie-Noakes, *Liverpool's Historic Waterfront*, London, 1984.

N. Ritchie-Noakes and M. Clarke, 'The Dock Engineer and the Development of the Port of Liverpool', in V. Burton (ed.), *Liverpool Shipping, Trade and Industry*, Liverpool, 1989.

J. Robinson, 'The Barry Dock Works, Including the Hydraulic Machinery and the Mode of Tipping Coal', *Min Proc ICE* CI (1889–90), pp. 128–84.

L.T.C. Rolt, *The Making of a Railway*, London, 1971.

N. de la Puerta Rueda, *El Puerto de Bilbao como Reflejo de Desarollo de Viscaya, 1857–1913*, Bilbao, 1994.

A.W. Skempton, 'Engineering in the Port of London 1789–1808', *Transactions of the Newcomen Society* 50 (1978–9), pp. 87–108.

A.W. Skempton, 'Engineering in the Port of London 1808–34', *Transactions of the Newcomen Society* 53 (1981), pp. 73–96.

W.N. Slatcher, 'The Barnsley Canal: Its First Twenty Years', *Transport History* 1 (1968), pp. 48–66.

S. Smiles, *The Education of the Working Classes*, Leeds, 1845.

S. Smiles, *Self-Help*, London, 1859.

S. Smiles, *Lives of the Engineers*, London, 1862 and 1874.

K.G. Smith and A. Jarvis, 'Princes Jetty, Liverpool: A Case Study of a 19th Century Concrete Maritime Structure', in A. Jarvis and P. Rees (eds), *Dock Engineers and Dock Engineering*, Liverpool, 1993.

H. Spencer, 'Railway Morals and Railway Policy', *The Edinburgh Review* 100 (1854), pp. 420–61.

R.A. Stephenson, 'The Development of the Liverpool Docks System', *Transactions of the Liverpool Nautical Research Society* 7–9, pp. 61–76. (These volumes were bound as one.)

R.W. Stevens, *On the Stowage of Ships and their Cargoes*, London, 1869.

P. Sulley, *Ancient and Modern Birkenhead*, Liverpool, 1907.

D. Swann, 'The Engineers of English Port Improvements 1660–1830' (2 parts), *Transport History* 1 (1968), pp. 153–67 and 260–76.

J.A. Tallis, R.D. Taylor and T.J. Dishman, 'Restoration of Albert Dock', *The Structural Engineer* 64 (1986), pp. 291–8.

M. Taylor (ed.), *Reports of the Late John Smeaton*, London, 1837.

R.H.G. Thomas, *The Liverpool & Manchester Railway*, Newton Abbot, 1980.

G. Thornton, 'Method of Blasting Rock for the Lyttleton Harbour Works, Canterbury, New Zealand', *Min Proc ICE* LVI (1878–9), pp. 275–6.

W.G. Wales, 'Caissons and Gates for Closing Lock- and Dock-Entrances', *Min Proc ICE* CXXII (1894–5), pp. 343–54.

F. Watson, *The Life of Sir Robert Jones*, London, 1936.

T. Webster, *The Port and Docks of Birkenhead 1844–52*, London, 1873.

I. Weir, 'Port of Liverpool Quay Walls', unpublished MSc dissertation, University of Liverpool, 1993.

W.H. Wheeler, 'Bars at the Mouths of Tidal Estuaries', *Min Proc ICE* C (1889–90), pp. 116–216.

D.M. Williams, 'The Quality, Skill and Supply of Maritime Labour: Causes for Concern in Britain, 1850–1914', in L.R. Fischer *et al.* (eds), *The North Sea: Twelve Essays on Social History of Maritime Labour*, Stavanger, 1992.

G. Woodward, 'Staite and Petrie: Pioneers of Electric Lighting', *Proceedings of the Institution of Electrical Engineers* 136 Pt A (1989), pp. 290–6.

## Obituaries and Memoirs

Hugh Bovey, *TLES* XXXIII (1912), p. 382.

John Brodie, *Min Proc ICE* 240 (1934–5), pp. 787–9.

William du Port, *Min Proc ICE* CVI (1890–1), pp. 319–21.

Major Eric Dougall, *TLES* XL (1919), p. 450.

John Ellacott, *Min Proc ICE* CXVI (1893–4), pp. 353–4.

Jesse Hartley, *Min Proc ICE* XXXIII (1871–2), pp. 216–22.

John Bernard Hartley, ibid.

Sir John Hawkshaw, *Min Proc ICE* CVI (1890–1), pp. 321–35.

George Fosbery Lyster, *Min Proc ICE* CXXXIX (1899–1900), pp. 357–66.

Anthony George Lyster, *Min Proc ICE* CCXVII (1923–4), pp. 447–8.
Sir Robert Rawlinson, *Min Proc ICE* CXXXIV (1893–4), pp. 386–91.
Isaac Ridgeway, *TLES* XL (1919), p. 450.
C. Graham Smith, *Min Proc ICE* LXXVIII (1883–4) pp. 445–6.
James Walker, *Min Proc ICE* XXII (1862–3), pp. 630–3.


## Parliamentary Material

*Royal Commission on Local Government*, BPP 1835 (116) XXVI.1.
*Select Committee of the House of Lords on the Liverpool Dock Bill*, 1844.
*Select Committee on Railway Labourers*, BPP 1846 (530) XIII.425.
*Royal Commission to Enquire into Harbours of Refuge*, BPP 1847 (411) LXI.1.
*House of Lords Sessional Papers: Reports, Committees* XXI (1850), pp. 131–49.
*Select Committee on Local Charges on Shipping*, BPP 1856 (332) XII.1.
*Return of the Number of Lives Lost through Accident During the Last Two Years*, BPP 1871 (488) LVI.591.
*Select Committee of the House of Commons on the Liverpool Dock Bill, 1873.*
*Select Committee of the House of Lords on the Liverpool Dock Bill, 1873.*
*Select Committee on Employers' Liability*, BPP 1876 (372) IX.669.
*Select Committee to Enquire into Schemes by Local Authorities for Providing Electricity*, BPP 1878–9 (224) XI.375.
*Select Committee of the House of Commons on the Manchester Ship Canal Bill, 1883.*
*Royal Commission on the Port of London*, BPP 1902 (1151) XLIII.222.


## Other Anonymous Publications

*A Report of the Proceedings of a Court of Enquiry into the Existing State of the Corporation of Liverpool*, Liverpool, 1833. (Liverpool Corporation)
*Report of the Special Committee on Dock Extension*, Liverpool,1872. (MD&HB)

*Proposed Dock Extension*, Liverpool, 1872. (MD&HB)

'Discussion on Harbour and Dock Works' [covering four papers], *Min Proc ICE* LV (1878–9), pp. 49–120.

'The Suction Dredger *Leviathan*', *Engineering*, 23 April 1909, pp. 570–4.


## Supplementary Material

J. Bird, *The Major Seaports of the United Kingdom*, London, 1963.

R.A. Buchanan, *The Engineers: A History of the Engineering Profession in Britain*, London, 1989.

C. Colson, *Docks and Dock Construction*, London, 1894.

B. Cunningham, *Dock & Harbour Engineer's Reference Book*, London, 1914.

B. Cunningham, *Port Administration and Operation*, London, 1925.

B. Cunningham, *Port Studies*, London, 1928.

F.M.G. Du Plat-Taylor, *Docks, Wharves and Piers*, London, 1928.

G. Read and M. Stammers, *Guide to the Records of Merseyside Maritime Museum*, St. John's, 1995.

L.F. Vernon-Harcourt, *Harbours and Docks: their Physical Features, History, Construction etc.*, Oxford, 1885.

# Index

# rkenhead Docks, 1991

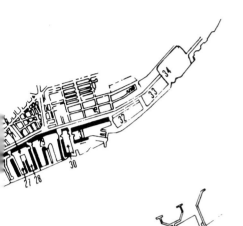

## Key to Dock Names

| | | | |
|---|---|---|---|
| 1 | Seaforth Container Terminal Royal Seaforth Docks | 21 | Princes Dock |
| | | 22 | Canning Dock |
| | | 23 | Canning Half-Tide Dock |
| 2 | Gladstone Dock and Branch Docks Nos 1 & 2 | 24 | Salthouse Dock |
| | | 25 | Albert Dock |
| 3 | Hornby Dock | 26 | Wapping Dock |
| 4 | Alexandra Dock and Branch Docks Nos 1, 2, & 3 | 27 | Kings Dock No 2 |
| | | 28 | Kings Dock No 1 |
| 5 | Langton Dock | 29 | Queens Dock and Branch Docks Nos 1 & 2 |
| 6 | Brocklebank Dock and Branch Dock | 30 | Coburg Dock |
| 7 | Canada Dock and Branch Docks Nos 1, 2 & 3 | 31 | Brunswick Dock |
| | | 32 | Toxteth Dock |
| 8 | Huskisson Dock and Branch Docks Nos 1, 2, & 3 | 33 | Harrington Dock |
| | | 34 | Herculaneum Dock and 4 Graving Docks |
| 9 | Sandon Dock | 35 | Cammell Laird's Fitting out Basin |
| 10 | Sandon Half-Tide Dock | | |
| 11 | Wellington Dock | 36 | Morpeth Branch Dock |
| 12 | Bramley-Moore Dock | 37 | Morpeth Dock |
| 13 | Nelson Dock | 38 | Egerton Dock |
| 14 | Stanley Dock | 39 | Vittoria Dock |
| 15 | Collingwood Dock | 40 | East Float |
| 16 | Salisbury Dock | 41 | West Float |
| 17 | Trafalgar Dock | 42 | Bidston Dock |
| 18 | East Waterloo Dock | 43 | Wallasey Dock |
| 19 | West Waterloo Dock | 44 | Alfred Dock |
| 20 | Princes Half-Tide Dock | | |